FALL OUT

THE UNOFFICIAL
AND UNAUTHORISED GUIDE
TO *THE PRISONER*

FALL OUT

THE UNOFFICIAL
AND UNAUTHORISED GUIDE
TO *THE PRISONER*

ALAN STEVENS AND
FIONA MOORE

First published in the UK in 2007 by
Telos Publishing Ltd
17 Pendre Avenue, Prestatyn, Denbighshire, LL19 9SH
www.telos.co.uk

This Edition 2013

Telos Publishing Ltd values feedback. Please e-mail us with any
comments you may have about this book to: feedback@telos.co.uk

ISBN: 978-1-84583-862-1 paperback

Fall Out: The Unofficial and Unauthorised Guide to The Prisoner © 2007
Alan Stevens and Fiona Moore
Foreword © 2007 Ian Rakoff
Index prepared by Ian Pritchard

British Library Cataloguing in Publication Data.
A catalogue record for this book is available from the British
Library.

Acknowledgements

The authors would like to acknowledge the invaluable help of, in no particular order, Andrew Pixley (for encouraging us to write this book, and being an unfailing source of advice and support throughout), Ian Rakoff, Dave Barrie, Rick Davy, Daniel O'Mahony, Jim Smith, Matthew Peacock, Matthew Kilburn, Lawrence Miles, Alice Dryden, Marcus Hearn, Rupert Booth and Jon Blum, Nick Lewis, and David and Rosemary Howe and Stephen James Walker (for seeing us through the publication process). We would also like to acknowledge the exhaustive research done by, among others, Roger Langley, Max Hora, Steven Ricks, Roger Goodman, Robert Fairclough, the various members of Six of One and The Unmutual, and the authors of the publications and websites we have listed in our Bibliography, who have provided us with innumerable insights into the production. Finally, we were greatly assisted by the staff of the Robarts and OISE Libraries at the University of Toronto, the Bodleian Library at Oxford, and the British Library, but we would particularly like to single out the staff of the Merrill Collection of Science Fiction and Fantasy, who proved extremely helpful in tracking down rare *The Prisoner*-related material.

Table Of Contents

Foreword

The Prisoner was deeply threatening and no-one knew why, which, on some levels, probably included McGoohan. The mirror that it was, portrayed a reflection far from clear. It was unpalatable, for sure. It was irritating and annoying as intended, precisely as designed. No easy answers.

The kind of egomaniacal madness in the project, the thinker-artist, moralist, driven by a fervour bordering on religious mania. McGoohan was unquestionably a lot more then a mere actor, but also a lot less than a sophisticated intellect of the ilk of Orson Welles, and McGoohan, despite all the lofty feature film protestations, was certainly not accompanied by the calibre of cast and crew that came out of the Mercury Theatre.

The training ground for *The Prisoner* was Pinewood Studios, with its overall factory product, making run-of-the-mill, mechanical entertainment governed more by the pocket than anything else. I cannot deny the sporadic intelligence sparked amongst the unit, which often highlighted the series. That's being better than what many basically were and consequently the series remains the inexplicable, mysterious high point in most of the participants' careers, including my own.

Derogatory though what I've suggested might seem, it is this very limitation that places *The Prisoner* simultaneously in an enduring realm of greatness and mediocrity. Had anything akin to the cultured intellect of an Orson Welles governed the production the result would have been more artful but less socially significant, less identifiable for the proletarian beast and its cousin, Everyman. It would've been more of an art and less of a cult.

This unauthorised guide presents a fascinatingly broad canvas, superbly researched and reflective of extraordinary hard work. It is to be fully commended, and essential reading on the subject, easily encompassing most of what has been done before and supplanting the lot.

John Smith, the editor I assisted on 'It's Your Funeral' and 'The General', was entirely responsible for bringing my writing to McGoohan's attention. John's generosity of spirit was distinctively unusual in the closed-circuit world of freelance editing. I suggested to him that he might go down in history as being the only editor willing to re-employ me.

John's big achievement was to bring life into the 'Dance of the Dead' episode when no-one else wanted to touch it with a proverbial bargepole. The other unusual aspect of John was that he was nearly as tall as McGoohan, or maybe he just deliberately hunched over whenever he stood next to Number Six.

John's prime observation on the series, delivered in his unflagging self-effacing manner was much in tandem with my own.

'Put it this way: this bunch, they're all just jobbers, like me.'

In regard to 'Living in Harmony', some thought the Western an intrusion on the ethos of the series, whereas I thought it inevitable; after all, didn't Hollywood instigate the genre, to embody the mythical land of moral conflict as an open sided canvas on which to paint the eternal battle of right versus wrong?

I initially struck a chord with McGoohan that prompted him to assure me that when the series continued beyond episode 17 I'd be working closely with him as he'd originally promised. I think his interest in my writing was due to the fact that he suspected, or perhaps knew, that I had a history of political subversion in my past, coupled with moral concerns that we shared. This also explains why I hold such a particular slant on the series and allocate prime credit to Patrick McGoohan, because of what he is, irrespective of what he did or didn't do. McGoohan was the driving force and moral intelligence. No-one else could have done what McGoohan did.

Seeing McGoohan as a two-fisted maverick, a scrapper, I think of Jack Dempsey, World Heavyweight Champion 1919-1926. Jack garnered a cluster of nicknames, 'The Manassa Mauler',

'Nonpareil' and, most appropriately, 'The Giant Killer', the slayer of ogres. If that doesn't capture the spirit of Number Six, I don't know what does.

Ian Rakoff
January 2007

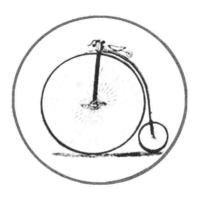

Mission Statement

Before we begin, we would like to take a couple of pages to outline our feelings about *The Prisoner*, the areas we will be covering, and how, precisely, we intend to approach the series in the subsequent chapters. This may seem rather self-indulgent, but *The Prisoner* is a series that has received a lot of critical attention from authors with a variety of different viewpoints and agendas, and, in view of this, it is worth setting out what we intend to do straight away, to avoid confusion or disappointment later on.

It is tempting to try to explain *The Prisoner* in terms of a single, or overriding, theory or metaphor. It has, for instance, been seen as an allegorical representation of the battle of the individual against society; a fantasy or hallucination in the protagonist's mind; a *The Truman Show*-style comment on the media; and many other things. However, when one tries to apply a single theory to the series, one usually winds up having to explain away aspects that don't fit with that theory, and consequently failing to explain precisely what it is all about. This elusive quality sets *The Prisoner* apart, not only from conventional spy series, but also from many of the more allegorical and conceptual television programmes.

The reason for this situation lies in the nature of the series' production. It is not actually the product of a single author-figure, or of a particular set of definite circumstances. The various players who brought the series about had different, even conflicting, agendas: Patrick McGoohan wanted to develop a programme that challenged the conventions of the series with which he had become strongly associated, *Danger Man*; George Markstein wanted to produce a relatively straightforward, if claustrophobic and paranoia-laced, spy story; David Tomblin brought in more experimental and surreal ideas influenced by new developments in European cinema. Furthermore, all the different writers on the series had their own ideas about what it should be, in terms of its genre as well as its message, and the scripts had different, sometimes unexpected, geneses. To this, one can add the happenstance and accidents that affect the production of any television programme. The result is a series that combines and crosses genres rather than adheres to a single 'vision', with some stories resembling thrillers and others being written more along science fiction, psychological or downright surreal lines. *The Prisoner* thus defies easy analysis, by virtue of not adhering to a single message or vision.

It is also worth remembering that *The Prisoner* was intended, at least partly, as a subversion of the familiar spy-story genre. Consequently, at least part of its conscious mandate involved the subversion of linear interpretations. A story may develop along lines familiar from a dozen spy stories (for example the heroic escape from the Village in 'The Chimes of Big Ben'), but then transform it abruptly (for example when the end of that story reveals that the Prisoner has not in fact left the Village at all). In a situation like this, where expectations are regularly built up and undermined, one cannot expect a single explanation or narrative to cover all the possibilities.

Consequently, this book has been written not with a view to making a definitive pronouncement on *The Prisoner*, but to enable viewers of the series to find out about and explore the different possibilities open to them, and ultimately to make up their own minds about it. This is not to say that it is endlessly interpretable, nor that all interpretations of it are valid; some fit better than others, and some make more sense than others in particular contexts. To present all theories as equal would be to produce a fairly dull and wishy-washy book. Likewise, we as the writers have our own biases and views, which will inevitably creep into the analysis, with which the reader may not necessarily agree; also, recognising that this is a series that invites the viewer to interpretation, and indeed to playing with concepts of interpretation, we are not arrogant enough to believe that our conclusions are necessarily the best or the only ones. What we intend to do is to present some of the ways in which the series can be interpreted, and discuss the problems and advantages of each position; if we agree or disagree with a particular conclusion, we will outline why we take this stance rather than simply embrace or dismiss it.

That having been said, there are a number of things this book will *not* do, to wit:

- Enumerate facts, figures, lists of statistics and technical data. This has been done before, and there is no point in our reinventing the wheel. This is not to say that we won't refer to these types of material, but when we do, it will be to support an argument or explain an interpretation rather than as an end in itself.

- Tell gossipy and/or salacious anecdotes about the production and the people involved. If an anecdote is relevant to understanding a particular episode, then fine, but the subtitle 'unofficial and unauthorised' doesn't denote a tabloid approach to the media.

- Be too analytical. Neither of the authors is from a media studies background and, while this undoubtedly has its place, we are writing with a popular audience in mind.

- Be the 'last word' on *The Prisoner*. There's always something new and different to say about a good programme, and *The Prisoner* is no exception.

We would like to say, however, that we are deeply indebted to people who have, in the past, written books with a more factual, analytical or anecdotal slant than our own, and would encourage people to seek out other volumes on *The Prisoner*. To this end, we have included a Bibliography of our key sources, for those who wish to read further, and also to allow people to judge for themselves where our influences may be coming from.

We should also, at this point, distinguish between two similar phrases that will crop up frequently throughout this book, *subtext* and *subtextual*. A *subtext* is a reading that is deliberately placed within a narrative by the author, for instance, a distrust of excessive computerisation in 'The General', or, arguably, Christian spirituality in the 'Dem Bones' sequence of 'Fall Out'. The *subtextual*, however, involves those aspects of a narrative that creep into the work non-deliberately, informed by the writer's background, concerns, the times in which they live, and so forth. We will be uncovering different subtexts and subtextual messages throughout the analytical portions of this book.

As with our earlier book, *Liberation: The Unofficial and Unauthorised Guide to Blake's 7*, then, what we propose to do is not to pronounce definitively upon *The Prisoner*, but to provide a guide that will be analytical, concise and, we hope, be a repository of ideas that viewers can play around with as they watch or rewatch the series. Read what we have to say; then agree with us, disagree with us, come up with different ideas using the same data we have presented; but you are welcome to use us as a starting-point for your own explanation of the wonderful, complex series that is *The Prisoner*.

As a final note, regarding the attributions of the characters: since there is little consistency in the way the character names are rendered in the official credits, we have chosen in the 'Credited Cast' sections on the episodes to give them exactly as they appear on screen, but in the 'Analysis' and 'Synopsis' sections to retain the convention of spelling out all numerical names ('Number Eight' rather than 'No 8', for instance). The broadcast dates and times given are those of each episode's initial UK transmission, and we have also indicated which of the regional ITV networks was first to broadcast the episode.

Alan Stevens
Fiona Moore

I Helped Patrick McGoohan Escape: The Production Of *The Prisoner*

'The object of the television series *The Prisoner* was to create a feeling of unrest about life today. It was an abstract expression of the world we are living in, and a warning of what would happen to us when gadgetry and gimmickry take over from creative people.' – Patrick McGoohan, contemporary interview.

The story of the making of *The Prisoner* is, as has often been remarked, every bit as convoluted and strange as the series itself, and, indeed, it is helpful, when analysing the series, to consider some of the events that were going on behind the scenes during its writing and filming. Readers interested in more detailed accounts are encouraged to peruse some of the volumes listed in the Bibliography.

PUSHED, FILED, STAMPED: ORIGINS OF *THE PRISONER*

Everyman Films was formed on 18 August 1960 by actor Patrick McGoohan and assistant director David Tomblin, who had met while both were working on *Danger Man*.[1] However, despite McGoohan's long-stated ambition to get into film-making (he was

---

1 *Danger Man*, effectively a precursor of *The Prisoner*, will be discussed in detail later in this volume.

particularly keen on making a film version of Ibsen's *Brand*: see '*The Prisoner* in Context' below) it was not until 1966 that the company had its first production approved. McGoohan, who was by this point the highest paid actor in the British television industry, approached Lew Grade with the idea for *The Prisoner* after announcing his effective resignation from *Danger Man*. Grade, a former cabaret dancer turned theatre impresario and agent, was one of the first people to become involved with independent television in the United Kingdom, setting up the Incorporated Television Programme Company (ITP, later to drop the 'Programme' and adopt the acronym ITC, by which it is best known) in 1954, and acquiring an independent television franchise, Associated TeleVision (ATV) in 1955 in partnership with others, incorporating ITC into the company as a wholly-owned subsidiary in 1957.[2] Grade was known for his innovative and idiosyncratic approach to programme commissioning: McGoohan later explained, as quoted in Carrazé and Oswald's *The Prisoner: a Televisionary Masterpiece*: 'I knew a man who backed hunches, and his decisions were his alone. Lew Grade, now Lord Grade, is such a man ... He didn't like reading scripts, but preferred to "hear" the idea, to see it in his mind's eye. After listening to the bizarre concept, he took a few puffs on his cigar, walked around the office a couple of times and said "It's so crazy it might just work. Let's do it! Shake!" ... and we did. And he gave me *carte blanche*. I was very fortunate.'

Grade's initial belief in the series is attested to by the fact that ATV subsequently agreed to fund *The Prisoner* to the tune of £75,000 per 50-minute episode, which was £35,000 more than its nearest ITC rival, making it the most expensive series of its day. He also, however, referred to it as 'the experiment' during its production, indicating that he was well aware that it was a potentially risky proposition.

The genesis of *The Prisoner* is generally attributed to a meeting of minds between McGoohan and writer/journalist/script editor

---

2 In the British context, 'independent television' refers to television programmes, companies and stations that are not connected with the BBC (British Broadcasting Corporation), and which obtain the bulk of their finances from advertising and overseas sales rather than from the 'license fee', a charge levied on all UK residents who possess televisions, which goes towards supporting the BBC and its productions. Independent television broadcasting companies collectively form an affiliated network known as ITV.

George Markstein. McGoohan was born in New York in 1928 to Irish parents, who very shortly thereafter returned to Ireland, where he spent the first seven years of his life before the family moved to England. McGoohan left school at 16, originally intending to become a Jesuit priest, but instead taking up a variety of short-term jobs while engaging in amateur acting on the side prior to landing a position as stage manager at the Sheffield Repertory. While there, McGoohan played his first professional role – filling in for another actor who was taken ill – and went on to become a member of the company (he also met and married Joan Drummond, to whom he is still married at the time of writing). McGoohan gradually rose through the ranks of the profession, going on to perform in the West End and to obtain a contract with the Rank Organisation, for whom he appeared in such films as *Hell Drivers* before he finally fell out with the management. He also worked frequently in the nascent medium of television. His starring role on *Danger Man* gave him the clout to push *The Prisoner* into production.

George Markstein, the other initial force behind the series, was born into a Jewish family in 1929 in Germany. He came to England in the 1930s when the Marksteins fled the Nazi regime. He worked as a journalist for *Stars and Stripes*, the US Army magazine, during the Second World War, and his ability to speak fluent German came in useful after the fall of Germany. Following the War, he continued in journalism (where he met Lewis Greifer, later to contribute to *The Prisoner*) and drifted into television (particularly independent television), becoming story editor on Associated Rediffusion's 1961 police series *No Hiding Place* and the war series *Court Martial*, an American co-production with ITC (his extensive post-*The Prisoner* credits, incidentally, also include developing Geoff McQueen's original screenplay *Woodentop* into a series format, which became ITV's long-running *The Bill*). Rumours persisted throughout his lifetime and afterwards that Markstein had been involved in espionage, but there has been no actual proof thus far; the rumours appear mostly to be based on the fact that many of his friends (including Moris Farhi, who contributed an unmade script to *The Prisoner*) credit him with an 'encyclopaedic' knowledge of spy lore, and that he once accused writer Paul Theroux of being a spy. He was also, by all accounts, a private and secretive man, which may have been an influence on the character of the mysterious figure at the centre of *The Prisoner*.

The question of which of the two – McGoohan or Markstein – should take the credit for coming up with the actual idea for *The Prisoner* has long been in dispute. McGoohan, in the 1984 Channel Four documentary *Six Into One: The Prisoner File*, said: 'It was in my mind from the very early days, since maybe about seven years old. The individual against the establishment, the individual against bureaucracy, the individual against so many laws that were all confining. The church, for instance: it was almost impossible to do anything that was not some form of sin.' George Markstein, by contrast, claimed that he came up with the idea on a train between Shepperton and Waterloo at 6.21 pm one day in 1966, while he was working on *Danger Man*. He said that it was based on stories he had heard, while working as a journalist attached to British Intelligence in the Second World War, about Inverlair, an establishment controlled by the Special Operations Executive (SOE) in Inverness, which was used for housing spies who, as it were, knew too much; although they were well treated, they were effectively kept prisoner, so that the information they had would not get out. Markstein asserted that he then worked up this idea and told it to McGoohan, who subsequently claimed it as his own. Lewis Greifer has confirmed that Markstein had discussed the idea with him long before it came to fruition. David Tomblin, on the other hand, has apparently attested that he and McGoohan jointly came up with the idea some years earlier. In the final analysis, it is probably fairest to say that McGoohan and Markstein were both working towards a similar concept, and found their ideas compatible, and that the subsequent attempts by each to claim sole credit must be seen in the light of their having fallen out.

The question of how many episodes were initially planned is also uncertain. McGoohan has stated that he thought the concept of *The Prisoner* would run to a seven-episode miniseries, but that Grade persuaded him to go with a 26-episode series, split into two production blocks, which would then form a first and second season and could be sold to the USA (some sources, notably Roger Langley, give different figures, up to 30 episodes; 26, however, is the most frequently quoted). In either case, *The Prisoner* gave no real indication, at this early stage, that it was to be anything other than a spy series with a slightly original twist on the concept, developed by a well-known actor (with some directing experience already to his credit on *Danger Man*) and a journalist/writer, and financed by a prominent independent television company with a view to selling it overseas.

BRIEFED, DEBRIEFED OR NUMBERED: PRODUCTION OF *THE PRISONER*

The production values on the new series were intended to be high from the start. Even though the ITV companies were still transmitting in black and white at the time, filming was done on 35 mm colour stock.[3] This was with a view to the possibility of US sales – a strategy that appears to have reaped great dividends, as McGoohan stated in a 1979 interview with Roger Goodman that Lew Grade was able to sell five other series (which were, in McGoohan's opinion, 'all rubbish') to an American network simply on the basis of a rough cut of *The Prisoner*'s opening episode, 'Arrival' (Ian Rakoff, however, has a slightly different story, saying that Michael Dann, Senior Vice-President of Programming for CBS, viewed a few of the series' early episodes and said that while he liked it, he did not think that American audiences would 'go for a loser'; McGoohan was uncompromising, but Lew Grade managed to persuade Dann to buy the series anyway, with the promise that it would change and everything would be resolved in the end). Beyond this, however, there are strong visual influences on *The Prisoner* from German Expressionism (principally Fritz Lang, F W Murnau and Robert Wiene), courtesy of production designer Jack Shampan. This gives the series a distinctive look, with attention to symbolic detail extending even down to the font used (the lack of capital letters in the modified Albertus font as seen in the Village signage, for instance, symbolising the suppression of the standout individual). McGoohan seems to have been particularly concerned about making the series more filmic: according to White and Ali in

---

3 The fact that the series was shot in colour rather than black and white may have contributed to its enduring popularity – certainly in the UK, as British television stations are reluctant to repeat black and white material, even in the digital age.

The Official Prisoner Companion, he insisted that the word 'television' should not be used on set.

Patrick McGoohan was, from the start, the dominating influence on the series. His official title was Executive Producer, meaning that he had overall creative control; however, rather than simply approving the decisions of others, he involved himself to a great degree in all aspects of production, apparently supervising costuming, effects, casting (Angelo Muscat was reportedly one of his finds) and scripting (editing most scripts and even rewriting large portions of some). Along with Robert Rietty, McGoohan did most of the uncredited overdubbing on the series, and particularly enjoyed doing silly voices (for instance, that of the bald man chanting nonsense syllables in the hospital in 'Arrival'). According to Eric Mival, the music editor on the series, McGoohan also was concerned about *The Prisoner* being viewed in the long-term, asking him if he thought the use of The Beatles' 'All You Need is Love' might ultimately date it. He certainly seems to have had a formidable reputation among the crew. Ian Rakoff says: 'He was an extraordinarily strong presence [but] his raw authority was accompanied by a definite softness, and an acute concern about stepping on our toes.'

Location filming began with a four-week shoot at Portmeirion in September 1966. The Portmeirion hotel complex in North Wales was founded in 1925 by architect Clough Williams-Ellis as a site for preserving 'rescued' old buildings of interest and for building new ones in attractive and interesting, predominately Italianate, styles. This has made it a long-time favourite filming location for British production companies, saving them the cost of going abroad to obtain exotic-looking settings. McGoohan allegedly hit on the idea of using Portmeirion after seeing it while filming *Danger Man*, although Markstein claimed that he himself came up with the idea after seeing a magazine article on the hotel and its creator. In *Six of One: The Prisoner File*, McGoohan said: 'This was a setting that could be beautiful enough, mysterious enough and confining enough to be the place for our man ... in isolation.'

Workloads on the series were heavy from the start, with the crew, according to David Tomblin, working a seven-day week and, often, a 16-hour day (and McGoohan, apparently, frequently going further: he would, according to Roger Langley's *The Prisoner in*

Portmeirion, work a full day in the studio from 7 am until nightfall and then drive through the night to arrive at the next day's filming location). According to Tomblin, where 15 to 20 set-ups per day was usual for a television production, *The Prisoner* involved 33 set-ups per day on average, and, in one 48-hour period, had no fewer than 104. Supporting artists for the location filming were recruited from the local labour exchange in Porthmadoc (which has made tracking down the names of uncredited cast members somewhat difficult for later commentators). Production was also disorganised and ad-hoc, even at a relatively early stage: Peter Graham-Scott, director of 'The General', recalls in *The Prisoner in Portmeirion* that he received a call from McGoohan on a Friday night asking him to take over an episode on the following Monday: 'The script arrived on a Saturday morning, giving me 48 hours to prepare it.' Angelo Muscat's costume was apparently improvised out of a donkey jacket, because wardrobe assistant Catherine Williams had been unaware of his small stature: when she had been unable to find the actor in the *Spotlight* directory and had asked propsman Mickey O'Toole for advice, he had told her as a prank that Muscat was a giant. Daily rushes of the filming were viewed at the Coliseum Theatre in Porthmadoc; as everyone involved was invited to come to these viewings, they technically constitute the first public screenings of *The Prisoner*. At the end of location filming, two parties were thrown, one for the extras, and one for the cast and crew.

Between October 1966 and March 1967, the studio filming and editing was done on the 13 programmes originally intended to make up the first series. Filming took place in and around MGM Studios at Borehamwood. There were two permanent sets – Number Six's cottage, and the Control Room and Number Two's office, which were the same set redressed – but otherwise filming took place on temporary sets (further details of filming can be found in the individual episode analyses below). In March 1967, the crew made a return trip to Portmeirion with McGoohan, to film inserts for several episodes, plus extensive footage for 'Many Happy Returns'; a third shoot apparently took place in August/September 1967 with Frank Maher standing in for McGoohan. In December 1966, a *The Prisoner* Christmas card was sent out to all crew members, showing a festive scene of the Village Butler, the penny-farthing, snow and holly.

After the completing of filming on the first production block of 13 episodes, the crew took a four-month break. Although the series was on schedule at this point (as 13 episodes being shot in a little over six months was average for a series of 50-minute filmed programmes at the time), it was well over budget. A further reason for pessimism about the show's future was that there had been a massive falling-out between McGoohan and Markstein about its direction. This dispute had been foreshadowed in the early departure from the series of acting co-producer Leslie Gilliat, who had previously produced, among other things, *The Great St Trinian's Train Robbery*. While Gilliat had been present at some of the location shooting, he had not liked the direction in which the series had been heading, and, apparently, McGoohan had refused to compromise. McGoohan's split with Markstein was of a similar nature. Markstein apparently wanted the series to be a more-or-less conventional spy story with an original twist (his 1974 novel, *The Cooler*, set in a fictional representation of Inverlair, renamed Inverloch, and revolving to a certain extent around chess, gives us some idea of what a straight Marksteinian version of *The Prisoner* might have been like) whereas McGoohan wanted something with more in the way of surrealism and allegory. Although Markstein had begun to express unhappiness with the series as early as on the shooting of 'Once Upon a Time' (which was sixth in filming order), he eventually left after 'Many Happy Returns' (thirteenth in filming order), feeling that his original concept had been compromised (he would later state that his departure was prompted by McGoohan's claiming sole creative credit for the concept, although this is more than likely to be a rationalisation after the fact). Ironically, in 'Many Happy Returns', Markstein briefly reprised his role from *The Prisoner*'s title sequence, of the nameless man to whom the Prisoner delivers his resignation. The split has coloured much of what both men have said about the series in subsequent interviews: McGoohan's periodic claim that the Prisoner was not a spy, but a scientist, for instance, must be considered in light of Markstein's fascination with espionage.

The departure of Markstein worsened the already tension-fraught atmosphere among the crew. At some point during the first production block, two scripts that had been commissioned by Markstein, 'The Outsider' by Moris Farhi (which had got as far as pre-production) and 'Don't Get Yourself Killed' by Gerald Kelsey, had been cancelled by McGoohan; following the break between production blocks (by which time Markstein had left), McGoohan and Tomblin solicited scripts from members of the crew, the only one of which actually saw production was 'Living in Harmony' by David Tomblin from an idea by Ian Rakoff (who says that he had been pitching the story to both McGoohan and Markstein for some time prior to this). All of this increased the pressure on the cast, crew and McGoohan, whose control on the series had now become even more extensive. Rakoff's memoir *Inside The Prisoner* emphasises the dire straits the production was in at the time, saying that McGoohan agreed to take a role in the Hollywood film *Ice Station Zebra* in the middle of making *The Prisoner* in order to put the money he earned from the film towards subsidising the production of the television series. Rakoff recalls being paid his wages out of Tomblin's own pocket, and that Tomblin was pessimistic at the time that the programme would even be broadcast, saying, 'Residuals? That's the money the series won't be making.'

With the second production block formally beginning on 26 August 1967, work continued on the series as the screening began in autumn of that year – 'Do Not Forsake Me Oh My Darling' was filmed in September. However, although the second production block had originally been scheduled to comprise 13 episodes, only four were ultimately made, resulting in *The Prisoner* running to an unusual total of 17 episodes. There was no amusing Christmas card in December 1967: during the filming of 'The Girl Who Was Death' in mid-October, McGoohan announced to the crew that the next episode ('Fall Out', filmed in November and possibly into the start of December) would be the last.

Rakoff describes McGoohan around this time as becoming difficult to work with: 'It appeared that something new had been gathering force inside Pat, simmering away, heading for an implosion.' In a sense, just as there was a parallel between McGoohan's own resignation from *Danger Man* and his character's resignation from his secret service job at the outset of *The Prisoner*, there was also a parallel between McGoohan's increasing control over the *The Prisoner* and its increasing focus on the central character's psyche, and (as Fairclough notes in *The Prisoner: The*

Official Companion) between McGoohan's effective destruction of the series, whether deliberately or through events getting out of control, and his character's destruction of the Village.

McGoohan would later claim that the decision to end the series was his own, saying both 'It has knocked me out. I'm whacked. This is why I'm stopping. I just can't do any more' and, in more reflective moments, that the series had reached a natural end beyond which there would be no point in continuing. Whatever was behind the decision to end the series, it also meant the end of a production that was as chaotic and fraught with tensions as it was exacting and high quality.

MY LIFE IS MY OWN: RECEPTION OF *THE PRISONER*

Despite the expense lavished upon the series and its filmic qualities, the public reaction to *The Prisoner* was initially rather lukewarm. This is not surprising when one considers that it had been marketed to them as nothing more than an offbeat spy adventure (with even ATV publicity keeping up that expectation until almost the last minute); modern viewers coming to the series for the first time generally have the advantage of knowing beforehand that it is something rather stranger than that.

The press reacted with bafflement to incidents like the famous press conference on 20 September 1967 (midway through the filming of 'Living in Harmony') where McGoohan turned up wearing a Kosho uniform (Kosho being a bizarre contact sport cum martial art created for the series) and a Russian-style fur hat, in the cage from 'Once Upon a Time', accompanied by Angelo Muscat, Alexis Kanner, a penny-farthing and a group of attendants and waiters dressed as Villagers, and asked the assembled reporters questions rather than answering them; and ATV's press sheets attempting to explain 'Fall Out' to the public after the episode had been broadcast did little at the time to help matters.

The reaction to 'Fall Out' was so hostile that McGoohan allegedly packed up his family and left the country, first moving to Switzerland and then to America, to let things cool off. He later said: 'I was nearly lynched in England when the episode came out. Everyone wanted to know what it was all about. Was I on the

Communist side or on the British side, or what? They wanted all the answers tied up with ribbon and handed out.' And, elsewhere: 'I had to go into bloody hiding for two weeks or I would have been killed' (Rakoff, however, says that the departure for Switzerland did not come until some time after *The Prisoner* had been broadcast and McGoohan had rejected the two-film deal mentioned below). Hostility continued even after *The Prisoner* went into repeats, although the controversy which continued to generate did gradually encourage the development of a fandom for the series, which would ultimately lead to its eventual acceptance by the public as a genuine landmark in television production. The series was pre-sold to the US, largely due to the success of *Danger Man* and to Lew Grade's persuasive powers (see above), with its distribution and schedule negotiated for a year ahead; however, it was not much more successful there on its initial release than it was in the UK.

Everyman Films had planned another TV series, *The Outsider* (unrelated to the unmade script by Moris Farhi), which, according to an interview in *Inside The Prisoner*, Lewis Greifer, its creator, had first pitched to the company while *Danger Man* was still in production. However, Everyman Films was deeply in debt by this point (the debts incurred over *The Prisoner* amounted to at least £63,000, of which £32,000 was in taxes), and McGoohan also showed no interest in producing another series, also turning down the opportunity to make two ITC-funded films with David Tomblin and Terence Feely, one a story about a retired agent who settles in Ireland and becomes involved with the IRA, the other, significantly, a filmed version of Ibsen's *Brand*, simply because Grade would not increase the funding for the two pictures from £900,000 to £1,000,000. *The Outsider* reads, to modern eyes, rather like a Bizarro Universe version of *The Prisoner*, featuring as it does Patrick McGoohan as 'Johnny Quill', a *The Fugitive*-type loner who wanders the countryside becoming involved in other people's lives and delivering fairly preachy homilies on individualism. The pilot script, 'Noises Off' by Lewis Greifer, involves Quill convincing a property developer that village life is a good thing and should not be disrupted or challenged; the setting of the village in question is unclear, incorporating as it does both British and American elements. As this does not sound like the most promising of new projects, some might say that it is just as well that Everyman went bankrupt before production could begin on it, although it is more than likely that some of the elements had already made it into *The Prisoner*.

Everyman was formally dissolved in 1974, and David Tomblin has subsequently claimed that he never made a penny out of its solitary television project. Although McGoohan remained one of the highest paid actors in Britain at the end of the series, and ultimately retained a share of the profits, other writers, ironically, wound up turning to Markstein for help: as Chairman of the Writers' Guild, he was able to pursue ITC over royalties owing to them. One of these writers, Roger Parkes, said in an interview in *The Prisoner: The Original Scripts vol. 1*: 'When, after more than a decade, with the series aired many times over in virtually every country in the world, to a global audience of billions … would … a further share of what by then had to be astronomical royalties, finally start to come out? George, due for a bigger share than any of us, hoisted the torch high enough to set a lawyer on ITC. And this, finally, did unlock a trickle. That trickle, never more than a few hundred pounds a year, still continues today.'

In hindsight, Patrick McGoohan has also been given to expressing mixed feelings about the series. Shortly after its original transmission, he was quoted as saying that he didn't think it came off 100%, that he blamed himself for this, that the progression of the story needed to be more related to the original premise, that they should have had a year's preparation, and that it was an error to start with only five or six scripts. In more bellicose moods, however, he has defended the ending of the series, saying: 'Don't expect a final pay-off. There isn't one. There's no big tying-up of loose ends. You still want to know its message? Then it's this: the most dangerous thing in the world is an attitude of mind.' It is arguably this quality that has kept *The Prisoner* in the public eye ever since.

In his academic analysis of *The Prisoner, Be Seeing You*, writer Chris Gregory interprets the Prisoner's rebellion as being not just against the Village and the society it represents, but against the medium itself, given the series' controversial production and genre-bending aspects. As such, then, its production history gives us valuable insights into the psychology and practicalities that contributed to *The Prisoner*'s final form.

Illustrious Predecessors:
The Prisoner In Context

Much has already been written on the ways in which *The Prisoner* draws on both the popular and high cultures of its time – pop art, the reaction to the Vietnam War, the development of the spy thriller genre of novels and films, and so forth – such that little more needs to be said on these subjects. As a consequence, we will here focus on some of the series' less-often-discussed antecedents: the 1959 stage and television production of Ibsen's *Brand*, the post-war surreal comedy genre, and the fashion for psychoanalysis in mainstream film and television (particularly, but not exclusively, in Hollywood). *Danger Man* is a sufficiently influential subject to require a chapter of its own, which follows this one.

DEFYING IDENTIFICATION:
THE PRISONER AS GENRE-BENDER

While *The Prisoner* appears to belong to a particular genre (the spy series), it also adopts elements of other genres (science fiction, comedy) and uses the concept of genre to achieve its ends. *The Prisoner* was, bizarrely, both of its time (in terms of its imagery and themes) and ahead of its time (in terms of its postmodern attitude to narrative and series), and this tension is worth exploring.

As noted, the series was initially packaged and sold to its audiences as a spy thriller (hence, if nothing else, the hostile reactions of the original viewers to the ending, and the less hostile reactions of subsequent ones, who tend to have the series sold to them as a fantasy or a high-art piece). Although it has little in common with 'realistic' spy stories (like those in the TV series *Callan* or in the works of John le Carré), the 'fantasy' spy story (as seen for example in *The Avengers* and in the James Bond franchise) was a recognised subgenre, and thus the fantasy elements do not in and of themselves prevent *The Prisoner* from being seen as distinct from other spy series of the day. The style of some of its music strongly recalls that of *The Avengers* (particularly in 'Arrival') and of *Danger Man*. In plot terms, elements from the James Bond books and films make their way not only into the explicit spoof 'The Girl Who Was Death' but also into more serious episodes. In the film of Ian Fleming's *Thunderball*, for instance, the head of SPECTRE is referred to only as 'Number One', and his operatives all use numbers rather than names to designate themselves (this gave the original audience of *The Prisioner* an expectation that Number One would turn out to be a Blofeld-style villain). In the same film, SPECTRE threaten to blow up London with a nuclear warhead, and in *You Only Live Twice*, there is an underground base, complete with rocket, very like that seen in 'Fall Out' (which McGoohan wrote very shortly after the latter film's release in 1967). Chris Gregory, in his book *Be Seeing You*, points out that the idea of the Village as a global force, independent of East and West, recalls the SPECTRE-type independent organisations that populate the genre. *The Prisoner* thus fits within the spy-series genre in a number of ways.

The Prisoner is also not that distinct, in some respects, from its ITC stablemates. Like other independent-television spy series, it lacks continuity for the most part, and very few of the episodes need to be viewed in a particular order (see 'Essay 2: Story Order'). However, *The Prisoner* also subverts the genre in a number of ways. Whereas popular spy series of the time generally had stories that changed context from week to week (different location, different antagonist, different problem to solve), *The Prisoner* was almost exactly the opposite. Also, whereas these series were generally very commercial, made with an eye firmly on the financial bottom line (and, indeed, Lew Grade backed *The Prisoner* at least partly because he initially thought it would be a similar commercial success), and, as a result, tended to date very quickly, *The Prisoner* was initially a commercial failure, but has endured in the public consciousness long after the likes of *Jason King* have been relegated to the 6 pm slot on ITV4 (by 1995, even Lew Grade acknowledged its success when he announced that he wanted to produce a feature film remake).

Similarly, we have the issue of formula. Like other spy series of the time, *The Prisoner* is actually a formula series, albeit one that gives the lie to the idea that 'formulaic' television is inherently dull and repetitive. Its episodes frequently involve a pretty (usually unconventionally so) woman with whom the Prisoner forms an uneasy but friendly relationship; a person who appears to be both a member of the establishment and sympathetic to the Prisoner himself; a seemingly innocuous Village activity or event that the Prisoner tries to turn to his own advantage; a fight and/or chase scene (with only 'The Chimes of Big Ben' and 'Dance of the Dead' lacking fight sequences, and both featuring equally dramatic chases instead). There is always a strongly characterised Number Two, and a death of some sort is central to most episodes. Nine out of 17 episodes also feature doubles (and, if one is less strict on what one considers a double, the count becomes higher). However, *The Prisoner* rings clever changes on these ideas, such that it is difficult to notice that exactly the same formula underlies stories as diverse as 'Living in Harmony', 'Dance of the Dead' and 'A Change of Mind'.

The Prisoner also undercuts the spy genre by bringing in aspects of other popular culture genres. While, in the 1979 Goodman interview, McGoohan categorically rejects the idea of classifying *The Prisoner* as science fiction, there is a certain resemblance to such classic stories as *Quatermass II*, which dealt with paranoia and fear focused around the idea of an alien force taking over British bureaucracy, with the added concern that it was difficult to tell who was working for whom, and *Quatermass and the Pit*, which is in part about the power of denial and the influence of the darker aspects of the human psyche. There are also connections to the prison-camp film, notably *The Colditz Story*, which featured Eric Portman (Number Two in 'Free for All') as a British senior officer and Richard Wattis (from 'The Chimes of Big Ben' and *Danger Man*). The Prisoner's own fictional escape attempts mirror the real-life schemes of the imprisoned officers (some of the real-life attempts even outdo the Prisoner's in their bizarreness and ingenuity), and the nature of the Village community – international, polyglot and subject to both formal and informal surveillance strategies – mirrors that of fictional, semi-fictional and real prison camps. *The Prisoner* thus collaborates with, subverts and combines genres.

Chris Gregory says that McGoohan invites the audience 'to share in the vicarious "thrills" of the action-adventure, secret agent and science fiction genres, while confronting them with a series of political, psychological and philosophical concerns'. In the fusion of these elements, he poises the relationship between reality and fantasy, and between significance and pure escapism, arguing that *The Prisoner* uses genre conventions to draw the audience into debates not normally the purview of genre television. In his interview with Tom Goodman, McGoohan, repeating a phrase he had heard sometime earlier, asks which came first, McGoohan or McLuhan; he then, with regard to popular culture, attacks the television viewer for his/her complacency in absorbing the message of programmes without question. *The Prisoner*, of course, forces the viewer to question the programme they are watching.

A MAN IN ISOLATION: IBSEN'S BRAND

The 1959 production of Ibsen's *Brand* at the Lyric Theatre Hammersmith (which was subsequently televised by the BBC) is a notable antecedent to *The Prisoner*, not only because it brought Patrick McGoohan to the attention of the public (to say nothing of Ralph Smart, executive producer of *Danger Man*, who cast him partly on the strength of his performance) as an actor capable of tackling difficult and controversial dramatic parts, but also because the play itself was a strong influence on the development of the series' central character.

In the play, which was translated and adapted by Michael Meyer from Ibsen's original (a five-hour-long script that had formerly been deemed unstageable by most), McGoohan played the title character, Brand, a priest in an isolated Norwegian village who is obsessed with the idea that he must give everything to God, saying repeatedly 'you must give all or nothing'. In living up to this ideal, he loses his mother, his wife and his son, is undercut by the village's authority figures, is driven out by the disillusioned villagers and is finally killed in an avalanche. The story is clearly a favourite with

McGoohan; he planned to produce a film version of it right after the completion of *The Prisoner*, and was still interested in doing so years later, as mentioned in the Goodman interview. Although he had also appeared in a 1962 production of Bridget Boland's play *The Prisoner*, which involves an unnamed cardinal in an unnamed Eastern European country being interrogated by an unnamed man (the part played by McGoohan), this has only a superficial connection to the subsequent series, and it is *Brand* that continually recurs in McGoohan's interviews on the subject.

The play demonstrated clearly that McGoohan was excellent at portraying dedicated loners. Michael Meyer said regarding his performance, 'What he wasn't good at … was relationships. He was very like Laurence Oliver in that. Laurence Oliver was never in his whole career able convincingly to act a son, a husband or a father. He could act the kind of father who can't make contact with anyone, like in *The Entertainer*, [and] possibly *Long Day's Journey*, but relationships he couldn't, and Pat wasn't good at that either. But what he was very good at was at acting loners, or people who can't make contact. Brand was someone who couldn't really have a close relationship, even with his wife.'

McGoohan's powerful performance as Brand thus anticipated his role as the protagonist of *The Prisoner*, another man willing to sacrifice all to maintain his personal integrity. The two characters have a lot in common. While Brand is more intense than the Prisoner, both are powerfully individualistic men who find themselves pitted against an uncomprehending community, and who are capable both of superhuman acts of resistance and of a certain amount of emotional cruelty in staying free of the influence of the community's norms and values. Brand shows a mounting egomania, mirrored in *The Prisoner*'s focus on the Prisoner to the exclusion of other characters, and is ultimately destroyed by his egocentricity, just as 'Fall Out' can be seen, in part, to consider the dangers of focusing on the ego to the exclusion of all else. Like the Prisoner, Brand is explicitly asked by the villagers to lead them, and he refuses, but nonetheless paradoxically remains a leader figure to the community. Both men continually form allegiances which are disastrous and doomed: the deaths of the various members of Brand's family anticipate how the Prisoner's relationships with apparently friendly Villagers seem always to end in tragedy and/or betrayal. Whether consciously or not, the character of Brand is a clear influence on that of the Prisoner himself.

The Prisoner's unwillingness to compromise is also anticipated in *Brand*. When Brand inherits his mother's money, he is encouraged to leave the community and go south so that his son might recover from his illness in the more temperate climate, but in the end he refuses to leave his post, even though he knows it will lead to the death of his son, because the villagers are afraid that he will desert them and fear the spiritual consequences. Ultimately, Brand becomes the enemy of all compromise, saying to the uncomprehending villagers (foreshadowing the Prisoner's own exhortations to the populace in 'Free for All') 'Compromise is the way of Satan! Your enemy is within you! Within you! A worm sapping your strength!' The implication at the end of 'Fall Out' that the Prisoner has left the Village to spread a both liberating and destructive rebellion throughout the world recalls Brand facing the fatal avalanche at the end of the play.

Moreover, the two men have similar relationships with the authorities of their respective villages. In *Brand,* the local Mayor and Provost co-opt Brand's idealistic desire to rebuild the village church for their own political ends. The Provost, in a speech which could have come straight out of *The Prisoner*, warns Brand against setting himself apart from the community: 'Every man must curb his individuality, humble himself. And not always be trying to rise above his fellow men. The man who fights alone will never achieve anything of lasting value. Well, goodbye. I have to preach a sermon on the duality of human nature and must take a little light refreshment first.' The Provost later addresses the villagers in another Prisoneresque attempt to suppress individualistic behaviour: 'My children, what can you achieve? Humble people born into a humble village, were you created to shake the world? You have your humble tasks allotted you. To attempt more is presumptuous and wrong. You will only be preyed upon by the ruthless and the mighty. My children – my sheep – .' Ultimately, the villagers are deterred from listening to Brand by virtue of a politician's lie, when the Mayor claims that there is a shoal of fish in the harbour and they all rush off to catch them, in an indictment of how people willingly trade freedom for material comfort. Furthermore, the religious themes of the play, and the issue of the relationship between God and society ('The voice of the people is the voice of God,' claims the Provost at one point) would also influence *The Prisoner*, and its exploration of temptation and sacrifice on the part of a truly faithful man.

As the Prisoner famously echoes and blends himself into his creator McGoohan's own life, too, aspects of Brand anticipate McGoohan's relationship with *The Prisoner*. Both Brand and McGoohan were men of integrity, with McGoohan's desertion of *Danger Man* to the mystification of all those who could not understand why he'd give up a financially and culturally successful series, and working himself into a near-breakdown over *The Prisoner*, echoed Brand's own self-sacrifice in the name of his beliefs. Like Brand putting his inheritance money into the building of the church, McGoohan also reportedly put up some of his own money to finance the production. Also like Brand, he put his career on the line with a gamble over something he really believed in. Peter Sallis, who played the Doctor and the Provost in the production, described McGoohan by saying: 'At times he was terrifying on the stage; to be with, I mean. You saw this look of God going right through you. And he sustained it.' This is an impression shared by many who worked on *The Prisoner*. McGoohan's behaviour thus has much in common with that of the character whose story influenced *The Prisoner*.

THE PALACE OF FUN:
CONTEMPORARY COMEDY AND SPOOFERY

Another influence on *The Prisoner*, despite its ostensible pigeonholing as a drama series, was British comedy of the 1950s and 1960s, particularly the savage, satirical and surreal type that grew up in the wake of the Second World War. While *The Prisoner* lacks actual laugh-out-loud gags and plays itself straight for the most part, it is a mark of its nature as a genre-busting series that it is able to draw ideas and tropes from comedy and successfully apply them to a dramatic context.

Britain in the 1950s and early 1960s was a country that had been through a massive social disruption, involving the loss of its empire as well as about ten years of economic austerity, and a sudden return to social conservatism which, after the socially and sexually liberal period of the war, brought about feelings of disassociation and alienation among many. This unease, however, gave rise to a new form of comedy, exemplified chiefly by the radio series *The Goon Show*, which was surreal, repeatedly played with dramatic and comedic conventions and made sophisticated use of the audio medium, referenced contemporary popular culture, and occasionally worked in pointed social commentary under the guise of comedy, for instance sending up the British media's attempts to sanitise the events of the War into ripping dramatic yarns. Also of note is the 1960s radio series *Round the Horne*, which, while less overtly anarchic, also engaged in knowing send-ups of popular culture (including, in later series, spy stories and films), as well as exploding social conventions through its continued references to the then-still-criminalised homosexual male culture.

The influence of such programmes can be seen in *The Prisoner*, most obviously in its occasional moments of biting humour (the title 'Living in Harmony' being superimposed over a scene of extreme violence, for instance, or the representative of the 'Anarchists' denouncing Number 48 as antisocial in 'Fall Out'), but also in its fondness for sending up or exploding dramatic conventions. 'The Girl Who Was Death' knowingly satirises spy series, taking this to such ludicrous extremes as having Mr X don a Sherlock Holmes-style deerstalker and cape; and, by continually pulling the rug out from under the Prisoner's escape attempts, almost every episode subverts the audience's anticipation that the virtuous hero will triumph over his evil adversaries.

By the time *The Prisoner* was conceived, however, the surreal comedy genre had moved to television, which brought about a new twist in the form of overt contemporary political satire. Programmes like *That Was the Week that Was* and *BBC3* (not to be confused with the present-day digital channel BBC Three) used comedy and satire actively to skewer the political establishment, in contrast to the generally reverent humour styles of the pre-war era (of which *Punch* magazine is usually cited as the chief example). This, consequently, paved the way for *The Prisoner* to engage in active criticism of the British political establishment, with its portrayals of the Prisoner's superiors as invariably in cahoots with the Village authorities (if indeed they are not one and the same), and the Village's own system mirroring the worst excesses of contemporary political societies ('elections' that are largely a pretence at democracy, for instance, or supposed rebels being co-opted into doing the work of the system they revile). While it may not engage in overt political satire, then, the development of this genre of television enabled *The Prisoner* to take the form that it did.

Finally, however, the Prisoner is also in line with the rise, during the period, of such surreal comedy, or comedy-drama, films as *The Magic Christian, What's New, Pussycat?, Help!* (which featured both Leo McKern and Patrick Cargill) and *The Magical Mystery Tour* (which came out over Christmas 1967 to the bafflement of the general public, causing a correspondent in *TV Times* to remark about 'Fall Out': 'I have come to the conclusion that it was part two of *The Magical Mystery Tour*').

One such film with a particular connection to *The Prisoner* is *Casino Royale*, which was in production at the same time, but was released early enough to be a heavy influence on 'The Girl Who Was Death'. Both productions, as well as sharing the acting talents of Colin Gordon, were partly filmed at the same studio, MGM in Borehamwood, making the possibility of comedic cross-fertilisation even more likely (the back lot used for the sequence where 'Jimmy' Bond faces a firing squad is the same one on which 'Living in Harmony' was filmed). Like *The Prisoner*, *Casino Royale* features bizarrely explained doubles (with seven people calling themselves James Bond at the eponymous casino, at least one villain-created double of Bond, a set-up in which every British agent, male or female, adopts the alias 'James Bond' and the number '007', and a climax that features an American Indian, a seal and a dog all bearing the number, a plot to use doubles of world leaders for nefarious ends, and Mata Bond, who, to judge by her portrait, is a perfect double of her mother; Moneypenny is also stated to be a double of her own mother). We see a German spy school with décor modelled on German expressionist art and a diminutive assistant who apparently runs on batteries (see not only the Butler but also Granny Bug in Thomas M Disch's *The Prisoner* novel *I Am Not a Number!*), a Head of School who strongly denies being who she claims to be, and various rooms in which we see people doing strange and pointless things (as in the Village Hospital).

The film also involves Prisoneresque themes of hallucinations and the idea of images echoing, or becoming, reality. Mata Bond, at one point, causes a group of generals to believe that war has been declared by showing them stock footage of warfare (following which she escapes from Germany to Britain in a London black cab). Le Chiffre tortures Bond (played by Peter Sellers) by pressing a button to induce a set of hallucinations which then abruptly become real, and is killed by an image on a TV screen breaking through it and shooting him. The film also has an eye motif that echoes the similar motif in *The Prisoner*. Visually and thematically, then, the film both shares ideas with and influences the series.

The ending of the film is also reminiscent of 'Fall Out'. In the finale, James Bond (played here by David Niven) unmasks the hidden villain, who turns out also to be James Bond ('Jimmy' Bond, played by Woody Allen), anticipating the Prisoner's discovery that Number One is himself, and the whole thing then degenerates into a bizarre free-for-all involving all the Bonds, stock footage, and the largely unexplained presence of cowboys, Indians and the French Foreign Legion before the casino finally blows up, killing all participants. *The Prisoner*'s intelligent lunacy thus finds both a precedent and a parallel in *Casino Royale*.

MOTHER KNOWS BEST: PSYCHOANALYSIS IN POPULAR ENTERTAINMENT

It is also worth noting, given its psychotherapeutic themes and premises, that *The Prisoner* was made at a time when psychoanalysis was a popular subject for film and television in post-war Europe and North America. In the prosperous, and mechanistic, America of the 1950s, the concept of psychiatry fitted in with the pro-science attitude of the day: mental health was equated to physical health, and therapy to curing a physical illness with exercises and pills. Consequently, films and television programmes began to focus on the mental state of their protagonists and antagonists as part of the story, rather than simply on their actions. The most notable example is Alfred Hitchcock's *Psycho* (and its numerous imitators), in which the villain is motivated by Freudian feelings about his mother, but there are others in diverse genres, such as *Harvey* (in which James Stewart's giant invisible rabbit friend serves as a metaphor for homosexuality); a number of late-entry film-noirs, such as Fritz Lang's *Secret Beyond the Door* (which evokes Freudian psychoanalytic theory in explaining the characters' bizarre obsessions); and the spate of vampire and monster films produced by the Hammer Studios and others (expressing the ambivalence towards sexual desire inherent in 1950s and early 1960s culture). The interpretation of *The Prisoner* as an exploration of its protagonist's psychological state (for instance, the fact that his fiancée is his boss's daughter in 'Do Not Forsake Me Oh My Darling' suggesting that he has a peculiarly Oedipal streak) is thus a development of the era's popular interest in psychoanalysis.

More than this, however, *The Prisoner* actually constitutes a critique of the embracing of psychoanalytic theory. Not simply in terms of its portrayal of psychoanalytic techniques as invasive, brutal, and mind-altering (in a contemporary interview, McGoohan said, 'The inquisition of the mind by psychiatrists is far worse than the assault on the body by torturers'), but through its implicit critique of the use of psychoanalytic ideas by advertisers and politicians. Post-war advertising, heavily influenced by Freud (indeed, Freud's son-in-law was a pioneer of advertising techniques), gradually eschewed text-heavy promises of quality services in favour of visceral images and ideas (sexy ladies placed next to cars; housewives in transports of delight at the sight of a washing machine, etc.) to spark an emotional response that overrides the consumer's intellect. McGoohan has quite famously railed against the use of simple, physical wants (particularly sexual ones) to sell products, notably in the Goodman interview. This trend also shows a tendency towards infantilisation: advertisers, and subsequently politicians, have increasingly appealed to infantile gratification – the satisfaction of simple, visceral desires – rather than entering into active, complex debates with their audiences over the merits of their product or platform. In *The Prisoner*, the Villagers are perpetually placed in an infantile position; encouraged, through childish activities, into an equally childish dependence on their superiors. One might also note the influence upon *The Prisoner* of Maoist imagery, with its focus on spectacle, bright colours and contrasting images, and easily-remembered, catchy soundbites, as an indictment of the suppression of discourse inherent in any political system that focuses on emotion and spectacle at the expense of issues. As McGoohan said in another contemporary interview, 'The function of any art is to speak ahead of the times, to herald the warnings that are not obvious, but are there in the atmosphere'. Critiques of the use of psychoanalysis, and of the contemporary media's fascination with it, are inherent in *The Prisoner*.

The Prisoner thus, as a genre-bending spy series, is able to incorporate not only aspects of 'straight' spy series into itself, but also displays influences from Ibsen, from the anarchic and satirical post-war British comedies, news programmes and films, and from psychoanalysis, as well as questioning and critiquing the concepts of genre, popular culture, comedy and psychology. Although on one level *The Prisoner* may have been part of its era's pop culture, on another it smacks the audience, both contemporary and subsequent, with a metaphorical mailed fist.

Drake's Drum:
Danger Man and *The Prisoner*

Any volume giving serious consideration to *The Prisoner* must also acknowledge its connections to the series Patrick McGoohan made immediately beforehand, *Danger Man*. *Danger Man* was one of the first secret agent series on either small or big screen (anticipating the James Bond films by two years, and premiering in the same year as *The Avengers*). It was also ITC's first foray into contemporary storytelling; previously it had focused on series based on such literary or folk characters as Robin Hood or the Invisible Man

.

DANGEROUS SECRETS: THE HISTORY OF *DANGER MAN*

The main creative force behind *Danger Man* was Ralph Smart, an Australian writer-producer born in London, who had previously served on such well-known independent television series of the 1950s as *The Adventures of Robin Hood*, *The Adventures of Sir Lancelot* and *The Buccaneers*. He created the series, wrote, script-edited and directed some episodes, served as producer on the first series and executive producer on the second and third (and also brought over a number of crew members from the ITC series he had just finished work on, *H G Wells' The Invisible Man*). According to writer Roger Marshall, Smart had originally intended to produce a series of televised James Bond adventures, with Bond creator Ian Fleming's blessing, and had approached McGoohan to play the part after seeing him in the 1959 production of Ibsen's *Brand* at the Lyric

Theatre Hammersmith. McGoohan, however, turned down the part because he considered the character of Bond to be too promiscuous, and, when Fleming also withdrew his permission, Smart carried on with the idea of doing a secret agent series featuring a different agent, John Drake. McGoohan was also approached independently by producers Albert R 'Cubby' Broccoli and Harry Saltzman to play James Bond in the film series, first in 1961 and again after Sean Connery departed the role, but turned it down on both occasions, for the same reason. It was reportedly ITC supremo Lew Grade who approached McGoohan to play John Drake, on the basis of his performance in a 1958 television production called *The Big Knife*. According to an article in *Starlog* (Issue #135, October 1988), McGoohan, upon reading a first script for *Danger Man*, then wrote to ITC explaining what he would and would not do, the latter including firing guns, womanising and using excessive violence. Later he explained this by saying: 'Television at the time was ... a guest in the house. I felt that just as one tries to behave properly as a guest, it behoves one playing on television to behave properly.' In a 1961 interview for *Photoplay*, he noted: 'Well it might have turned out to be terrible and trashy ... But I don't think *Danger Man* has. There are a number of ridiculous episodes which make my blood boil whenever I watch them, but on the whole there have been some pretty fair films in the batch. They could have been worse had the original conception of John Drake been portrayed. This painted him as a rough, tough, sexy guy, who hits below the belt in his fights, is always using a gun and makes a pass at every pretty girl. I fought against this. It took a little time but eventually the character was ironed out. Personally I detest violence ... one of the reasons why I always stay in on St Patrick's night.'

The first series consisted of 39 25-minute episodes screened in 1960-1961. They were initially made to be shown by ITC's parent company Associated TeleVision (ATV) and other channels in Britain's Independent Television (ITV) network that chose to purchase the series; however, Lew Grade always had an eye on selling programmes abroad, particularly to the lucrative American market (hence the fact that *Danger Man* was shot on 35 mm film, the preferred format of American networks). Stylistically, the first season also had a number of elements blatantly aimed at the American market: there is a strong influence from *Dragnet*, a popular American police series featuring voice-over narration and a jazz soundtrack; Drake is said to be Irish-American (notably in 'The Sanctuary'), with McGoohan affecting a mid-Atlantic accent throughout. He is said in most episodes to work for NATO (although this is fairly ambiguous: in some episodes he appears to act on a freelance basis, doing work for corporations and friends as well; and occasionally, for instance in 'View from the Villa' and 'Find and Return', he appears to work for NATO on a paid contract basis rather than as an employee) and the title sequence makes it plain that he works out of Washington, DC. There was also an attempt to imitate the American 'moralising' style of television drama in the unfortunately racist 'A Position of Trust', which involves a *Reefer Madness*-style portrayal of drug addiction. Ironically, despite this, the series bombed in the US, failing to secure a place in a network schedule and instead going straight into syndication. However, the pacy, contemporary style of *Danger Man* did ensure that it had some success elsewhere in the world, particularly in Europe.

This, coupled with the sudden mania for all things secret-service in the wake of the first James Bond film, *Dr. No* (1962), was enough to cause ITC to relaunch *Danger Man* three years later for a new series, screened in 1964-1965. The episodes were extended to 50 minutes in length, although they remained very fast-moving and exciting. Moreover, with a nod to the embryonic James Bond franchise, the action was relocated firmly to Britain, and Drake made British (aside from in three episodes, 'Fair Exchange', 'Fish on the Hook' and 'Don't Nail Him Yet', in which he affects an accent that fluctuates between received pronunciation, mid-Atlantic and Irish; these were the first three episodes in production order, meaning that this is probably a holdover from the previous series). These new episodes see Drake working for M9, a fictitious branch of the British secret service, which uses a travel agency, World Travel (possibly a nod to the name of the company supplying most of the stock footage for the series, World Backgrounds), as its cover. However, they lack some of the more Bondian elements of the original series, with Drake abandoning his Aston Martin in favour of a Mini Cooper, and with a number of episodes questioning the morality of spying and the secret service (in 'Yesterday's Enemies', for instance, M9 arrange to have a rogue agent, Archer, killed without informing Drake of their intentions; and in 'Judgment Day', Drake's superiors turn out to be willing to use a former Nazi scientist's work, without consideration for where his evidence was obtained). The reformatted series was a success in the USA under the title of *Secret Agent*, with a catchy theme tune, 'Secret Agent Man', which has achieved a certain amount of popularity independent of the show.

The third series, screened in 1965-1966, was also popular and well-made, but artistically was starting to drift.[4] Concepts from the first two series began to be reused (Drake being framed for murder by enemy agents; Drake having to rescue a compromised spymaster in a Communist country; Drake posing as a butler; and so forth). The Bondian gadgetry that had started to feature heavily in Series Two became even more prevalent (in 'Someone is Liable to Get Hurt', for instance, Drake is revealed to sleep in a bed with a TV screen in the footboard and other sorts of communication devices in the headboard). All of this may well explain why McGoohan then decided to leave the series. As he later commented: 'I enjoyed doing *Danger Man*, but I thought we'd done enough, and the ideas started to get a bit thin.'

The 'fourth season' of *Danger Man* thus consisted of only two episodes, 'Koroshi' and 'Shinda Shima', story-edited by George Markstein (whose first credit on the series was as 'script consultant' for the Series Three episode 'Not So Jolly Roger'), which, while not precisely constituting a two-part story, are linked in terms of their location (Japan) and could be broadcast either separately or, with slightly different footage, as a single, feature-length compilation – which is what was done in the US, under the title 'Koroshi'. These are also the only colour episodes of *Danger Man* – although McGoohan claimed in the 1979 Roger Goodman interview that he had urged Lew Grade to make the series in colour from the start – and due to this are the only episodes to get regular repeats on British digital television at present. Unfortunately, they are also among the episodes that most approach the James Bond formula, and – featuring as they do secret orders of Japanese assassins whose members are almost entirely European, and diabolical masterminds

---

4 The second and third series were sold, though not always screened, in blocks of 32 and 13 episodes respectively.

with bases under volcanic islands and heavy machine-guns built into their desks – tend to give a false impression of the overall style and credibility of the series.

McGoohan's abrupt departure from such a successful series may have been a surprise to audiences and production people alike; however, his view that it had run its course seems to be borne out by its history, and also speaks of a strong sense of artistic integrity on his part.

A MAN TO BE TRUSTED: *DANGER MAN* EXPLORED

Seen from the perspective of 40 years on, *Danger Man* actually stands up quite well in terms of its stories and presentation, compared with most of its contemporaries. The series is graced with a staggering number of extremely good fight sequences with spectacular choreography, and some episodes are quite powerful: good examples are 'No Marks for Servility', in which Drake poses as a butler to entrap a criminal, and which features a tour-de-force performance from McGoohan, and the abovementioned 'Judgement Day', in which Drake is forced to defend a Nazi war criminal against an Israeli paramilitary organisation, despite his own feelings about the situation. While the use of stock footage backgrounds and sets to represent foreign locations may look a little unconvincing to modern eyes, it must be remembered that at the time the series was made, international travel was still beyond the reach of many Britons; although the rise of the cheap package holiday meant that people were becoming interested in foreign holidays, even Spain and Italy were still considered fairly exotic.

While generally good, the series does suffer from a few problems. It has a tendency to go in for gratuitous gadgetry in some episodes, and its portrayal of women is generally fairly conventional, with most of the female characters appearing to be in their mid-twenties (with occasional older women usually being either crazy eccentrics or stunningly beautiful) and tending to fall into only a few stereotypical categories: enemy agent who defies Drake; enemy agent who has a change of heart and helps Drake; innocent caught in the crossfire who winds up helping Drake (or, in some episodes, getting in his way); or damsel in distress. In terms of multiculturalism, the series is something of a mixed bag. Certain stories could be easily characterised as either casually or explicitly racist (notably 'The Blue Veil', in which Middle Eastern Arabs are characterised as ignorant, avaricious slave-traders in a 'feudal' society; 'A Position of Trust', featuring unscrupulous Asian drug-traders and a weak-willed British civil servant who can nonetheless be induced to do the right thing through an appeal to old school ties; 'A Very Dangerous Game', with the Chinese villain being played by a White actor in make-up and with a bad, Fu Manchu-like accent; and 'The Mercenaries', which takes place in an African state in which only one Black character actually has a line, and which has a very stereotypical portrayal of African traditional spirituality). However, others, notably 'Loyalty Always Pays', 'The Galloping Major', and 'Parallel Lines Sometimes Meet', portray both White and Black characters with equal intelligence and sensitivity. The first two stories are both sympathetic portraits of African politicians under threat from political pressure and internal corruption, and the latter, although it is set in Haiti, manages to avoid most of the clichés about zombies and voodoo (and when these do appear, it's plain that they are the result of a local mine-owner exploiting local legend to stop people investigating his operations), and gives us a memorable Caribbean M9 agent, played by Earl Cameron (who also played a local secret agent in 'The Galloping Major', and was later to appear in *The Prisoner*) and policeman, played by Clifton Jones (later to become a regular on *Space: 1999*). Mention should also be made of 'The Colonel's Daughter', again a sensitive take on the social and political consequences of decolonialisation, but this time set in India, and featuring Zia Mohyeddin as an incisive Indian policeman named Khan (12 years before the actor's appearance in the role of the equally incisive Pakistani policeman Old Man Khan in *Gangsters*).

Although fans of the series tend to emphasise the idea of *Danger Man* as providing a kind of moral contrast to the womanising, gunslinging and hedonistic James Bond, it has to be said that it tends to want to have its cake and eat it too in the moral area. While Drake almost never kills anyone personally, and rarely fires a gun, villains do have a tendency to be accidentally killed or incapacitated around him (for example in 'A Time to Kill', in which a gun goes off as Drake struggles with the villain), or to be killed by other, less scrupulous characters, relieving Drake of the necessity of taking on the moral burden of killing them himself. While Drake may not use guns often on his enemies, also, he is seen to fire an assault weapon accurately from the hip in 'Someone is Liable to Get Hurt', indicating that he is quite capable of gunplay if warranted. Likewise, although the series does not go out of its way to blatantly glamourise spying, it still has Drake travelling to lots of exotic, beautiful locations, having exciting adventures and meeting lovely women (even if he never does much more than actually meet them).

It is thus tempting to speculate that McGoohan felt a sense of conflict in playing Drake, a man involved in covert operations whose controllers are not necessarily good people, and whose activities involve blackmail, fighting, subterfuge and other dubious activities, and yet at the same time wanting to impose a sense of morality on the series, which informed the subsequent premise of *The Prisoner*. Whether or not this is actually the case, there are a number of connections between the two series.

DON'T NAIL HIM YET:
DANGER MAN'S INFLUENCE ON *THE PRISONER*

Beyond the professions of their central figures, there are a number of connections between *Danger Man* and *The Prisoner*. There are at least three episodes of the former series that are thematic precursors of the latter, and several others that are interestingly prescient. Also, on a production level, a number of crewmembers and actors from *Danger Man* wound up working on *The Prisoner*, with David Tomblin, Brendan J Stafford, Don Chaffey, Rose Tobias-Shaw and Masada Wilmot being only five of their number. This is not particularly surprising, however, as a lot of television work is done through producers and directors bringing their networks with them from production to production: *Blake's 7* and the BBC adaptation of *The Day of the Triffids* share a large number of crewmembers due to producer David Maloney having worked on both. On a more personal level, the director of 'The General', Peter Graham-Scott, said that he interpreted 'Fall Out' as McGoohan's revenge on Lew Grade for the punishing schedule of *Danger Man*. McGoohan directed a few episodes of *Danger Man*, including 'The Paper

Chase'. The theme tune of the series in the US also contained the prescient lines 'They've given you a number and they've taken away your name,' which some might argue fits the Prisoner better than Drake.

There are other, thematic, connections. Drake is something of a cipher; if anything, he appears to have less of a private life than the Prisoner does, making him a character who seems to be heading for some kind of identity crisis. The fact that *Danger Man* has a sort of 'repertory company' of actors, i.e. that the same performers frequently feature in different roles (Jane Merrow, for instance, plays two different Communist translators in two different episodes, Series Two's 'A Date with Doris' and Series Three's 'The Man who Wouldn't Talk'), seems like an interesting anticipation of the duplicates that keep appearing in *The Prisoner*; or perhaps the latter programme is referencing the casting practices of the former.

A number of *Danger Man* episodes exist that have superficial connections with *The Prisoner*. Chief among these is the series' first screened episode, 'View from the Villa' (the pilot, 'A Time to Kill', was screened second), which features Portmeirion standing in for the fictitious Italian village of Pollicentra – although there is little other connection, aside from the fact that McGoohan appeared on location there, and that from the perspective of viewers of *The Prisoner* it seems curious to see 'the Village' in this context (various parts of Portmeirion would go on to appear a total of seven times in *Danger Man*). 'Have a Glass of Wine' features a Napoleon-obsessed villain, an arguable precursor of the character of Schnipps in 'The Girl Who Was Death'; Drake says to him, 'It is said that some people who admire Napoleon do so out of a sense of personal inadequacy.' The episode 'A Very Dangerous Game' has a denouement in which a clock being heard chiming on tape gives away the game (as with 'The Chimes of Big Ben'), and Drake says 'Be seeing you' (later to become a Village catchphrase in *The Prisoner*) at one point, as he does also in 'Whatever Happened to George Foster?'. The ironically-titled 'The Prisoner' involves doppelgängers and a man attempting to escape from a luxurious location (although there the similarities decidedly end). There are also connections between *Danger Man*'s 'Koroshi'/'Shinda Shima' and *The Prisoner*'s 'Hammer into Anvil' and 'The Girl Who Was Death'; these are discussed in the episode reviews below. Although

'Koroshi'/'Shinda Shima' was made before *The Prisoner*, it was screened afterwards, and, in one ITV region, was actually screened *during* the run of *The Prisoner* (see the Analysis for 'The Girl Who Was Death').

A number of other *Danger Man* episodes revolve around the ideas of secret organisations and of the negative consequences of agents resigning. 'Fair Exchange', by Wilfred Greatorex, has as its premise the case of a secret agent who has resigned, but who believes that she is being pursued, and it is unclear whether her pursuers are her own former employers, or her former adversaries, or simply the fantasies of a lunatic; we also learn in this story that Drake lives at No 7 in a London mews. In 'Such Men are Dangerous', Drake infiltrates a secret organisation that mirrors M9 in terms of its activities and set-up, which is based on a large estate (with a fleet of numbered jeeps providing the main mode of transport); the gates close on him as he enters, in a very Prisoneresque fashion, and shortly afterwards he again says 'Be seeing you.' In the third series, 'Two Birds with One Bullet' features a sequence in which a drugged and hypnotised politician is induced to unwittingly reveal his secrets as a flashing light plays over his bed, and 'The Paper Chase' features both the Village Supervisor, Peter Swanwick, as an American actor playing poker, and Aubrey Morris from 'Dance of the Dead' as a mad Italian. More than this, however, at one point we encounter Nandina, a beautiful older woman (played by Joan Greenwood of Ealing comedy fame), who is implied to have some sort of past (or possibly current) connection with espionage, who rents out rooms to international fugitives, whom she keeps under surveillance with a sophisticated system of cameras, and has a pair of thugs keen to enforce her will. At one point, Drake, waking up after having been knocked unconscious, says 'Where am I?' to which Nandina responds 'You're in the Villa San Nicola de Tollentina,' amusingly anticipating the familiar 'Where am I?' 'In the Village' dialogue.

COLONY THREE

There are, however, three episodes of *Danger Man* that have stronger connections with *The Prisoner*: 'Colony Three', 'The Ubiquitous Mr

Lovegrove' and 'Dangerous Secret'. 'Colony Three' features Drake infiltrating a Soviet installation that is a replica English village, staffed with English people who ostensibly live as ordinary villagers; Soviet agents are sent there to be immersed in English day-to-day culture until they learn how to pass perfectly as English people (in a later episode, 'To Our Best Friend', Drake encounters a Soviet agent who was trained to pass as an Englishwoman in such an installation, and makes brief reference to his own encounter with it)[5]. Although ostensibly named Hamden, the town is continually referred to by the agents as 'the Village': it also has a Number Two figure in the person of Donovan, the Director, and a room in which the Soviet agents are taught to resist the interrogation techniques that the British will use on them if they are captured. We also learn that 'none of the residents can leave the Village, ever', as they will be killed by the extreme Siberian environmental conditions outside it if they are not captured first; as Richardson, a Soviet agent, puts it, 'You're quite free to go where you like in the Village, only don't wander outside it.' Richardson also makes the Prisoneresque remark: 'Geography is a matter of physical illusion. Lines on a map, words on a signpost. It's this that gives a place its identity. After all, you are where you recognise yourself to be … All countries are countries of the mind.' The situation is thus like that in *The Prisoner*, only seen from the perspective of the Villagers rather than of the Prisoner: as Donovan says to his new recruits, 'this village is one of our best-kept secrets. I regret that you had to be brought here – in the dark – but we couldn't risk the possibility of a security leak.' We even have a *The Prisoner*-style plot unfolding in that Randall, a British Communist who shares a room with Drake, is taken aback by the set-up he discovers in Hamden and begins a Prisoneresque fight against the system, whereas Drake, for obvious reasons, gives a good impression of trying to fit in with it as best as he can. At the end of the story, when Drake asks about the possibility of rescuing Janet Wells, a young Englishwoman, from Hamden, we learn that both sides are denying that she exists, because of the unofficial nature of the installation (allowing the British government conveniently to avoid doing anything about her situation).

---

5 A remarkably similar premise would appear two years later in the *Mission: Impossible* episode 'The Carriers', although whether there is any direct connection between the two is unknown.

THE UBIQUITOUS MR LOVEGROVE

'The Ubiquitous Mr Lovegrove' is certainly the most surreal and offbeat episode of *Danger Man*. The story takes place, for the most part, in a dream or hallucination that Drake has following a car accident. In terms of its surreal imagery alone, it strongly anticipates *The Prisoner* – for instance it has a ball flying through the air as a recurring motif (as it was a child's football flying at him that caused Drake to lose control of his car); a man dressed as an undertaker selling insurance; a wobble-cam sequence down a hall with eerie marble busts; recurring heartbeat sounds and hysterical laughter dubbed over the action; clocks stopped at 12 (the time of Drake's accident) and a doctor's eye-chart printed backwards. Various characters throughout the story turn, with no explanation, into doubles of Mr Lovegrove (Drake's boss for this adventure), and Drake himself looks in the mirror at one point to see Mr Lovegrove reflected instead (later, when fighting a casino employee who has previously transformed into Lovegrove, he winds up literally fighting his own mirrored reflection, through camera trickery). We also have the implication that there are two identical men, both named Drake, wandering around London, in an anticipation of *The Prisoner*'s continual duplicates and implication, notably in 'Free for All', that there may be more than one Number Six in the Village.

More than this, however, the story anticipates the psychological themes of *The Prisoner*, in that Drake seems to have a number of issues about his identity. The story turns on a casino owner, Mr Alexander, learning of Drake's identity as an agent and using it to blackmail him; Drake also, as noted above, fights his own double, learns that there is another Drake who is identical to him, but whom he has never met, and sees himself turn into another man before his eyes in the mirror, all of which foreshadow the issues of personal identity and fear of sublimation into the group reflected in the later series. There is also a bit of knowing humour about the lack of realism of spy fiction, when an agent, reading *From Russia with Love* (complete with a picture of Sean Connery on the cover), has the following exchange with Drake: 'Why do I never meet a beautiful Russian spy on a sleeping car?' 'Possibly because the Treasury would send you a memo afterwards asking why it was necessary for you to travel first class'. Desmond Llewelyn, who had by then established himself in the role of Q in the Bond films, also appears as a casino doorman, in another knowing wink to the audience that anticipates *The Prisoner*'s postmodern stylings.

DANGEROUS SECRET

This late-Series Two story seems almost like a non-surreal version of *The Prisoner*, in that it revolves around a scientist who discovers a bacterium that could be used for germ warfare, and then, horrified by the ethical issues this raises, destroys his notes and goes on the run rather than let his discovery be used for nefarious ends (recalled in the later series in the strong implication in a number of episodes that the Prisoner resigned for ethical reasons, and in 'Do Not Forsake Me Oh My Darling' that the potential misuse of a scientific discovery specifically was the trigger). The scientist then finds himself cornered in a hotel in France with representatives of four separate factions (English, French, Russian and Chinese) all determined to get hold of his secret, and even those who seem sympathetic at first actually put the pressure on as soon as they can. Drake again says 'Be seeing you' at one point in the proceedings; we also have the following exchange between Drake and the British agent Fenton regarding the scientist: 'Have you ever made a stand on a point of principle, Mr Fenton?' 'I find it quite enough to do my duty.' 'He probably thought he was doing his.' 'You can't be serious.' 'I take it you are one of the school that believes in blind obedience?' 'I certainly do.'

THE MAN WHO WOULDN'T TALK:
IS THE PRISONER JOHN DRAKE?

Perhaps the most common question raised regarding the two series is whether or not the Prisoner and John Drake are one and the same person. This might seem an odd question to people who haven't seen *Danger Man* (or have seen only the atypical 'Koroshi'/'Shinda Shima' episodes) and know it only as The Spy Series That McGoohan Did First, since McGoohan has tended to be rather overly critical of *Danger Man* since leaving it, implying that it was for the most part a superficial romp. An examination of *Danger Man*, however, provides strong arguments both for and against the possibility.

While nothing within *The Prisoner* itself actually confirms that the two are one and the same (some fans of the series have suggested that Number Two addresses the Prisoner as 'Drake' during the Schoolboy sequence of 'Once Upon a Time'; however, this is a result of the last word of the line 'Come and see me in the morning break' being misheard by North Americans, who use the alternative term 'recess' for a recreation period during school), nothing actually disproves it either. Some extra- or semi-canonical works have equated the two, most notably the novels *Who is No. 2?* and *A Day in the Life* (Jean Marie Stine, the author of the latter book, has gone on record, in an online interview, as saying that she and David McDaniel, the author of the former, both believed the Prisoner to be Drake, but that they deliberately said so in their books just in order to see if McGoohan was reading the manuscripts, as they knew that he would delete all such references). Other works, such as *I Am Not a Number!* and *The Prisoner's Dilemma*, are more ambiguous on this point, while the graphic novel *Shattered Visage* chooses to engage in postmodern games with the idea.

Similarities between the two characters include the fact that both are secret agents (albeit, in the case of the Prisoner, one who has resigned); both maintain friendly, but not sexual, relationships with women; both have multiple identities (as revealed in 'Do Not Forsake Me Oh My Darling'); Drake sometimes (for instance in 'I Can Only Offer You Sherry' and 'The Paper Chase') wears a black polo-neck shirt with a black or very dark suit, like the one the Prisoner favours when out of the Village; Drake appears in some episodes to be quite fluent in Spanish (in 'A Man to be Trusted', for instance, he is seen choosing a thick volume on voodoo and obeah in Spanish for bedtime reading), just as the Prisoner is apparently familiar enough with the language to be able to quote Cervantes at will in 'Hammer into Anvil'; Drake has a number of different bosses, with none lasting more than a few episodes (one, Hardy, was played by the same actor who would later play Fotheringay in 'The Chimes of Big Ben'), rather like the Prisoner's rotating array of Number Twos; and one of Drake's bosses, Hobbs, has a print of a penny-farthing on his office wall. The picture of the Prisoner used for the shot of him being 'x'ed out' in the title sequence, and seen also in the posters in 'Free for All', is a publicity still of McGoohan from *Danger Man* (although this could equally be one of *The Prisoner* crew's notorious inside jokes). Although Drake does serve his government more or less unquestioningly, he is seen in a number of episodes experiencing private doubts about what he does, and so it is not much of a stretch to consider that the Prisoner might be a future Drake who has finally found these doubts too overwhelming to allow him to continue in the service. If one takes the interpretation that the events of *The Prisoner* are a fantasy, a dying vision or a kind of afterlife, then it is quite possible that the person having the fantasy or vision is Drake.

However, there are also a number of differences. Where Drake never actually seems to have romantic relationships with women at all, the Prisoner has a fiancée; also, Drake never goes against his employers to a serious degree (even when he acts against orders, it's always in the best interests of Britain, or NATO, or whoever happens to be employing him at the time). Drake drives either an Aston Martin or a Mini, neither of which suggests the sort of person who would favour a hand-built Lotus 7 kit-car of the type driven by the Prisoner. Although some have suggested that 'The Girl Who Was Death' is evidence that the Prisoner is Drake, this interpretation hinges on the idea that the story that the Prisoner is telling to the children is one of his real adventures, when it is equally likely (if not more so) that he is making it up, and also, while *Danger Man* did sometimes verge on the unrealistic, it never went to the extremes of self-parody of the plot of this episode.

It is thus impossible, on the basis of evidence from the series, to say categorically whether or not the Prisoner is Drake. On the production level, opinion seems equally divided. Patrick McGoohan has firmly maintained, at least since *The Prisoner* was first aired, that the Prisoner is not Drake; George Markstein has equally firmly maintained that he is. Tony Sloman, the film librarian on *The Prisoner*, has claimed that the continuity sheets for early episodes had 'Drake' as the Prisoner's character name (although, since the script for 'Arrival', like later scripts, refers to the character simply as 'P', this seems rather unlikely), but that Markstein told him they were changing this so as to avoid paying royalties to Ralph Smart for the use of his character. It has also been pointed out that

McGoohan's abrupt departure from *Danger Man* left both audiences and ITC baffled as to why he would leave a successful show, in a parallel to the Village authorities' difficulty with accepting the Prisoner's stated reasons for his resignation: as Max Hora puts it in *The Prisoner of Portmeirion*, 'In real life, McGoohan got tired of being "John Drake" ... and decided to do something different. So really, John Drake had to "resign" from *Danger Man* because Patrick McGoohan wanted to make *The Prisoner*.' The two thus have some connections in real life, despite not necessarily being one and the same.

Our conclusion, based on the evidence we have reviewed, is that Drake may not be the Prisoner *per se*, but that the similarities between the characters mean that Drake is a kind of conceptual forebear to the Prisoner, and the Prisoner likewise is someone whom Drake might have become, under particular circumstances. Indeed, the differences between the Drake of Series One and the Drake of Series Two are, if anything, more marked than those between Drake and the Prisoner. The two characters are thus not explicitly one and the same, but they are linked to such a degree that a viewing of *Danger Man* does cast interesting light on the origins of *The Prisoner*.

THE PRISONER

An ITC Production
by
Everyman Films Limited

Script Editor:
George Markstein (1-12, 16)

Producer:
David Tomblin

Executive Producer:
Patrick McGoohan (1-13, 16)

Production Managers:
Bernard Williams (1-12, 16)
Ronald Liles (13-15, 17)

Director of Photography:
Brendan J Stafford BSC

Art Director:
Jack Shampan

Camera Operators:
Jack Lowin (1-12, 16)
Len Harris (13-15, 17)
Bob Kindred (17)

Editors:
Lee Doig (1, 9, 10, 12, 16)
Spencer Reeve (2)
Geoffrey Foot GBFE (3-5, 7)
John S Smith (6, 8, 11)
Eric Boyd-Perkins GBFE (13, 15, 17)
Noreen Ackland GBFE (14, 17)

*Assistant Editor to John Smith:
Ian L Rakoff (6, 11)

Theme Music:
Ron Grainer

Cameraman (2nd Unit):
Robert Monks (1, 2, 4, 7, 8-9)

Assistant Directors:
Gino Marotta
Ernie Lewis (13)

*Second Assistant Director:
Seamus Byrne

Incidental Music/
Musical Director:
**Wilfred Josephs (1, 2, 9)
Albert Elms (3-8, 10-17)

Sound Editors:
Wilf Thompson (1, 2, 4, 6, 7, 12-17)
Peter Elliott (3)
Stanley Smith (5, 8)
Ken Rolls (6, 10, 11)

Sound Recordists:
John Bramall (1-12, 16)
Cyril Swern (13-15, 17)

*Sound Effects:
Cinesound

Music Editors:
Bob Dearberg (1, 2, 9)
Eric Mival (3-8, 10, 12-17)
John S Smith (11)

Casting Director:
Rose Tobias-Shaw

Continuity:
Doris Martin (1-6, 8, 9, 11, 12, 16)
Josie Fulford (7, 10)
Ann Besselman (13)
Phyllis Townshend (14, 15, 17)

Set Dressers:
Kenneth Bridgeman (1-12, 16)
Colin Southcott (13)
John Lageu (14, 15, 17)

Make-Up:
Eddie Knight (1-12, 16)
Frank Turner (13-15, 17)

Hairdressing:
Pat McDermot (1-12, 16)
Olive Mills (13-15, 17)

Wardrobe:
Masada Wilmot (1-12, 16)
Dora Lloyd (13-15, 17)

*Wardrobe Assistant,
Portmeirion:
Catherine Williams

*Fight Arrangers:
Frank Maher
Jack Cooper (13)

*Film Librarians:
Tony Sloman (1-12, 16)
David Naughton (13-15, 17)

Made on Location
and at
Metro-Goldwyn-Mayer
Studios,
Borehamwood,
England

Not credited on screen

Credited only in alternate version[6]

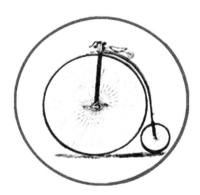

---

6 As will be discussed later in this book, alternate prints of 'Arrival' and 'The Chimes of Big Ben' exist.

Episode 1:
Arrival

First UK Transmission Date: Friday 29 September 1967: ATV Midlands/Grampian, 7.30 pm – 8.30 pm
Writers: George Markstein and David Tomblin
Director: Don Chaffey
Credited Cast: Patrick McGoohan (The Prisoner); Virginia Maskell (The Woman); Guy Doleman (Number Two); Paul Eddington (Cobb); George Baker (The New Number Two); Angelo Muscat (The Butler); Barbara Yu Ling (The Taxi Driver); Stephanie Randall (The Maid); Jack Allen (The Doctor); Fabia Drake (Welfare Worker); Denis Shaw (Shopkeeper); Oliver MacGreevy (Gardener / Electrician); Frederick Piper (Ex-Admiral); Patsy Smart (Waitress); Christopher Benjamin (Labour Exchange Manager); Peter Swanwick (Supervisor); David Garfield (Hospital Attendant); Peter Brace (1st Guardian [1st Croquet Player in alternative version]); Keith Peacock (1st Guardian [2nd Croquet Player in alternative version])
Known Uncredited Cast: Frank Maher (Double for Patrick McGoohan); Fenella Fielding (Telephone Operator/Loudspeaker Voice); William Parry (Villager Fighting in Goldfish Pond); Seamus Byrne (Rover's First Victim); Jill Hennessy (Location Double for The Maid); Heulwen Vaughn-Hatcher (Double for Barbara Yu Ling); Lilian Llewellyn (Passer-by); Patrick McGoohan (Additional Voicework)

SYNOPSIS: A nameless man drives to an underground location in Westminster and angrily tenders his resignation to an official at a desk. He returns home, followed by a hearse. While packing to leave, he is gassed. When he awakes, he discovers that the view outside his window has changed from a familiar London street to a strange Italianate vista. Going outside, he learns that he is in a place known only as the Village, and that it is impossible to make contact with the outside world. He is invited for breakfast by a man calling himself 'Number Two', who inhabits the Green Dome, attended by a diminutive butler. Number Two has a good deal of data on the man, and wishes to know why he resigned. He takes him on a tour of the Village, by helicopter and then by taxi. The man will not conform to Village life, refusing to register at the labour exchange, dismissing his housemaid, smashing his radio and attempting to leave the Village, whereupon he is attacked by one of the 'Rover' creatures/devices that enforce discipline in the Village, and by two strong men, and is hospitalised. While in the hospital, he encounters an old acquaintance, Cobb, in the next bed; Cobb apparently commits suicide, and the man (who has been given the designation Number Six, though he rejects this), attempts to investigate, in the process discovering that a new man is now bearing the designation of Number Two. The Prisoner makes contact with a woman who claims to have been a friend of Cobb's, and to have planned an escape with him; she offers to help the Prisoner escape through providing him with an electropass, which will neutralise Rover and allow him to steal the helicopter. The Prisoner identifies her as an agent for Number Two assigned to him, but attempts this escape plan anyway, only to be brought back to the Village by an autopilot. Cobb is revealed to be alive and working for 'new masters', apparently the people behind the Village.

ANALYSIS: The key functions of 'Arrival' are to set up both the Village and the Prisoner's situation within it, and to introduce the principal themes of the series. These things are accomplished effectively, but as a consequence of the complicated nature of the set-up, it comes across as a rather strange, dual-focused episode.

'Arrival', or 'The Arrival' as it was originally titled, was written by George Markstein and David Tomblin, both of whom had worked with McGoohan on *Danger Man,* and both of whom would prove key influences on *The Prisoner*. It is unusual in that it effectively consists of two consecutive stories in a single episode. The first story, conceptually, ends with the Prisoner being attacked by Rover on the beach. The subsequent events regarding Cobb and Number Nine are the second story, with their own plot and development. Although one can draw parallels between the maid in the first story and Number Nine in the second (in that both are women who appeal to the Prisoner's sympathy, yet are actually working for the establishment in doing so), neither Nine nor Cobb appears in the first, meaning that they are brought in without foreshadowing. This structure serves an obvious function within the series: had the two stories been developed into two separate episodes, the change of Number Two and the recurrence of the themes of escape plans, betrayals, women in apparent distress and mystery surrounding the real-world powers behind the Village, would have been lost on those viewers who saw only one of the two. The concept of the Village must be introduced, and the Prisoner situated within it, before events can begin to unfold. However, one problem that it causes is that the second part of the episode feels distinctly underdeveloped, with Nine being given little time to worm her way into the Prisoner's affections, and both she and Cobb being rather hastily established.

The fact that Guy Doleman left early and abruptly during the location filming (causing problems, most notably in the initial Rover-attack sequence, in which cut-in studio footage and doubles are used to cover for his absence) might lead some to suspect that the initial change of Number Twos was happenstance. However, this is clearly not the case: Doleman returned to do studio work later on, and the original script makes it plain that a changeover of Number Twos was always intended to happen within 'Arrival' – in particular, one cut line has Two remarking on the subject of Cobb's death, 'Sorry about him, he's one of the reasons I've taken over.' Although the early genesis of *The Prisoner* did involve a number of happy accidents – the replacement of the unwieldy mechanical Rover with the iconic weather balloon (see 'Essay 1: Rover'), for instance – there were always intended to be two Number Twos in 'Arrival'.

NO ESCAPING IT: THE VILLAGE

The key purpose of 'Arrival' is to establish the Village, and in the process to expose a number of complex themes. Right from the start, for instance, images of infantilisation pervade the story. Adult villagers are shown playing like children – we see old people climbing the rigging of the Stone Boat and tossing balls (the Prisoner's question about 'St Vitus' Dance' refers to an expression usually used of hyperactive small children); the man at the labour exchange plays with what seem like large tinker-toys; the 'welcome' card in the Prisoner's cottage is held by an antique doll; ice-cream flavours are announced over the tannoy; and the ostensible leader of the Village, Number Two, wears a school scarf. Physical aspects of the Village also fit in with this, with Rover resembling nothing less than a giant bouncing ball or toy balloon; and the constant references to 'number one' and 'number two' recall childish scatological slang. The aptitude test at the labour exchange is like tests that were finding favour in the 1960s as a way of establishing the intelligence of children without reference to social background. We also hear three children's tunes at significant points in the action: 'Pop Goes The Weasel' is played when the Prisoner goes to meet Number Two for the first time (and when Number Two takes him to see the Old People's Home); the waiting Villagers at the labour exchange are all, surreally, humming 'Boys and Girls, Come Out To Play' (which is echoed in the incidental music played over the group therapy room); and the Admiral is humming 'What Shall We Do With A Drunken Sailor?' (not a children's tune originally, but one that has arguably evolved, in bowdlerised form, into such).

One possible significance to the infantilisation imagery could be the relationship of the Prisoner to the Village and its administration. Childhood is the stage of life in which, arguably, one is most truly known by other people: like the parents of a child, the Village administration knows the Prisoner's favourite foods, slipper size, and so forth, can make an accurate guess as to what he is thinking in the surveillance photos in his dossier, and watch over him in much the same way that he is watched over by the grandmotherly woman who sits by his bedside in the hospital (calling him 'son' when he awakes). The early sequence in which the Prisoner goes on a headlong race through the Village, now pursuing the mysterious figure in the bell tower, now rushing to the restaurant, now attempting to leave the Village by taxi, and finally being led by his sighting of the maid to discover which cottage is his own, suggests that the Village is manipulating him, leading him on through glimpses of Villagers and conveniently-arriving modes of transport. At the same time, however, the Village authorities do not know the answers to key questions about the Prisoner, most notably why he resigned. In a way, the Village's relationship with the Prisoner parallels that of a parent with a child: on the one hand, there is their detailed knowledge of his background and history from birth, and on the other, there is the Prisoner's demand to be recognised as an independent person who does not have to justify himself to them.

In contrast to the themes of childhood, however, the Village set-up also incorporates themes of death. When the Prisoner arrives in the Village (having collapsed in his flat and been removed in a hearse), it is deserted; the tolling of a bell heralds the Prisoner's first glimpses of living Villagers. The undertakers from the opening sequence later appear drinking tea or coffee outside the Old People's Home. The Diary in Cottage Number Six has no dates on it, suggesting that the Village exists outside ordinary time. Cobb's funeral is also a key sequence in the story: initially, according to the original script, the event was to have been a much more sombre affair, with a funeral march and Rover (which, at the time the script was written, was a mechanical device) having its light covered by a black cloth. It was also to have been shot in a local churchyard, an idea abandoned partly because the sequence would have shown the nearby village of Porthmadoc in the background, and partly because the film-makers were unable to get permission from the families of the deceased; however, the final sequence, with its jaunty tunes in place of a march, cheerily-dressed villagers (with black umbrellas being the only concession to mourning) and graveyard set up on the beach (with consequent implications of impermanence and instability) instead give a disconcerting sense of death as a cause for celebration and frivolity, themes that will recur again and again in the series. Significantly, given the avoidance of religious statuary (although Portmeirion contains a statue of the Buddha, left over from the filming of *The Inn of the Sixth Happiness,* a statue of a saint, and a few deities/saints in niches, the production team appear to have shot around all statuary representing non-classical deities as much as possible) and of references to religion elsewhere in the series, the script specifies that no church should be seen in the graveyard.

There is also the implication that the Village is all happening, as it were, in the Prisoner's head: as Max Hora puts it in *The Prisoner of Portmeirion*, 'It all comes back to the "bad dream" theory where things are not necessarily consistent … Did it all really happen or was it only happening in the Prisoner's own mind? On this level, the viewer need look no further than his or her own mind to discover the exact location of the Village.' Despite occasional details like seeing a pair of Mini Mokes driving past with ambulance sirens blaring, it is hard for the viewer to envisage daily life going on in the Village outside of the Prisoner's own immediate ambit. The characters give no evidence of well-rounded backgrounds: it is hard to picture an undertaker going to the Citizen's Advice Bureau, or the Admiral having a spat with his wife (indeed, having a wife at all), or the taxi driver relaxing after work with a drink in the pub in the company of the Gardener and Electrician. Although the maid in the cottage says she grew up in the Village, we don't know how much of what she says is the truth. The people queuing up at the labour exchange don't react at all when the Prisoner and Number Two jump the queue; later, all the Villagers freeze, as if they were robots or people on film, when Rover appears. When Rover kills its first victim, the fact that we see three separate men under attack (first the man with the sunglasses, then a shot that was cut from 'It's Your Funeral' of Rover attacking Mark Eden, then finally Patrick McGoohan's screaming face as Rover suffocates the man, taken from 'The Schizoid Man'), the sequence ending with a shot of the Prisoner's own face being enveloped by Rover, means that there is almost a suggestion that the apparently interchangeable Villagers and the Prisoner are, in fact, one and the same – as if all the people we encounter are the products of a single mind.

While all of this adds to the suggestion that this is a massive psychological game played against the Prisoner rather than a real village, it also gives the general impression that perhaps it doesn't really exist at all. We also get surreal touches like the presence of the two identical Villagers: although Fairclough suggests that they are clones, there are other explanations, particularly as actual and apparent doubles are recurring themes within the series as a whole, and could again be taken as evidence of a mindgame or that the Village is imaginary (indeed, the abovementioned funeral procession was originally to have contained another possible double, as Number Two was to have been seen in that sequence despite having just concluded a voiceover a few seconds earlier; although he could have had time within the story to join the procession, the juxtaposition of his voice in one location with his physical appearance in another would have given viewers a double-take). We also are exposed to dream logic on the Prisoner's initial arrival, when he sees a man at the top of the bell tower, but, when he climbs the tower, finds that his observer has apparently transformed into a (female) stone statue. All of this flags up the recurring theme of psychoanalysis, also seen in the hospital sequences with 'group therapy' taking place under purple lights (with all participants sporting blindfolds and straitjackets) and a man, disconcertingly dressed in the Prisoner's old clothes, chanting gibberish (an overdub by Patrick McGoohan himself) as he observes a ping-pong ball; like the 1969 Bonzo Dog Doo-Dah Band album *Keynsham*, the subtext of which draws parallels between interrogation and psychoanalysis, the ambiguities between manipulation and therapy will recur throughout the series.

The Village is also associated with the world at large, at the same time as it emphasises its own isolation. The opening sequence of London shows it as very like the Village, unnaturally sunny, sparsely populated with people in bright clothing and pretty little cars, and strange gothic buildings such as those in Whitehall. The Village itself is explicitly global: the Chinese taxi-driver speaks French (commenting 'French is international'), and implies that there could be Poles and Czechs in the Village; the shopkeeper speaks an unidentified foreign language casually; Greek letters are seen on the doctor's keyboard in the hospital; Cobb reports being picked up in Germany, and even his *'au revoir/auf Wiedersehen'* exchange with Number Two at the end of the story could be seen as indicating internationalism as much as that Cobb has defected to East Germany. Maps of the world, and of outer space, are seen in the Control Room, suggesting that the individuals in it are not only monitoring the whole world, but the known universe. The taxi-driver remarks that the Village is 'very cosmopolitan, you never know who you'll meet next,' Portmeirion itself is a mix of architectural styles, and even the surveillance busts (echoed in what appear to be a series of miniature busts briefly visible on the shelving above the desk in the Prisoner's cottage) show a mix of times and cultures. The name of the place, 'the Village', is simply a description of what it is, no more meaningful than the other words on the map, such as 'the mountains' and 'the sea'; it has no street names, historical monuments or other indicators of a past or of an outside culture. At the same time, however, the phone exchanges, taxi services and maps are exclusively local, and the Town Hall is said to be used for meetings, amateur theatricals and so forth, as with the town hall of any small town or village, in a kind of exaggerated version of the close-knit parochialism that still can be found in British villages (this also features strongly in *The Avengers*, and would be sent up extensively later on in *The League of Gentlemen*). In Number Two's expression, then, the Village is 'quite a world on its own.' The original end titles sequence, still present in the alternate print of the episode (which will be discussed in detail below), encapsulates this tension between universality and containment: the small wheel of the penny-farthing spins out to become the Earth within the Universe, then the Universe becomes contained within the large wheel of the rematerialising penny-farthing and the Earth becomes the small wheel, symbolically encapsulating all of the cosmos within the Village.

The penny-farthing symbol itself has been repeatedly referred to by McGoohan as an ironic symbol of progress. Precisely what is meant by this is best illustrated by his remarks in his interview with Roger Goodman: 'Not just because it looked pretty, there was a very specific reason for it, and that is it symbolised progress. I think that most of the progress we have is not progress at all … The Earth is running out of oil, gasoline, and they're plumbing things too far, too soon, too quickly. And … if only people would – if we could stop and be grateful for what we've got, and try and save what we've got instead of building bigger and better jets, bigger and better fighters, bigger and more efficient guns and tanks and all this stuff, we'd be better off. So I was saying that as an ironic symbol to progress.' The penny-farthing is particularly significant in this regard in that it is a fairly useless bit of technology, difficult to ride (note that in the Village it is only ever leaned upon, or pushed) and, as the Prisoner observes regarding the Village taxis, it would generally be more productive to walk. However, much as the Prisoner is encouraged to take a taxi instead of walking, so consumers in Western society are encouraged to use the latest technology, regardless of whether it actually is a step forward or, like the penny-farthing, a useless, even counterproductive, piece of equipment that is nonetheless promoted as being an advance or improvement. The penny-farthing thus permeates the Village as a symbol of how sometimes technological 'advances' constitute a step backwards rather than forwards.

Finally, the iconic '60s/surrealist imagery of the series lends the Village a distinctive attractive-yet-disconcerting look. The cordless phones that appear would have seemed stranger to a '60s audience than they do now (the original script seems to assume a more conventional telephone), but the sight of Number Two using one as a dictaphone continues to highlight the oddness of the device to modern viewers. Credit cards, although unusual at the time (having first been introduced in Britain in 1966) would not have been unknown as a concept. The surveillance society portrayed is also an idea with a long genesis (*Brave New World, Nineteen Eighty-Four*, etc) but was still far enough from the immediate public consciousness of the 1960s to seem strange and repressive. The scene in which the Prisoner smashes his radio, and yet the music keeps on playing, is a direct steal from the Marx Brothers' surrealist comedy *Duck Soup*. Stripes feature throughout the Village, on shirts, dressing gowns, capes, and even on the mugs (taken, as an inside joke, from Portmeirion's own china range) that the camera lingers on in the Village Store, perhaps echoing the bars of a symbolic 'prison' and the stripes on a prisoner's uniform. Similarly, round, Roverlike objects appear throughout, from Two's chair, to the statue of Hercules holding the world on his shoulders and the electronic Eye in the Control Room, down to the airborne ping-pong ball in the hospital therapy room. We see penny-farthings everywhere, and at least one bicycle with an attached awning (as well as, bizarrely, a blue-painted stagecoach). The Village itself famously invites comparison with a holiday camp, with its badges, tannoys, information boards and house signs (based on signage actually extant at Portmeirion), but at the same time subverts expectations when, for instance, what seems to be a castle turns out to be a hospital, or when a 'Residents Only' sign appears (as there are no non-residents in the Village). Clever shooting also makes the Village look larger than it is, and makes it impossible to fully get a grip on the geographical relations between places; the ornamental lighthouse at the end of the real Portmeirion village appears for the only time in this episode, for instance. Lava lamps feature everywhere, even in laboratories, as if they were regular lamps: most are the 'Astro' model common in the 1960s (with the Prisoner's house containing one with a now-rare copper base) but Number Two's office features what seems to be a custom lamp made from two 'Imperial' globes stacked on top of each other (this is very similar to one seen in Doctor Noah's headquarters in *Casino Royale* and, since the two productions were both filmed at the same studio, may well have been the same lamp), and what looks to modern eyes for all the world like a computer screensaver of lava-lamp bubbles on Number Two's wall-sized monitor screen.

A SMALL TOWN IN GERMANY: COBB AND NUMBER NINE

Once the Village has been established, the narrative then moves on to the story of Cobb and Number Nine (whose number is the inverse of a Six). Although this initially seems fairly straightforward, a closer reading reveals several ambiguities. The most common interpretation of Cobb's story is that he is a British agent who was captured and taken to the Village, which is run by a foreign (and probably Communist) power, where he was induced to defect, making the story a fairly simple piece of cold-war fiction. This might be supported by the fact that Cobb was allegedly picked up in Germany (with East Germany being a popular setting for spy stories of the day), and says '*auf Wiedersehen*' at the end of the episode as he announces that he is off to meet his 'new masters.' However, Cobb (who is the only person in the story to be named, rather than numbered or described) never specifies that he was in *East* Germany at any point, and the Village itself is distinctly international. Although Number Two is trying to get information out of the Prisoner, talking about how valuable the information he has is, and revealing that he has been under surveillance for a long time, he never says who it is that wants this information, and some of the information that the controllers of the Village have would be difficult for a foreign power to gain access to at such speed (as he is evidently kidnapped on extremely short order after resigning). It is worth bearing in mind that although a foreign power would obviously want to get information out of a British spy who resigned, the British authorities would also want information: namely, if he is planning to defect, if he has been bribed or blackmailed, and what he could reveal about his former employers. Although the implication is strong that the Prisoner has been captured by a hostile foreign power, or at least that the British secret service has been completely infiltrated by such a group, one can, even at this early stage, read other possibilities into the scenario.

The motivations of Number Nine are also less straightforward than they first appear. The Prisoner initially suspects that she is working for the Village authorities, against him. But in fact her reactions at the end suggest that she really did want to help him: in a brilliant bit of acting, her eye twitches nervously as she watches his failed escape attempt (this does not appear in the alternate version, in which her conversation with the Admiral takes place before the Prisoner is recaptured), and she reacts with shocked realisation to the Admiral's 'We're all pawns here, m'dear.' Her conversation with Number Two also indicates that she apparently does not know that Cobb's death was faked; and Number Two's comments during the conversation deliberately imply that he does not suspect her of plotting with the Prisoner, since he refers to the Prisoner attending the brass band concert as a positive, innocuous action. However, it also appears that the escape scenario with the stolen electropass has been set up some time prior to the story, giving three possibilities for consideration. First, that in fact, Cobb was working for the authorities all along, and the escape plan with the electropass was intended to break Number Nine, not Cobb. When the Prisoner arrives, the extant scenario is turned around to fit his situation instead, 'killing' Cobb in order to redirect the woman's energies onto him, playing on both his and her feelings about Cobb. The second possibility is that Cobb was in the same situation as the Prisoner, being worked on by various agents within the Village, including Number Nine – but that he was 'turned' prior to the events of 'Arrival' through the efforts of other inmates, and, with this achieved, both Cobb and, without her knowledge, the woman are set onto the Prisoner instead. The final scenario is that the whole situation is an elaborate set-up of at least four weeks' standing and involving action in the outside world as well as in the Village, aimed at the Prisoner himself, which would seem to make less sense at first than the idea that this is an adaptation of an extant plan within the Village; however, as we have observed earlier, the Village repeatedly seems to operate only for the Prisoner's benefit, so this scenario makes sense in the context of Village logic.

DANGER MAN? THE PRISONER ESTABLISHED

The story also establishes a number of literal and symbolic elements about the Prisoner himself. He is portrayed in many ways as a secret agent in the John Drake mould: like TV secret agents everywhere, he has a number of esoteric skills, such as martial arts and helicopter piloting, and his reason for resignation was a matter of principle (suggesting, again, a government operative with a heart of gold). We hear an anecdote about another secret agent, Chambers, who he tried to talk out of resigning, but who vanished before he could see him, suggesting parallels with the Prisoner's own situation. Christopher Benjamin, who had already appeared in *Danger Man*, is seen here in the first of several *The Prisoner* roles, and McGoohan's *Danger Man* publicity photo is used in the resignation sequence. The Prisoner is also, from the outset, identified with McGoohan himself; they share a birth date (4.31 am, 19 March 1928), and the Prisoner is first seen presenting his resignation to a man played by George Markstein, story editor on *Danger Man*, suggesting, as noted elsewhere, McGoohan's own departure from a conventional spy series to a more esoteric one of his own devising (the extended title sequence of the first episode has the Prisoner going through a set of doors marked 'Way Out' as he resigns, which could be taken as indicating a departure from his job/series, as well as foreshadowing the twisted geography of the Village, and/or providing something of a comment on the 'way out' nature of the series that follows). The Prisoner thus has parallels both with McGoohan's most famous television role at the time, and with McGoohan himself.

The Prisoner's character and situation are also established on a symbolic level. His role within the Village, for instance, is highlighted in the sequence in which he deliberately places a round peg in a square hole, but the hole deviously irises to become round. We also see themes of freedom and constraint: the Stone Boat, for instance, is something that gives the illusion of being able to move, and indeed is spoken of by the Admiral as if it can move, but is ultimately static, much as the helicopter seems to offer escape but is in fact outside of the Prisoner's own control. Objects in the village are identified as 'free' – the board as 'free information,' the pond as 'free sea,' leading the viewer to question the various meanings of the word 'free.' The Prisoner's declaration that he is not a number, but a person, liberates him symbolically not only from his former employers, but from all their bureaucratic preoccupations, classifications and so forth.

PRINTS OF WALES: CHANGES FROM SCRIPT TO SCREEN

The changes that 'Arrival' underwent between the initial script and the final version highlight the way in which the themes of the story were developed. The 'round peg into square hole' sequence at the labour exchange initially featured the Prisoner using his fist to hammer a peg into a hole that it didn't fit, implying that he would force the Village to come round to his point of view, rather than, as in the final version, the Village adapting deceptively to turn his rebellion into conformity. The Butler transformed between script and screen from a formal, athletic type into the minuscule, dour Angelo Muscat, providing one of the series' more unconventional and arresting images. Number Two's residence also shifted from the 'Unicorn' house (referred to in the original script as the Georgian House) to the more iconic (and, perhaps, more connotative of surveillance and authority) Green Dome, following a reconnaissance visit to Portmeirion in 1966. Other changes are more superficial: the Prisoner originally does not approach the information board but meets the taxi driver at a taxi rank; a scene involving two villagers fighting and then falling into the 'goldfish pond,' before being 'arrested' by two gardeners (called 'PMCs: Public Minded Citizens,' by Number Two), was cut, although the beginning of the fight can still be seen briefly (and in a slightly different form, as the fight now starts in the goldfish pond) in long shot when Number Two is addressing the Prisoner through a megaphone; the scene where Rover subdues the Prisoner originally took place in the woodland, not on the beach; and the two stuntmen who fight him were initially credited as '1st Croquet Player' and '2nd Croquet Player', because a sequence showing them playing croquet and speaking dialogue, which was filmed, was dropped after one of them, Keith Peacock, was killed while working on the BBC police series *Softly Softly*. In an indication of one of the directions in which the series might have gone, also, a 'Palace of Fun' that was mentioned in the ITC press release about the series and featured in an unmade script (see 'Unmade Stories 1: The Outsider'), but never actually appeared, is mentioned on the fold-out Village map and the legend on the information board (where it is designated 'Fun Palace').

The fact that an alternate print of 'Arrival' exists[7] also serves to expose the way in which the themes of the series were developed. The series initially premièred in Canada, a month before its first UK broadcast, and early edits of 'Arrival' and 'The Chimes of Big Ben' were sent to Canada but never transmitted. A 16 mm film print has since been discovered of the alternate 'The Chimes of Big Ben'; for many years, only a video copy of the alternate 'Arrival' was known to exist (thanks to its accidental transmission on an American PBS station in the 1970s), but a 35 mm film print was later found. Many of the changes are fairly superficial: the opening sequence is slightly different, for instance, featuring, instead of the familiar Ron Grainer theme music, an alternative composed by Wilfred Josephs (which was itself the second attempt at a theme tune for the series, the original one by Robert Farnon having also being rejected as unsuitable), with Patrick McGoohan's name appearing earlier, the gassed Prisoner rushing to the window and pulling down the blinds for some inexplicable reason, and the reawakened Prisoner reacting with far-too-comic astonishment to the sight of the Village; and the Prisoner is knocked down by Rover at the end of the story. Other changes are more significant: a dubious remark by the Prisoner to the taxi-driver that this is an 'unusual job for a girl' was cut from the final edit; the labour exchange sequence did not originally feature the chanting of nursery rhymes; the final title sequence was changed; and Rover's initial appearance did not originally have it attacking a hapless Villager. McGoohan's insistence that nothing indicating overt sexuality should occur in the series also becomes evident in a comparison between the two prints of the sequence where the

---

7 George Markstein has apparently claimed that 'Arrival' was initially intended to be a 90-minute-long pilot episode for the series; however, no other evidence has emerged supporting this.

Prisoner walks past the Butler towards the helicopter; in the original, he looks back in the direction of a pretty girl in a bikini and, although it is ambiguous whether he is looking at her or at the Butler, the transmitted sequence features no girl and no backward glance. These changes all add up to produce a sharper and more complex portrayal of the themes of the series.

Finally, a number of things appear in 'Arrival' that foreshadow later stories and developments. We get a brief glimpse at the surreal numbering system on the information board, which only goes up to 120 and, since it has no sevens, features two sixes, two threes, two 51s, 2c, 8c and two digits that are either an I or a 1, foreshadowing 'Free for All' and, indirectly, 'Fall Out' (judging by the accompanying legend on the board, one of the I or 1 characters indicates the Town Hall but, significantly, it is unclear what the second indicates). The theme of chess (from the chess set in the Prisoner's cottage through the repeated games with the Admiral), and the idea of the Villagers all being pawns, foreshadows 'Checkmate'; we also have a moment of inadvertent symbolism when the Prisoner crosses the lawn and an alternating checkerboard pattern of light and dark green squares is visible, as this sequence was filmed after the human-chessboard sequence in 'Checkmate' was completed, and one can still see where the grass was pressed down by the giant chessboard. The maid's initial contact with the Prisoner, in which he reacts to her sexually-tinged introduction by ordering her out (with attendant ambiguity over whether it is the maid service, or the sexual advance, that he is rejecting), highlights McGoohan's refusal to allow images of explicit sexuality within the series. Similarly, the maid first saying that she is happy in the Village, then breaking down in tears, and then having those tears revealed to be a sham as well by Number Two, brings in the recurring theme that people in the Village may not necessarily be who or what they claim to be.

'Arrival' is thus very much an establishing episode for *The Prisoner*, focusing on developing the Village scenario and introducing viewers to the central characters and concepts, while at the same time highlighting themes of compassion, betrayal and shifting motivations, which will pervade the series through to its final episode.

Essay 1: The Music Of The Spheres: The History And Meaning Of Rover

THE ORIGINAL ROVER

'Rover,' the white balloon-like object (or possibly creature) that defends the Village, is one of the most memorable pieces of Village iconography. The presentation of Rover as a large white globe was something of a last-minute addition. The original Rover (which was, by many accounts, designed by McGoohan himself) was a device that, to judge by surviving film footage and photographs, strongly resembled the futuristic hovercraft seen in *Casino Royale* (1967), but with black and white panelling. Although it was subsequently described, particularly by McGoohan, as a brilliant, state-of-the art device (in a 1977 interview with Warner Troyer in Toronto, McGoohan claimed that it could travel on water as well as land), other accounts suggest that, in fact, it was abandoned at least partly because it could run only on flat surfaces (another reason, cited by Steven Ricks in his book *The Prisoner: I am Not a Number!* , is that the two-stroke engine that powered the device was so loud that it drowned out dialogue). The surviving footage reveals it to be an awkward object, looking rather like a kind of gigantic fairy-cake on wheels, fitted with a police light.

The appearance of the original Rover also has interesting implications regarding some of the Village iconography. The Butler's umbrella, for instance, has a black-and-white pattern very like that of the original Rover's panelling (meaning that, had the original device been used, the diminutive, unnumbered Butler would have served as a kind of visual pun on Rover's appearance), and the flashing blue light motif seen throughout the series (see, for example, 'Free for All' and 'The Schizoid Man') would have been echoed in Rover's light. The original Rover's appearance is frequently alluded to in earlier scripts; the change to the form eventually seen on screen appears to have taken place during the writing of 'Checkmate', where the script treats Rover as mechanical, but additions made to it in late 1966 refer to the globular Rover instead (albeit with its noise still described as a 'siren').

THE BUBBLE

The genesis of the idea of having Rover as a giant whitish bubble is uncertain, and subject to contradictory accounts. The device is, in fact, a weather balloon, two metres in diameter, filled with helium, air and French chalk; smaller ones (inflated to about one-third to one-half the size) appear in 'The Chimes of Big Ben' and 'Free for All' (for the scene in 'Arrival' in which a tiny Rover is seen on top of the fountain, propsman Mickey O'Toole used an ordinary toy balloon, cut in half and tied 'like a haggis'). Various accounts attribute the idea of using a weather balloon to members of the crew having seen such a device in a BBC documentary on weather, or to their being inspired by the bubbles of a lava-lamp in the bar in which they were discussing what to do about Rover. McGoohan has claimed that he had the idea through seeing a weather balloon floating near Portmeirion at a fortuitous moment. Production manager Bernard Williams has made a near-identical claim. Legend further has it that, once the basic shape of Rover had been decided upon, Williams was promptly dispatched to buy some weather balloons; but another account reports a panicked phone call to props buyer Sidney Palmer, who, after the idea of using a large rubber ball as seen in the *Horse of the Year Show* had been rejected, suggested meteorological balloons as the solution. The balloons were in fact ordered directly from the manufacturer, in Birmingham, and proved slightly problematic in that they tended to burst during filming, and to be only partly controllable: for the scenes in which Rover apparently herds the Prisoner along, it had to be tethered to McGoohan's ankle to keep it floating after him. While it has been said that the practical reason for the Villagers freezing when Rover bounces through the Village is that, in order to get the balloon to go where they wanted it to go, the team wound up releasing the balloon from the end-point of its trajectory and then filming the sequence in reverse (such that it appears to arrive at its destination rather than depart from it), the original script reveals that the Villagers were intended to freeze even when the mechanical Rover, which would have had no such limitations, was to be used. Nonetheless, it is true that some of the Rover sequences were filmed in reverse, presumably for the abovementioned practical reason (viewers may particularly note the peculiar reverse movements undertaken by McGoohan towards the end of the 'Arrival' sequence in which the device is introduced). The eerie noise that provides the finishing touch was created by Wilf Thompson, and is a synthesis of the noises made by an inner tube filled with shotgun pellets, a man screaming and Gregorian chanting (the alternate versions of 'Arrival' and 'The Chimes of Big Ben' have an additional noise that sounds something like an aqualung). It is tempting to assume that, in Moris Farhi's unmade script 'The Outsider', the Pilot's initial pose as being from the Meteorological Office is a kind of inside joke about using weather balloons as Rover; however, since Farhi also refers to Rover's 'flashing light', this must be simply a weird coincidence.

Rover's origins and nature are deliberately mysterious. Roger Langley, in *The Prisoner in Portmeirion*, describes Rover as part-mechanical, part-organic, which is exactly as it appears in the series. Some of the time it seems to be controlled by the Village authorities, but on other occasions it appears to act independently (as in 'The Schizoid Man', for instance, in which we see it patrolling the streets after dark). It also sometimes seems to have preset routines and instructions, as when, in 'The Schizoid Man', Rover kills Curtis rather than the Prisoner, not, apparently, deliberately, but because the Prisoner gave the correct password first, and thus, although Curtis did give the correct password, he was overruled. In a filmed, but cut, sequence from 'It's Your Funeral', when Rover is seen killing Mark Eden's character (a portion of which was reused in 'Arrival', as noted in the episode review), it was to have been seen filling with blood, an idea abandoned on grounds of it being too horrific. However, the lack of any explanation for the device's existence, actions and motivations is enough to give it a bizarre, nightmarish quality.

The novels frequently take the opportunity to expand on, or explain, the set-up as seen in the televised episodes. Thomas M Disch's *I Am Not a Number!* describes a Village in which the balloons, called 'Guardians' (the term in the series referred to the human guards), are graded according to size and pastel shade: only one, a fawn-coloured balloon that is the only one with the ability to kill, is actually called 'Rover' (aside from the shading and the use of the name 'Guardian', this does not actually contradict anything that we see in the series, and is an interesting elaboration on the Rover system). At one point, Number Two makes a radio broadcast through Rover. David McDaniel picks up on the idea of classified balloons in *Who is No. 2?*, referring to them as differentiated into 'herders' and 'killers'. *The Prisoner's Dilemma* has, as a comment on post-9/11 paranoia, the Village stores selling egg cartons of miniature Rovers as 'Home Security Systems'.

NUMBERS AND CIPHERS: SYMBOLISM AND ROVER

Rover's ultimate representation as a round, blank object does allow it, fortuitously, to fit in with Village iconography, if anything, more so than the black-and-white device. Circles abound in the Village: the doorways in the Prisoner's house and in the hospital are rounded; Villagers play with balls and display umbrellas; there are frequent images of globes, round lamps and penny-farthing wheels. In a happy accident, the sculpture of Hercules that dominates central Portmeirion has the hero holding up a very Rover-esque ball on his shoulders. The rising Rover also looks like the rising globes of lava in lava-lamps (particularly Mathmos' 'champagne mist' range of lamps, introduced in 1965 and discontinued in the 1970s, which featured opaque, off-white lava in a pale amber solution). In particular, Rover recalls the white, eye-shaped camera/light of the Control Centre (which is often intercut with shots of Rover: see particularly 'The Chimes of Big Ben') and Number Two's chair, which rises into the centre of the room in an exact, if colour-reversed, parallel of Rover's rise from the sea. Finally, as pointed out in one of Fairclough's articles for the De Agostini release of *The Prisoner* DVDs, there is a similarity between Rover and the Village hearse, in that the hearse is seen in London silently policing and attacking citizens, and that they are even filmed in a similar way.

Symbolically, however, Rover is a void, or a cipher: it is, essentially, Number Zero, the expression of the will of the Village authorities and a kind of social control made manifest. This is picked up on in the exchange on page 256 of *The Prisoner's Dilemma*, describing Rover as 'a thought balloon.' … 'For the thought police?' … 'No wonder it's empty.' Director Don Chaffey describes it as 'faceless, suffocating bureaucracy'; it could equally be read as an all-seeing eye. Its very blankness and mutability give it the quality of a nightmare monster, in keeping with the dreamlike nature of some of the series. McGoohan himself, quoted in *The Prisoner: a Televisionary Masterpiece*, apparently described it as 'The Unknown, or the invasion of privacy. Or hidden bureaucracy. Or interviews. Or death. Or taxes. Or whatever.' Rover thus represents what the viewer, or even the writer, finds most disturbing about the Village.

The blank, uncommunicative appearance of the device means that it is possible to read any emotion, or none, onto it. *The Prisoner's Dilemma* has one character, when attacked by Rover, have a weird vision of television news and commercial images, from which he emerges, broken of all rebellion and determined to be a file clerk, suggesting that, as implied in 'Free for All', Rover is a kind of televisual or literal expression of the mediasphere, displaying and reflecting popular images. Rover's destruction at the end of 'Fall Out', to the tune of Carmen Miranda singing 'I, Yi, Yi, Yi, Yi (Like You Very Much)' can be taken as the Prisoner's unleashed ego filling up the void that is Rover, and destroying it in the process.

The choice of the name 'Rover' also echoes this absurdity, being largely unexplained and inexplicable beyond the fact that the device has the ability to rove. The only story in which it is actually named onscreen is 'The Schizoid Man', although the name appears in the scripts as far back as 'Arrival'. In 'The Outsider', Farhi takes the name to mean that it is doglike, having the Pilot ask if Rover is a 'dog' and having the device actually sniffing around people at points in the story (it is also explicitly singular, an idea abandoned when the weather-balloons came in to replace the mechanical device). In *The Prisoner's Dilemma*, the authors speculate that the name is a kind of attempt to make light of something terrifying by giving it a frivolous nickname, as was frequently done with bombs and planes in the Second World War.

Rover's strength as a piece of imagery arises from its simplicity and from the lack of history and motivation attributed to it, causing a simple weather balloon to achieve iconic status as a symbol of surveillance and control.

Episode 2:
The Chimes of Big Ben

First UK Transmission Date: Friday 6 October 1967: ATV Midlands/Grampian, 7.30 pm – 8.30 pm
Writer: Vincent Tilsley
Director: Don Chaffey
Credited Cast: Patrick McGoohan (The Prisoner); Leo McKern (Number Two); Nadia Grey (Nadia); Finlay Currie (General); Richard Wattis (Fotheringay); Angelo Muscat (The Butler); Kevin Stoney (Colonel J.); Christopher Benjamin (Number Two's Assistant); David Arlen (Karel); Peter Swanwick (Supervisor); Hilda Barrie (No. 38 [No. 36 in alternative version]); Jack LeWhite (First Judge); John Maxim (Second Judge); Lucy Griffiths (Third Judge)
Known Uncredited Cast: Frank Maher (Double for Patrick McGoohan); Fenella Fielding (Loudspeaker Voice); Helweun Vaughan-Hatcher (Double for Nadia Gray); Robert Rietty (Additional Voicework)

SYNOPSIS: As Number Two urges the Prisoner to take part in the Village's upcoming arts competition, a new prisoner, Nadia (Number Eight) is installed in the cottage next to the Prisoner's. She attempts to escape by swimming out to sea, but is captured and taken to the hospital. Witnessing her treatment, the Prisoner agrees to take part in the arts competition provided that Nadia is left alone. The Prisoner learns that Nadia knows the Village's location (Lithuania, 30 miles from the Polish border), and enlists her in an escape plan. The Prisoner wins the competition with an abstract piece called 'Escape', and purchases one of the runner-up pieces, a tapestry, with his prize money. That night, he and Nadia convert his sculpture and the tapestry into a boat with a sail, and sail to a bay where they meet a contact of Nadia's, who seals them up in a packing crate to be shipped to London. The Prisoner exchanges his watch with that of Nadia's contact, as his own has become water-damaged. Upon arrival in London after a long journey, Nadia is taken away and the Prisoner is questioned by his former colleagues Fotheringay and Colonel J. Hearing the chimes of Big Ben, the Prisoner realises that the clock is giving the same time as his watch, which should have given the time as being an hour later. He exposes the whole set-up as a Village fake, and Nadia is revealed to be a Village agent.

ANALYSIS: Filmed fifth in sequence (followed by 'Once Upon a Time', facilitating the presence of Leo McKern in both stories), 'The Chimes of Big Ben' is one of *The Prisoner*'s more ordinary and less imaginative stories. However, it is at least partly redeemed by certain clever ideas and sequences (notably the Prisoner's defence of his art exhibit), and by its development of the nature of the Village.

NOT ANOTHER SPY STORY: 'THE CHIMES OF BIG BEN' IN CONTEXT

The story of 'The Chimes of Big Ben' is, if anything, disconcertingly close to one that might have been seen in a conventional fantasy spy series of the time, such as *The Man from UNCLE*. The plot is full of Soviet agents, daring escapes from behind the Iron Curtain, a boss with a clipped accent and a letter for a name (Colonel J) and a super-clever hero who comes up with James Bond-esque plans, develops highly unlikely skills for a single episode only (in this case, stone-tool-making), and rumbles the villains' game with a clever contrivance. The plot, also, hangs on a whacking great convenience (namely, that Nadia's Resistance friend is waiting for the Prisoner and Nadia on the beach; if Nadia is supposed to have been kidnapped without warning, as he was, you would think that the Prisoner would have become a bit suspicious) and is verging on the unbelievable anyway (as the makeshift boat has no keel, the 'sail' is too loosely woven to work properly, and the oar has to double as a tiller, meaning that steering would be impossible if there is no wind). The episode also, like many ITC series of the time, features a rather obvious bit of stock footage (here, when the Prisoner chops down a tree). The whole idea of a building or office being mocked up in order to convince a spy that he is not where he thinks he is, is a stock feature of a number of post-war spy thrillers, most famously *The Ipcress File*. As Vincent Tilsley had written extensively for independent television (largely ITC and LWT), including detective and spy series, and as Don Chaffey was a veteran of a number of ITC spy series, the conventional spy-thriller nature of 'The Chimes of Big Ben' probably owes much to their track records.

The story also comes across as weak in other ways. The escape attempt, for instance, works on only one level – i.e. that it has all been set up by the Village – when it should really work on more than one, maintaining an ambiguity over whether or not it is genuine until the very last moment, to avoid careful viewers seeing through the plan early on. Although Nadia is a fine character and the first of the woman-in-apparent-distress type that will crop up over and over again in *The Prisoner* to good effect (Tilsley had originally intended her to be more of a romantic interest for the Prisoner, and was reportedly not pleased when McGoohan scaled down heavily this aspect of their relationship), unfortunately actress Nadia Grey comes across as rather cold and unsympathetic; she may arguably have seemed less so in the '60s, (she also appeared in Fellini's *La Dolce Vita*, at one point famously wearing nothing but a fur coat, a sequence referenced in her choice of outerwear in the final scene of 'The Chimes of Big Ben'), but to a modern viewer she bears too much of a resemblance to the android woman in *Mars Attacks!* to seem in any way vulnerable or appealing. The story is also not helped by the fact that it was made mostly in the studio or on the Borehamwood back lot, and consequently looks a bit rough – the beach up which Nadia is dragged by the three Rover balloons is clearly not the beach that the Prisoner finds her on later. A double for Nadia Grey was used in the Portmeirion scenes and in the sequence where the Prisoner and Nadia exchange information while ostensibly flirting (a change apparently made due to McGoohan's reluctance to show him in romantic scenes with his leading lady, and another source of irritation for Tilsley, who had originally wanted the sequence to take place on the Prisoner's bed), and although, to be fair, this is not apparent on first viewing, once the viewer knows it to be the case, it becomes unfortunately rather too obvious.

One common complaint about this story is that, although it comes second in the transmission order, the Prisoner appears to have been in the Village for quite some time, got over his initial shock and developed a well-established pattern of resistance (see 'Essay 2: Story Order'). Its placement does, however, serve to highlight its parallels with 'Arrival'. Nadia's awakening in what seems to be her own flat mirrors the Prisoner's own entry to the Village, and the Prisoner's behaviour towards her, evidently intended to try to find out where she stands (he at one point asks her who Number One is) echoes that of the various people he met on his own arrival: he is friendly to her, gives no sign of being anything other than happy in the Village, greets neighbours with 'Be seeing you', and explains to her about the greeting and the taxi system. All of this, incidentally, casts new light on the behaviour of the characters in 'Arrival': was the taxi-driver, for instance, a warder, or just another prisoner doing a model-citizen act in order to ascertain the Prisoner's loyalties? Number Two later asks the Prisoner for information on Nadia, much as Number Nine (one number away from Nadia; the original script had Nadia as Number Seven, which brings her symbolically closer to the Prisoner himself) was asked for information on him, and Nadia also accuses him of working for Number Two, just as the Prisoner did Number Nine. The character is also played by an actress with the same first name as herself, which serves to emphasise the parallels between McGoohan himself and the character he portrays. Nadia's escape attempt parallels the Prisoner's adventure with the Mini Moke, and, in a cut scene, we would have learned that Nadia had been assigned as the Prisoner's maid, recalling the maid in 'Arrival'. 'The Chimes of Big Ben' also reuses a slightly extended version of the location footage of the Prisoner watching the helicopter from the first episode; and the sequence where the Prisoner watches the helicopter arrive as he plays chess with the General parallels the sequence in 'Arrival' where Number Nine watches the helicopter leave as she plays chess with the Admiral (both the Prisoner and Number Nine, incidentally, are playing white at that point). The position of 'The Chimes of Big Ben' in transmission order certainly casts new light on the events of the preceding episode.

BEHIND THE IRON CURTAIN?
THE VILLAGE IN 'THE CHIMES OF BIG BEN'

The Village set-up seems to have changed slightly between episodes. The accepted currency has switched from 'credit units' to 'work units' (and the Prisoner now has enough of them to buy both whiskey- and vodka-substitute); the music stops when the Prisoner puts the radio in the fridge (unlike in 'Arrival', when it continues long after he has smashed the speaker); the Admiral has been replaced with the near-identical General; and the Village is directly identified as being somewhere near the Polish border (but see below). The emphasis in the tannoy's speech on the democratically-elected nature of the Village council could be a dig at the Soviet Union's false elections, used to justify their governance of Eastern European countries, or alternatively a more general comment about the idea of democratic language being used as a fig leaf for oppression. When Rover attacks Nadia, it does not smother its victim's face as in 'Arrival', but seems to send her into a kind of hallucinatory vortex (suggesting that it carries drugs). In this story, the Village has a definite curfew: while this will also appear to be the case in some later episodes (for example 'The Schizoid Man'), others will appear to show a more relaxed attitude to Village events after dark (for example 'The General' and 'Free for All'; whether these are exceptions made for special events or indicative of changes within the Village set-up is unclear from the stories in question).

These variations, whether they are deliberate or (as possibly in the case of the works units) inadvertent continuity errors, give the Village the feeling of being a postmodern environment or dream landscape, continually changing without anyone remarking on it. The fact that, when the Prisoner leaves Colonel J's office, he walks into a square with a band in it but the band starts playing only when he arrives, again leaves one with the impression that the Village may all be a creation of the Prisoner's own mind and have no physical existence; it could also be argued that Fotheringay's lack of remorse at selling out his old school chum, and Nadia's at similarly betraying the man she has flirted with extensively throughout a journey of several hours, suggest a weird lack of emotion consistent with them being ciphers rather than real people. Chris Gregory, in *Be Seeing You*, suggests that the sequence showing the crate apparently travelling on planes, boats and trucks also implies that the whole montage, at least, takes place only in the Prisoner's mind, as in reality the pair made only a short trip back to the Village; however, this is ambiguous, as, considering the lengths the Village administration go to in order to affect the Prisoner's mind elsewhere, they could have arranged to have him driven/flown/etc around the countryside for a while. A sequence that apparently involved Number Two pursuing a truck carrying the crate in a helicopter, which would have made it plain that it was *not* in the Prisoner's imagination, was cut from the original script, leaving the question open as to how much, if any, of what we see has physical existence.

This episode is one that, however, appears to give a definite location for the Village, in that Nadia states that it is in Lithuania, on the Baltic, 30 miles from the Polish border. At the same time, though, it is careful not to give too much credence to this. Early on, when the General says that he would like to have had the Prisoner in his regiment, the latter counters with 'Which regiment? Which army?' and the former does not answer, leaving it uncertain where they are and whether or not, indeed, the Village exists physically at all. One sequence present in the alternate print of the episode but cut from the final version shows the Prisoner using a triquetrum, an ancient Greek navigational device for working out one's position using the stars (the image of the sky used was a plate from Kubrik's *2001: A Space Odyssey*, which was being filmed at the same studio at the same time); had this sequence been retained, it would have carried the implication that the Prisoner has a reasonable idea of where he is geographically, and, since he does not then contradict Nadia's story about the location of the Village, this would have implied that it was correct. A line in the original script saying that he was able to work out only that he was in the Northern hemisphere was cut, presumably on credibility grounds (the Greeks were the premier naval power of their day, so the device can't be that inaccurate), and the sequence underwent a number of drastic changes from script to screen, suggesting that the team had problems with the idea from the start. So, although a definite location is given for the Village, the story as it stands leaves open the possibility that this is false information.

Once again, too, we get the implication that the Village is the world itself, and vice versa. This is highlighted early on in Number Two's conversation with the Prisoner on the beach, in which Number Two says that once East and West become mirror images of each other, the Village will be the model for the whole world (leading the Prisoner to comment about wanting to be the first man on the moon). The sequence was originally to have been much longer, and to have included the following exchange:

NUMBER TWO: What do you think of nationalism? As such?
P[RISONER][8]: Depends on whose side you're on.
NUMBER TWO: Nationalism's a disease, but it breeds its own antibodies … that's why it doesn't matter who Number One is.

Number Two goes on to say that the Village was created for 'the very worst nationalistic motives', but is developing an international community. This line may have been cut because it makes the Village's origins less ambiguous, but it also ties in with the idea that the Village is a symbolic representation of the world itself. The end titles of the alternate print also pick up on this idea, but with more apocalyptic implications: in this sequence, the penny-farthing fades out, leaving the Earth and the universe as the small and big wheels: the universe then expands out, and the Earth fills the screen, to be replaced finally by a red screen and the word 'POP,' in a kind of foreshadowing of the explosive exodus from the Village in 'Fall Out'.

This theme also recurs in the scenes set in Colonel J's office. The globe (identical to one in the Prisoner's own house) and the two white globe lamps are motifs continually recurring in the Village (and, in the latter case, recalling Rover); the red telephone parallels those in Two's office and the Control Room; and the Prisoner's house, Nadia's house and Colonel J's office all have identical existences both in the Village and in the world at large. Colonel J's office also contains navigational instruments (recalling the Prisoner's triquetrum), abstract paintings and naval images (recalling the Prisoner's and Nadia's own escape by sea using an

---

8 In the scripts, the Prisoner is inevitably designated simply as 'P'.

ostensible piece of abstract art). When Colonel J starts in on the Prisoner, the latter responds that J (played by Kevin Stoney, who is visibly acting with his moustache, and also sporting a drooping eyelid sustained in a recent car accident) reminds him of Number Two, bringing up the idea that we see the same systems and types of people over and over, wherever we are; and the deal that the Prisoner strikes with J regarding his cooperation for Nadia's safety is similar to the one he struck with Number Two earlier in the story.

BESIDE MYSELF:
DOUBLES, PSYCHOANALYSIS, AND CHILDISHNESS

The theme of doubles features again, albeit more subtextually, in this story, particularly when viewed in conjunction with *Danger Man*. Christopher Benjamin's appearance, coming immediately after those he made in 'Arrival' and the *Danger Man* episodes 'Koroshi'/'Shinda Shima', means that (if one counts the *Danger Man* two-parter as a single production) he has now featured in three McGoohan-related productions in a row, as three different characters (given that his credit here is 'Number Two's Assistant' rather than 'Labour Exchange Manager' as in 'Arrival', and he is dressed in Village gear rather than a suit). Benjamin's role was to have been more extensive, with him being the one to interrogate Nadia (on screen, this is done by the Supervisor), but there is no apparent reason why his scenes were cut – or why he was, in the final version, redubbed by Robert Rietty (who also provided the Supervisor's voiceover during the interrogation scene, and briefly overdubbed Leo McKern with the line 'Wait, what?') – beyond, possibly, anxiety on the director's part at having the same actor appearing in two quite different roles in what became consecutive episodes. The role of Fotheringay is one that would also have given a moment of recognition to viewers of McGoohan's earlier series, as Richard Wattis (whom McGoohan reportedly chose himself to play this role) had a recurring part as John Drake's boss Hardy in the first series of *Danger Man*. Some less explicable doubles are also seen when the tannoy begins her 'Good morning, good morning,' speeches: in both cases, we see the Prisoner apparently standing in one location and then almost instantly reappearing in another quite distinct one (in the first case, his appearance on the balcony outside the Green Dome is followed by a shot of him in bed in his house; in the second, he is first seen on top of the bandshell and then emerging from the Green Dome), foreshadowing some of the peculiar visual imagery of 'Free for All'.

Given that episode writer Vincent Tilsley subsequently became a psychotherapist, it is unsurprising that this story also emphasises the series' psychoanalytic themes. Number Two's continual reporting of the Prisoner's behaviour into a dictaphone has more than a touch of the therapist about it, particularly when he goes on to say that the Prisoner 'will be cured,' and will come to him whimpering to discuss any dream or bad feeling; he remarks on the Prisoner's 'rising egomania' and suggests that he take up arts and crafts as a kind of occupational therapy. We again see the group therapy room, and another shaven-headed man in the hospital, with the obvious implication that brain surgery is being carried out. Nadia's 'treatment' is like a sadistic form of post-suicide-attempt counselling: in a cut line, Number Two says that they are testing her to ascertain the 'depth of neurosis,' as 'a characteristic of neurosis is the inability to choose between different courses of action.'

The themes of infantilisation also continue, with the group therapy sequence again being accompanied by the 'Boys and Girls, Come Out to Play' musical sting, and the establishing shot of the beach featuring two old people building a sandcastle while younger Villagers play with a ball. We also learn something about the Prisoner's own schooldays, namely that he was top of his class at woodwork at the age of 15, and, in a cut line that appears in the alternate print, that he and Fotheringay were at school together. The arts and crafts exhibition, as well as recalling activities at holiday camps, is also something associated with children; as the entries on exhibit were all done by the children of the production team, there is at least one picture apparently done by a small child, leaving it open whether there are children in the Village, or whether the adult Villagers have become infantilised.

IT MEANS WHAT IT SAYS: THE PRISONER HIMSELF

This episode also reinforces what we have learned about the Prisoner in the preceding one. The themes of rebellion continue, with the Prisoner likening himself to Prometheus when he threatens to discover fire, and defiantly putting three sugars in his tea in a sequence apparently added by either McGoohan or Chaffey (as it does not appear in the original script). In a cut line, the Prisoner explains that he resigned as a matter of conscience, but Number Two is not interested. The parallels with John Drake, the conscientious secret agent, are emphasised in another cut line, when the Prisoner describes the Village: 'It's a place where people are sent. People who resign from dirty, filthy jobs because they think their conscience is worth something. But other people think what they have in their heads is worth even more.' However, the situation of the Prisoner is also developed when Number Two (in a performance by Leo McKern that is nothing short of brilliant, particularly in his habit of apparently finding everything irresistibly funny) refers to himself as a prisoner too, confined to the Village for knowing too much, and likens himself to his charge.

The Prisoner's defence of his art exhibit, 'Escape', is one of the strongest and most important sequences in the story. Again, we see themes of rebellion subverted: although he appears to have made the only piece that does not feature a representation of Number Two, Number Two in fact looks through the holes in the sculpture as he says to the judges 'Don't let me influence you'; and after he leaves we can clearly see an ink drawing of Number Two through one of the holes. The Prisoner's explanation of his work (and the old lady judge's ignorant attempts to pretend that she understands what he is saying) seems almost like a prophetic send-up of the sort of analysis that would be subsequently applied to *The Prisoner* itself (not least, some critics might say, in the present volume!), and of McGoohan's own tendency to obfuscate in interviews. Asked what the sculpture means, the Prisoner replies 'It means what it is,' and then turns the question onto the judge, asking him what the piece represents to him. 'A church door,' replies the judge, in the only mention of churches in the series at all. The Prisoner later elaborates: 'This other piece … Along the same general lines, but more abstract, representing freedom or a barrier, depending on how you look at it. The barrier's down, the door is open, you're free, free to go … to this, the symbol of human aspirations. Knowledge, freedom, escape.' Asked, 'Why the cross piece?' he responds 'Why not?' All of which is seemingly as meaningful yet ultimately meaningless as Number Two's description of the Prisoner as 'Our very own Epstein.' A few lines were cut from the sequence, ostensibly because they pertained to religion: originally the Prisoner's response to 'A church door' was to have been 'Right first time, a barrier to truth and progress', and his reply to the question about the cross-piece was similarly to have identified it with religion and, at the same time, oppression: 'Our escape leads us back to discipline, faith, organisation. In fact, religion.' However, another reason why they were removed might have been that they suggested a genuine symbolism to the piece, whereas in fact the twist is that the title and function of the piece are totally literal: the art exhibit *is* a boat, and as such it *is* escape in the most literal sense. Symbolically, then, this scene emphasises the problems of reading too much into any given text.

ROBINSON CRUSOE: DESIGN AND TECHNICAL DETAIL

Despite this warning not to take it too seriously, it is difficult not to notice recurring images of surveillance and freedom in the design. When we first see the unfinished 'Escape', it is lying on its side in the woods and looks very like an eye; the music track,'Tropical Forest', that plays in the final print as the Prisoner works (a different track of unknown name is used in the alternate print), would have been recognisable to many in the original audience as referencing that of the 1964 French series *The Adventures of Robinson Crusoe*, with attendant themes of isolation and escape. The cameras in the Control Room appear at times, from the pictures they relay, to be actually hovering over Nadia, which, given the strangeness of the series as a whole, comes across less as an error than as a kind of surreal comment on the ubiquity of surveillance. Tilsley's idea behind the non-alcoholic whiskey and vodka was that to him, the idea of having a full drinks cabinet but no actual alcohol seemed like the ultimate punishment.

On the repeating images front, Number Two's video screen,

when not in use, seems to show a 'screensaver' of red lava-lamp fluid, and chess sets appear again (at the Prisoner's cottage and at the Old People's Home, but also as the General's entry for the competition, with Number Two as the Black King, and quite probably, given its shape, the White King as well). The fact that the game between the Prisoner and the General would lead to 'checkmate in seven moves' is also interesting, as seven is the number that almost never features on the Villagers' badges in the finished series but was originally intended to be Nadia's number. Nadia's appearance in the control room at the end of the story foreshadows the ending of 'Free for All', with the slight distinction that when she drops her innocent pose, she does not drop her accent in the way that the maid will drop her pseudo-Slavic language in the latter episode.

Finally, on a minor point of distinction, 'The Chimes of Big Ben' is also notable as the first episode to feature the 'Where am I …?' introductory sequence, which is essentially a shortened version of the opening of 'Arrival' and recaps the series' main concepts: the resignation, the Village, Rover, the constantly changing Number Twos, and so on. An alternative sequence appears in the original script, designated as Standard Title Sequence Draft 1, essentially a shorter version of what became the finished introductory sequence, featuring, among other things, the mechanical Rover (clearly designated as such in the script) shepherding the Prisoner back to the Village across the beach, and an image of prison bars clanging shut over the Prisoner's face, which then recedes into an image of the Village (which ended up being used as the animation before the end credits in all episodes except 'Fall Out', albeit with the Prisoner's face coming up out of the Village rather than receding into it; the end credits described in the original scripts for 'The Chimes of Big Ben', as well as 'Arrival', 'Dance of the Dead', 'Checkmate', and the unmade 'The Outsider', also refer to a different version of this animation, in which the gates clang shut and then the Prisoner's face zooms up out of the Village towards them). The opening title sequence on the alternate print differs slightly from the final, having the Wilfred Josephs theme (which McGoohan had rejected) rather than the familiar Ron Grainer one, the introductory sequence accompanied by a more subdued voiceover from McGoohan, and the clip of the Prisoner being knocked down by Rover from the alternate print of 'Arrival'; it also varies from the title sequence seen on the latter print in that the title theme does not start until after the Prisoner leaves the underground car park, and the sound of (ironically) Big Ben chiming is overdubbed as we see the car pass Westminster.

'The Chimes of Big Ben' is one of the more conventionally structured, and also less thought-provoking, of the series' episodes. Fortunately for the viewer, however, it is less a harbinger of things to come than a look back at McGoohan's earlier series.

Episode 3:
A, B and C

First UK Transmission Date: Friday 13 October 1967: ATV
Midlands/Grampian, 7.30 pm – 8.30 pm
Writer: Anthony Skene
Director: Pat Jackson
Credited Cast: Patrick McGoohan (The Prisoner); Katherine Kath
(Engadine); Sheila Allen (Number Fourteen); Colin Gordon
(Number Two); Peter Bowles ('A'); Angelo Muscat (The Butler);
Georgina Cookson (Blonde Lady); Annette Carrell ('B'); Lucille
Soong (Flower Girl); Bettine Le Beau (Maid at Party); Terry York
(Thug); Peter Brayham (Thug); Bill Cummings (Henchman)
Known Uncredited Cast: Frank Maher (Double for Patrick
McGoohan)

SYNOPSIS: Number Two arranges for the Prisoner to undergo a
procedure at the hands of Number Fourteen, whereby, through the
agency of drugs and recordings, his dreams are controlled, and can
be viewed on a large display screen. Number Two has him dream of
attending a party at the house of socialite Madame Engadine, over
the course of which he will encounter three people, whom Number
Two suspects of having been instrumental in the Prisoner's
resignation. In the first dream, the Prisoner encounters A, a former
colleague who has defected and who encourages the Prisoner to join
him; the Prisoner goes with him to meet his new employers, but
fights with them. The next day, the Prisoner surmises something is
up, observing the injection mark on his wrist and recognising

Number Fourteen (whom he saw briefly before becoming fully unconscious) in the Village. On the second night, the Prisoner meets B, a female agent; at Number Two's request, Number Fourteen asks the Prisoner questions in the persona of B, but the Prisoner becomes suspicious and deflects the questions. The next day, the Prisoner finds the underground laboratory, investigates the set-up and substitutes water for the bulk of the drug. On the third night, C, the last contact, whose identity is unknown to Numbers Fourteen and Two, apparently proves to be Madame Engadine herself. She takes the Prisoner to a mysterious location to meet her master. Unmasked, this man is revealed to be Number Two; the dream Prisoner then comes to the laboratory and gives the dream Number Two an envelope containing holiday brochures, saying that he wasn't selling out. The dream Prisoner departs, leaving Number Two to consider his own future.

ANALYSIS: 'A, B and C' is the first episode in the transmission order to move away from introducing the Village or riffing on *Danger Man* into what most people think of as *The Prisoner*'s main territory, namely, psychoanalysis and mind alteration. However, it is more than that, being something of a televisual metafiction and exploration of the nature of the Village and its structure as well.

A, B AND TV: METAFICTION

Most immediately, 'A, B and C' is distinctive for being an early televisual metafiction. The story's premise, to a modern viewer, seems to recall the 'cyberpunk' novels and films of the 1980s, in which the brain is treated as a kind of unformatted computer into which virtual environments and characters can be introduced. However, although early examples of this genre can be found in the New Wave fiction of the 1950s and '60s (notably Philip K Dick's 'We Can Remember it for You Wholesale' and, in Britain, Daphne Castell's 'Who's In There With Me?'), these ideas would not come into general use for a good 15 years at the time of the story's genesis, and the more immediate referent for its premise is television production. We see characters introduced into an imaginary setting: notably, when the Prisoner appears on screen, the party fades up around him like a back-projection (which, of course, it is in reality); and when A appears on the small screen after the relevant tape is fitted, he is silhouetted against a blue screen – a technique that, although relatively new at the time, was a known way of 'inserting' an actor into another image, much as A, B, C and the Prisoner will all be 'inserted' into the party.

We also see the televisual nature of the story referenced in the on-screen images: when we first see the Prisoner on the display screen, it is in a third-person view of the resignation scene from the series' title sequence, looping over and over; when his eyes open, we see a first-person view of Number Fourteen; and then, when the party starts, we return to the third-person view. In an apparent inside joke referring to the fact that the production team were nervous about the budget at the time the story was made, A remarks 'I'm saving myself money' when the same actors who have portrayed Engadine's footmen also act as his henchmen. One of the story's earlier working titles was 'A Play in Three Acts', which refers to the structure of the story itself as much as to its events (although, of course, *The Prisoner* episodes, like most 50-minute commercial television plays, were always structured in four acts, allowing for advert breaks); the other working title, '1, 2 and 3', is close to the final one (note also that the vials of the drug are still labelled '1', '2' and '3' rather than 'A', 'B' and 'C'). The struggle for control over the story between Number Fourteen and the Prisoner could be seen as a battle over 'directorial' control of the action. Finally, the Prisoner himself makes the ultimate metaphysical transition when, after unmasking the man in the cul-de-sac (remarking as he does 'Mustn't disappoint the people who are watching,' meaning the viewers as much as Numbers Fourteen and Two), he walks out of the fiction into the Village, then into the lab (causing the watching Fourteen and Two to glance nervously at the door), to speak directly to a dream-Fourteen and dream-Two, foreshadowing the fourth-wall breaches in postmodern series such as *Monty Python's Flying Circus* and *Gangsters*.

Parallels with the real-life situation on the production also emerge in 'A, B and C'. At the time of its filming (13 February 1967 in the studio, with location footage done in March and April), rifts were beginning to appear between Markstein and McGoohan; by August, Markstein was no longer involved with the series. It may therefore be significant that 'A, B and C' features a plot in which a nervous Number Two is developing a straightforward spy story that is then hijacked by the Prisoner and turned into a psychedelic fantasy in which the mystery man turns out to be Number Two himself. Having done this, the Prisoner returns to the recurring image of McGoohan resigning from an institution represented by Markstein at a desk. These parallels may perhaps have owed something to the involvement of scriptwriter Anthony Skene and director Pat Jackson. Skene was a prolific writer whose credits also include *Upstairs, Downstairs, The Adventures of Sherlock Holmes* and a version of 'A, B and C' rewritten for the BBC series *Counterstrike* as 'Nocturne', and who may have had a partial influence on the look of *The Prisoner* as a whole (having written for ITV a surrealist drama on themes of individual freedom entitled *File on Harry Jordan*, screened in 1965, which featured Angelo Muscat as a silent butler; it was remade by YTV in 1978). He got on well with George Markstein, having previously been commissioned to write 'Dance of the Dead' for *The Prisoner*. Jackson was another *Danger Man* veteran who was a last-minute replacement for the original director, Michael Truman, who fell ill.The climax of the story foreshadows events later to be seen in 'Fall Out' – Number Two, desiring to find out who the Prisoner is allegedly selling out to, is shown a masked man, who, when unmasked, has Number Two's face, and the Prisoner then walks out into the 'reality' of the Village, paralleling the Prisoner's own (self) discovery and departure into 'reality' of the final episode.

A CHANGE OF MIND: PSYCHOANALYSIS

Where other stories in the series have hinted at themes of psychoanalysis, 'A, B and C' deals explicitly with concerns in this area. Most immediately, it references Freud's well-known theories about dreams as the expression of unconscious fears or desires, which could be affected by physical and mental stimuli (see Freud's monograph *The Interpretation of Dreams*, 1889); in this case, we see how the Prisoner wrests control of his mind from outside forces by learning to control his dreams, shouting 'It's dreamy! It's a dreamy party!' as he does. The sequence in which he straightens out the room by straightening out a mirror hanging crooked on the wall also symbolises his regaining control over his own mind. The idea of the Prisoner sneaking into underground caves that shelter secret projects seems like a metaphor for his journey into his own subconscious. We also have Madame Engadine's remarks about her mysterious boss: 'Even I work for someone ... I have never seen him. No-one has ever seen him ... He likes impressive offices' (the Prisoner asks 'How will I know him?' and Engadine replies 'He will know you'). All of this could be taken as a reference to Number One, Number Two, the id, or even, as they are approaching a church door at the time, God. Curiously, however, given Freud's interest in childhood experiences as an influence on adult behaviour, themes of infantilisation are kept to a minimum, with the party-guests' games being nothing unusual for drunk or otherwise inebriated adults in such a setting.

At the time, however, an area for much discussion and concern was the idea of modifying behaviour through physical action, such as drug-taking, electroshock therapy, hypnosis and so forth. Such devices were being used not only in the treatment of psychiatric patients but also in mind-control experiments sponsored by, among others, the British MoD and the American CIA (as described extensively in Anne Collins' 1988 book *In the Sleep Room*). The controversial nature of such activities seems to be reflected in the way the lightening-flashes at the start of the story obliquely reference James Whale's 1931 film *Frankenstein*. It is also implied that his physically sighting Number Fourteen is the catalyst that allows the Prisoner to overcome the 'treatment'.

Unsurprisingly, this story casts an interesting light over whether or not the events of the series, or some of them at least, take place in the Prisoner's head. In this case, many of the events literally take place within the Prisoner's mind; however, in that context, he also interacts with the ostensibly 'real' world of the Village, and aspects of the dream parallel Village life: the sequence at the climax in which he goes through a church door into a city street parallels the surreal discovery that the view outside the window of his London flat has changed into an Italianate vista; and the end of the sequence, when he walks up to a pair of doors, which close, and opens them to reveal the Village, into which he walks, is a parallel to the ending of 'The Chimes of Big Ben' (and a reversal of the animation that precedes the end titles). The fact that the events of the Prisoner's resignation also apparently play out continually in his mind suggest that the title sequence at the start of each episode may itself be a recurring dream or memory; note that, when the Prisoner is conditioned to believe that he is in the Wild West in the later episode 'Living in Harmony', the events of the resignation in the title sequence are transposed directly into a Western setting.

The story also contains a distinct homoerotic subtext regarding the character of A. Peter Bowles's decision to play A as a slightly camp man, who fixes his eyes on the Prisoner over his wine glass and licks his lips, lends the subtext to their conversation that, instead of being spies, these are two gay men, possibly even former lovers, one of whom is attempting to 'go straight', while the other is trying to persuade him to 'come back', with double-entendres about 'defecting' and 'going over to the other side'. 'I don't want a hint, I want you,' says A, looking very hard at the Prisoner. In a cut sequence, the returning Prisoner says to Engadine (who, amusingly, was earlier described in the original script as 'blowing kisses to other women'): 'I disappointed him. He wanted to buy something.' Engadine responds 'And you didn't want to sell?' to which the Prisoner, with a smile, says 'Sell what?' This idea is very much in keeping with the homophobia that pervaded the Cold War-era spying community, with fears of gay spies and civil servants being blackmailed by Soviet agents (to the point where the Royal Canadian Mounted Police actually invested a substantial amount of money in quack 'psychological' devices aimed at 'rooting out' homosexuals in their ranks – compare with the futuristic and fantastic mind-reading devices used in 'A, B and C'). The Philby scandal, which broke in 1963, also involved a gay man, claimed to have been 'recruited' both sexually and in a political sense at Cambridge, who, like A, made a high-profile defection; the title 'A, B and C' is thought to be a reference to Burgess, MacLean and Philby, the three key figures in the scandal. The story alludes to Cold War paranoia elsewhere, for instance in the implication that Village tap water is drugged, referring to Western fears of Communists putting 'something in the water'. While the original script was heavily pruned for references to sexuality (cut lines including the Prisoner's suggestive remark to B that 'Friends are better than lovers'), the references to the Philby scandal persist in the A sequence.

CRISIS HOTLINE: NUMBER TWO

'A, B and C' also falls into a particular subgenre of *The Prisoner* stories, in which, rather than trying to escape, the Prisoner focuses on baiting or manipulating Number Two (compare with 'Hammer into Anvil'). The sequence early on in which the Prisoner confronts Number Two with the needle mark on his wrist is clearly not an attempt to seek information, as he doesn't stay around to press the issue further or even to watch Number Two's reaction, but just to let him know that he knows something is up involving him and Number Fourteen. The headline on the Village newspaper, the *Tally Ho* (dated 10 February, the first date seen anywhere in the series, and the first time the newspaper physically appears) – 'Is No. 2 Fit for Further Term?' – implies that Number Twos have fixed terms, an idea upheld in 'Free for All' but not necessarily in other stories. There is also the interesting suggestion that Number Two sleeps in or near whatever area the spherical chair descends to, as he rises from the floor in a dressing gown with mussed hair, as if he has just woken up.

In keeping with the psychoanalytic themes of the episode, the story devotes some time to Number Two's own mental state. Not only does he have a clearly stress-induced stomach disorder (evidenced by his obsessive milk-drinking at tense moments) but the gigantic red telephone, exaggerated like the props in German Expressionist films, is featured ominously every time he starts to fear for his head. We also have the Prisoner's metatextual reference to Number Two when he comments to the girl wearing B's dress in the third party sequence, 'Haven't they killed you yet? Sorry, must have been thinking of someone else.' Although this refers directly to B, it could equally apply to Number Two's paranoia that his failure will cost him his head (figuratively or, as in 'It's Your Funeral', literally). The Prisoner's remark that the party is 'so wild it will end in tears' could also refer to Number Two's anxieties.

The casting of Number Two deserves mention here. Colin Gordon would also play Number Two in the story 'The General':

'A, B and C' was the tenth story to be made, and 'The General' the eleventh, and Gordon was asked to take over the role of Number Two in the latter story when the actor originally supposed to play him dropped out at short notice. Although 'The General' was originally intended to come after 'A, B and C', and indeed does in the final transmission order of the stories, there are indications that it was at one point intended to be transmitted first. For instance, Gordon in the title sequence for 'A, B and C' introduces himself simply as 'Number Two', not 'The new Number Two'; and the man we see in 'The General' is much more self-confident than the one in 'A, B and C', when one would expect the opposite if this were a Number Two whose attempts at getting the Prisoner to cooperate had been failing repeatedly. The problem, however, is that, in the Prisoner's initial confrontation with Number Two in 'A, B and C', their conversation implies that they haven't seen much of each other and that this Number Two is more hands-off than his predecessors, and, in 'The General', Number Two refers to himself and the Prisoner as 'old friends,' neither of which would be the case if 'The General' came first.

THE WORLD OUTSIDE: THE VILLAGE

With a financial crisis ongoing at the time this episode was written, Anthony Skene was encouraged by David Tomblin to make plentiful use of stock footage, but chose instead to base the action around sets that he found on the Borehamwood backlot, including some from *Casino Royale*, which coincidentally also featured Colin Gordon, and *The Dirty Dozen*. Most of the action thus occurs away from the Village, but the story does nevertheless take the time to explore some aspects of it. Again we see internationalism, with the Village now apparently, through the Prisoner's dream, containing Paris, and another Chinese girl selling flowers: according to the original script, the Prisoner's maid would have spoken only Arabic to him, and he only English to her, until their final meeting, when he would have wished her good night in Arabic and, after he fell unconscious, she would have responded in perfect English. We see Number Two talking to an evident superior on the telephone, although whether or not this is Number One is open to debate (see

'Essay 5: Number One').

A further suggestion that the Village is illusory comes in a cut sequence in which the Prisoner says to Number Fourteen, when they meet there, 'Some people speculate all the time on what things mean. Though this place encourages speculation … "Where are we?" leads to "Why are we here?" and – if you don't watch it – "Who are we?" For a bit at the start, I thought the whole Village was a dream.' Number Fourteen responds, 'Perhaps it is,' and the Prisoner counters with, 'And you're another dream inside it? I'm not so complicated.' This is later echoed in another cut sequence where, upon winning the key at the 'dreamy party', the Prisoner is given a bottle of champagne by Engadine, and fills people's glasses with it; he then spins the empty bottle in the middle of the circle of people, as in the familiar kissing game, saying 'Where are we? Why are we? Who are we?' He then asks 'Where are you?' and the bottle finishes pointing to Engadine, drawing deliberate parallels between his conversation about dreams with Number Fourteen and the events in the dream itself. At the party, also, the Prisoner says that he wants to go 'somewhere different, somewhere quiet, where I can think' (which he does, to wit, the Village) and Madame Engadine replies 'There is nowhere quiet' (which there isn't, as the quiet in the Village is an illusion). The shifting nature of the Village thus is highlighted in the dream sequences.

Chris Gregory has argued in *Be Seeing You* that, given what we know about the universality of surveillance in the Village, it is a contrived idea that the Prisoner can break into the cave system apparently unnoticed. However, the fact that something is seen, or recorded, does not mean that it will be acted upon, and since Number Two is asking Number Fourteen to conduct secret, dubiously tested experiments with drugs, it is likely that they wouldn't want attention drawn to the caves. Also, since elsewhere in the series we have seen that the Prisoner is aware of the cameras – he acknowledges one in this story with a salute – it could also be argued that he has noted where they are and is avoiding them.

Finally, it is also possible to see references to other aspects of 1960s culture in the story. The psychedelic 'dreamy party', at which the guests seem to have had more than champagne, to judge by the sight of elderly guests dancing and playing, is clearly influenced by the notoriously drug-fuelled parties of the day. It is possible that the partygoers playing catch with what appears to be an orange is a reference to *A Clockwork Orange* (which also features scenes of drug-induced mayhem), but may also be part of the series' own internal colour symbolism, picking up on 'Arrival''s Orange Alert. Number Fourteen's gender, and the fact that it is not remarked on, give the story a more modern feel than many of its less progressive counterparts (see 'Essay 3: Gender, Race and Sexuality'). On a more frivolous note, the Prisoner sports a new dressing gown, this one brown with black stripes where the previous one had been blue and white; Number Two's dressing gown breaks with the stripe theme, having a kind of purple check pattern. Sharp-eyed viewers can also spot that in the fight during the B segment of the story, the stuntman playing the Prisoner rips his trousers.

'A, B and C' would be mentioned in the film *Killing Zoe*, which also focuses on themes of drug use and rebellion. As such, 'A, B and C' typifies many of the elements that brought the series lasting fame, drawing on Cold War imagery to develop broader ideas about mind and culture in the late 20th Century.

Episode 4:
Free For All

First UK Transmission Date: Friday 20 October 1967: ATV Midlands/Grampian, 7.30 pm – 8.30 pm
Writer: Paddy Fitz (pseudonym for Patrick McGoohan)
Director: Patrick McGoohan
Credited Cast: Patrick McGoohan (The Prisoner); Eric Portman (Number Two); Rachel Herbert (Number Fifty Eight); George Benson (Labour Exchange Manager); Angelo Muscat (The Butler); Harold Berens (Reporter); John Cazabon (Man in Cave); Dene Cooper (Photographer); Kenneth Benda (Supervisor); Holly Doone (Waitress); Peter Brace (1st Mechanic); Alf Joint (2nd Mechanic)
Known Uncredited Cast: Peter Swanwick (In footage reused from 'Arrival'); Fenella Fielding (Telephone Operator/Loudspeaker Voice); John Frawley (Man with Bass Drum); Frank Maher (Double for Patrick McGoohan); Will Parry (Penny-farthing man); Brian Axworthy (Speedboat pilot in long shot)

SYNOPSIS: The Village is holding an election for a new Number Two. The current Number Two persuades the Prisoner to run for the office, on the grounds that if he becomes Number Two, Number One will no longer be a mystery to him. The Prisoner agrees to stand, announcing that he intends to thereby discover who are the prisoners and who are the warders. He is given as his assistant Number Fifty Eight, a girl who speaks no English. He gives an 'interview' that consists entirely of him refusing to comment, which is then written up in the *Tally Ho* newspaper as a legitimate interview. He meets the Village council, whom he accuses of being mindless. They insist that he undergo the Test, a mysterious process after which he suddenly becomes more cooperative, 'campaigning' with a series of meaningless political phrases. He attempts escape, but is brought back by Rover. He goes to a nightclub but becomes violent when he is unable to obtain alcohol; Number Fifty Eight takes him to a cave, the Therapy Zone, where he obtains bootleg alcohol and drinks with Number Two, passing out at the end. The Prisoner ultimately wins the election, and is given control of Number Two's office, where Number Fifty Eight slaps him back to his senses. He activates the microphones and tells the Villagers they are free to go, but nobody listens. He flees, finding himself in a cave where a group of men are watching Rover. He is attacked and subdued by the men and returned to Number Two's office, where he discovers that Number Fifty Eight (speaking perfect English) is now Number Two and he is still a prisoner.

ANALYSIS: 'Free for All' is one of the best-known episodes of *The Prisoner*, due to its structure as political satire and the fact that it was written, under a pseudonym, and (largely) directed by Patrick McGoohan himself (Don Chaffey was originally to have directed the interiors, but after he fell out with McGoohan, McGoohan shared the direction of these sequences with director of photography Brendan J Stafford). As such, it is one of the key points where McGoohan begins to assert his control over the series. However, it can be equally argued that the overt political satire actually serves to obscure a number of other interesting and surreal aspects of the episode.

SIX AND POLITICS: SATIRE AND SURREALISM

The political messages of this story are easily the first thing to strike the viewer. Images such as the Prisoner spouting fatuous political phrases under 'hypnosis', Number Fifty Eight turning out to be Number Two all along, the Prisoner's radical agenda becoming a conventional one and his truly radical ideas being ignored and suppressed, the cheap shot about the civil service, and the Villagers campaigning away in a curiously mechanical and robotic fashion, all make it easy for the viewer to draw the conclusion that the message of the story is clear: politicians are corrupt, the people behind the throne are the ones who rule, and democracy is a total sham. Much is also made of the fact that the story was screened at a time when, following a long period in which it was considered disrespectful to make fun of politicians, political satire was returning to Britain, with television programmes like *That Was the Week that Was* and theatrical revues such as *Beyond the Fringe* becoming both popular and controversial, and of the fact that the episode was screened at a particularly sensitive time in a British election year. However, these facts might make it easy to overlook aspects of the story: had it been screened in any other year, for instance, the audience might have taken it another way. And, considering that the controversy of the abovementioned programmes was less about their being general political satires in the vein of 'Free for All', and more about their skewering of particular individuals in politics, it might be worth asking whether 'Free for All' really is part of the cutting edge of satire of the day, or rather part of the same dramatic tradition as George Bernard Shaw's and Berthold Brecht's early 20th Century works. As an experiment, then, it might be worth looking at 'Free for All' less as a 1960s political satire, and more as an exercise in dramatic surrealism.

Although earlier episodes have contained surreal aspects (recurring doubles, for instance, and Rover's seeming mind of its own), this episode brings them to the fore. The Village again has a change of organisation and apparent ownership: Number Two's reference to 'the homeland' suggests both that it is run by a single power and that, given that this power is fonder of collectivist rhetoric than of nationalism, it is likely not Soviet; and his matter-of-fact remark that the Village has elections every 12 months, which is not mentioned at any other point in the series, appears to be at odds with the seemingly random replacement of Number Two in 'Arrival', and with the older Number Two's implication in 'It's Your Funeral' that all the other Number Twos have simply been replacements for him, and that he will shortly give way to an unelected successor. In this episode, we also see the geography of the Village change even as we watch it, when the door of Number Two's office suddenly ceases to lead out to the anteroom and instead leads out to the Rover cave, and when Number Two turns up at the Prisoner's door with disconcerting suddenness. In a scripted line obscured by the noise of the band and dialogue, the tannoy refers to 'us girls on the switchboard' being thrilled by the Prisoner's announcement of his candidacy, a bizarre touch since we only ever hear a single female voice over the tannoy, and she does not otherwise appear to have an existence outside of her role as announcer. All of these things lend a slightly *Through the Looking-Glass* aspect to the story, and give the Village an even more dreamlike quality than usual.

Dream logic is particularly pervasive in this story. As well as the shifting Village geography (*Through the Looking-Glass*, of course, being ultimately a story about a dream), the jumps of time, and such bizarre imagery as a plaster Chinese lion (very similar to one that actually forms part of the statuary at Portmeirion) apparently playing the drums, and four men and a surveillance bust watching Rover as if it were a television (the brutal fight sequence that follows is reported to have been cut from some regional UK transmissions on original broadcast, and was definitely cut from the 1970s repeats, then reinstated in the 1983 Channel Four transmission), once again we have a situation in which nobody within the story is a well-rounded character, and the bulk of the Villagers are a robotic, Greek-chorus-like mass who take their cues, positive or negative, from the Prisoner (an idea that was apparently undermined when recording began by the fact that the Welsh accents of the extras made it initially sound as if they were chanting 'sex for two' rather than 'Six for Two'; a less misconstruable pronunciation is used in the transmitted version). In a cut line, the Prisoner speaks to Number Fifty Eight in her own language after taking the Truth Test; and at one point in the televised episode, he appears to know how to say 'Be seeing you' in that language. Since the language is made up, this again implies that the whole scenario is taking place within the Prisoner's own mind. The Prisoner himself is the dominant personality in the Village; the only characters allowed any degree of development are the ones here to deceive and trick him (Numbers Fifty Eight and Two). The Prisoner is the prime mover of the Village; as such, this would appear to be his dream that we are drawn into as viewers.

The sequence with the Truth Test is also deserving of elaboration. In this scene, a circle and a square, representing lies and truth respectively, appear on a screen before a silhouette of the Prisoner, like a shadow-play. The two shapes collide as they make contact with him between his eyes, and apparently this turns the Prisoner into a fatuous politician, spouting random political phrases. We have no idea how this mind control is actually achieved, or what the mechanics behind the 'test' are; but by this point, we have been subjected to enough bizarre imagery that we are unlikely to ask questions. Essentially, this fact damns us, as we, like the electorate and the Villagers, are now accepting contradictory and counterintuitive ideas without question. If the Prisoner said to viewers themselves that they were free to go, would they move? Rather than simply being random surrealism, the imagery in 'Free for All' causes us to question our own motivations.

The sequence in which the Prisoner appears to become 'drunk' in the nightclub The Cat and Mouse, despite not having had any alcohol, and is then taken to the ironically- (and psychoanalytically-) named Therapy Room by Number Fifty Eight also reflects ideas of role and behaviour. Significantly, at this point in the story, the Prisoner is still hypnotised or conditioned into acting like a politician, and one thing that has been suspected of politicians ever since the Profumo incident has been their involvement in scandal. The Prisoner thus is not breaking free of his conditioning when he demands a drink (in the script, he is also described as 'lunging' at Number Fifty Eight, with associated sexual connotations), but acting the part of a politician off the rails (explaining why Number Two and the scientist are not surprised to see him). The assignment of role can also be seen in the Villagers' stony silence when the Prisoner wins, despite their having all voted for him: universally in democracies, it seems, once the candidate is actually elected as leader, the love that the electorate had for him or her during the election campaign dissipates and he/she becomes a figure for hate and criticism.

THE FAMILIAR REVISITED: DOPPELGÄNGERS, SURVEILLANCE, INFANTILISM AND INTERNATIONALISM

The now-familiar theme of doppelgängers similarly calls into question the motivations of the central character himself. In this story, we do not simply have duplicates along the lines of the Gardener/Electrician of 'Arrival', but we have Number One Hundred and Thirteen-b, the photographer, instantly transforming into a *Tally Ho* salesman (and when the Prisoner looks back from the

Tally Ho stand, he sees Number One Hundred and Thirteen-b waving at him from the other direction), and he and his colleague Number One Hundred and Thirteen turning up again as a television reporting team.[9] The Prisoner also twice observes himself: in the first case, he watches his own television broadcast, aping his own gestures; and in the second case, more bizarrely, we see a clip in the Green Dome of the Prisoner, dressed in his pre-Village black shirt and blazer, which, since the other images we see on the screen are all in real time, must be actually happening (a comparative search of 'Arrival' also yields no equivalent shots). The Prisoner is thus, physically as well as symbolically, 'not himself' and 'in two minds'. A duplication of personnel might also explain how Number Two manages to arrive at the Prisoner's cottage immediately after being seen in the Dome; and the Village council are, symbolically, extensions of Number Two: their numbers are all subcategories of two (2a, 2b, 2c and so forth: the highest letter we see is 2x, but the letters are non-consecutive and a few seem to be missing), leading one to wonder if the many different Number Twos we see over the course of the series are, in a way, one person. This is also the first and only story in the series to feature characters who are subcategories of numbers (although the information board seen in 'Arrival' has already implied that such exist). The surreal use of numbers can also be seen when the Prisoner and Number Fifty Eight use the information board: the numbers are non-consecutive, include 2b, 4d, 3e and, next to 68, 6h, possibly a confirmation that the Prisoner himself has a double and leading one to question where 6a through 6g are. All of this also casts in a doubtful light the Prisoner's assertion that he intends, over the course of his campaign, to 'find out who are the prisoners and who are the warders': the Number Six we see is both prisoner and warder, as are all the people in the story.

This is also flagged up in the theme of surveillance. As the Prisoner appears to be observing himself at two points within the story, we see a surveillance society taken to its logical extreme, as in Philip K Dick's *A Scanner Darkly*, an unsettling novel in which a police agent in deep undercover as a drug addict reports upon his own crimes as well as those of his fellow addicts, who, he comes to

---

9 Harold Berens, who played Number One Hundred and Thirteen, would also appear as the Boxing MC in 'The Girl Who Was Death'.

suspect, may all be police agents too. When we see the Prisoner's dreams in the hospital, what we see are images that the viewers have already witnessed from earlier in the story, and his dreams, as in 'A, B and C', are all in the third person. While this can be seen as an example of the familiar television convention of seeing flashbacks in the third person, it could also be taken, in the context, as another instance of the Prisoner metaphorically observing himself. The Prisoner is also not asked at any point why he resigned, perhaps flagging up the fact that his status as prisoner or warder is in question. Similarly thought-provoking is the sequence with four watchers, sporting sunglasses, and a surveillance bust, all apparently sitting around Rover and watching it as if it were a television, its 'skin' glowing like a television screen. First, this appears to suggest almost that the devices in the Village have a kind of life and existence of their own: if a bust can come to watch Rover, and Rover itself act as a form of entertainment, perhaps Jools Holland's dinner party in the 1987 spoof *The Laughing Prisoner*, in which Rover attends as a guest, is not so far-fetched after all. Second, in an episode in which a television appears as a *Nineteen Eighty-Four*-style surveillance device, the Village statuary relaxes by playing music in a nightclub, and the Prisoner observes himself, perhaps we are seeing a group watching a 'television' that is itself watching them (the idea that the figures on television are themselves watching the viewers is one that crops up over and over in the cartoons and popular fiction of the 1960s). This story thus turns the ideas of observer and observed, prisoner and warder, on their heads.

Earlier themes of internationalisation and infantilisation are also brought up and given a new twist. Number Fifty Eight speaks a language that McGoohan made up, which was uttered by actress Rachel Herbert using inflections taken from a tape of a Yugoslavian friend. The Village thus now not only includes people from everywhere in the world, but also, apparently, people from places that don't actually exist. Similarly, the themes of infantilisation are exaggerated: we see an elderly woman jive-dancing unselfconsciously to jazz music in The Cat and Mouse, and note again that the Prisoner's likes, dislikes and desires are known and anticipated by those running the Village, just as those of a very young child are by its parents, in that the Villagers have a placard and election campaign all ready for him even before he has decided to run (in the original script, the Villagers were initially to have turned up in the parade of Number Two's supporters holding blank signs, which they would then have turned around to reveal pro-the Prisoner placards, in a mix of anticipation and political commentary). The sequence where the Prisoner keeps saying 'No comment' to Number One Hundred and Thirteen, who then writes down instead what he wants to hear, as well as being a comment on the way that newspapers will make up a story regardless of what the actual facts may be, recalls familiar parent-child conversations ('You want to go on the swings, don't you?' 'No.' 'Come on, you really mean that you want to go on the swings.' 'No.' 'Right, we're going on the swings. You'll like it really'). Number Two also somehow knows the nonsense song that the drunken Prisoner has made up (in a cut scene, the Prisoner was to have been seen singing it in The Cat and Mouse, which would have made more sense of the later sequence). Now-familiar themes are thus taken to extremes in 'Free for All'.

Themes of isolation are also flagged up by the use of the tune 'For He's a Jolly Good Fellow' after the Prisoner wins the election. As well as being an obvious tune to associate with an election winner, the song has the same tune as the children's song 'The Bear Went over the Mountain'. As well as referencing infantilisation and Number Two's earlier remarks about being 'at the summit' (political and physical) and the mountain coming to Mohamat (as the name is spelled in the script), at the point at which Mohamat himself (the Prisoner) is coming to the mountain (the Green Dome), the song is also about the futility of change: 'The bear went over the mountain …/to see what he could see …/but all that he could see …/was the other side of the mountain …/Was all that he could see.'

HAVEN'T I SEEN YOU BEFORE?
REFERENCES BACK AND FORWARD

The story also recalls earlier episodes, and foreshadows episodes to come, particularly 'Fall Out'. The round peg/square hole metaphor from 'Arrival' is referenced in the Test sequence (involving as it does a circle and a square meeting), which is also set in the Labour Exchange, and the discussion between the Prisoner and Number Two about the food ('French.' 'International.') recalls the Prisoner's conversation with the taxi driver; there is again a mention of the Prisoner's preferences regarding milk and sugar being in his file. Spheres are referenced a few times in the dialogue (although two of the relevant lines were cut). We see undertakers in Number Two's entourage and outside the Town Hall (the Village Council also wear undertaker-style top hats, and the mechanical Rover's siren is described as sounding like 'an ambulance on an errand of death' in the original script). A sequence cut from the script was to feature an old man on a penny-farthing blowing up a balloon with 'Vote' written on it and laughing deliriously when it explodes (a modified version of this does appear in the sequence where the Prisoner says 'I am not a number, I am a person'). This would have linked the images of balloons/globes, penny-farthings and explosions from the abandoned end credits sequences: he would then have shouted 'We're him, and he is us.' In the original script, Number Two was to say of Number Fifty Eight, who was originally Fifty Seven, '[She] comes from a religious family'; this is thus a case of McGoohan censoring his own reference to religions and the number seven.

In terms of the future of the series, when encouraging the Prisoner to campaign, Number Two does not in fact promise him that he will learn the identity of Number One, but that 'Number One will no longer be a mystery to [him]'. In the Council chamber, we see Number Two on a dais, and above him an empty chair with a glowing, and at times blinking, blue eye, symbolising not only surveillance and conspiracy theory (as it recalls the eye-and-pyramid symbol associated with, among others, the Illuminati), but also the eye/I/aye/1 word-play that will become significant in the final episode: the Prisoner, in silhouette, is hit between the eyes by the shadow forms, at the supposed site of the third eye in Hinduism, as will be seen again with the blue light in 'The Schizoid Man' (note also that the mechanical Rover was to have had a flashing blue light).

'Free for All' is thus a deep and intelligent story, but not entirely for the reasons that many people think it is. More than a political allegory, it is in fact a deeply surreal comment on the established themes of the series.

Essay 2: Not a Number: *The Prisoner*'s Episode Order

For many years, a key debate among fans of *The Prisoner* has been the order in which the episodes should be viewed. While this debate has largely been resolved, albeit not as most of the contributors probably imagined it should be, we shall briefly revisit the issue here for what it tells us about the nature, and writing, of the series.

The origins of the debate lie in the fact that, while the series does have a definite opening episode ('Arrival'), and final two episodes ('Once Upon a Time' and 'Fall Out'), the rest of the stories not only do not appear to have a set order, but also seem to, at times, actively defy ordering (see the Analyses for the two episodes featuring Colin Gordon as Number Two, 'A, B and C' and 'The General', for a good example of this). The way in which the opening sequence for nearly every episode briefly recaps the Prisoner's kidnapping to the Village and introduces a new Number Two seems, in some ways, to suggest that each episode sees the Prisoner begin anew in the Village, further defying the idea of a definite order to the stories. 'Once Upon a Time' appears at first glance to suggest the existence of linear progression in its sequence of clips; however, these same clips cannot be in sequence, as scenes from 'Arrival' appear dispersed throughout. Furthermore, it is possible to discern some kind of progression within the series as screened, from introductory episodes through a series of more conventional action-adventure episodes through to a final spate of strange and postmodern stories, suggesting that there is intentionality to the episode order, if only the viewer could discern it, and/or smooth out any anomalies. The result has been that, as evidenced by the contributions in Max Hora's *The Prisoner of Portmeirion*, it is possible to argue convincingly for almost any order to the episodes (provided the opening and closing ones are in place).

Patrick McGoohan has further confused the issue by stating, in the Goodman interview, 'There were seven [episodes] that I would pick and put in line, and I'd just keep those and throw the rest away'. However, although much ink has been spilled trying to identify precisely which episodes constitute the 'magnificent seven', the nature of the production means that one cannot discern any sort of master plan, as it were, from the order in which the episodes were commissioned or made. Although 'Dance of the Dead' was third in production order, for instance, and is frequently cited as a possible candidate for the second episode of the series, it was promptly shelved when McGoohan took a dislike to it. 'Once Upon a Time' was filmed sixth in order, in keeping with McGoohan's initial idea of doing a seven-part mini-series, but, when the series was expanded into a 13-episode season, it was apparently briefly considered as a season finale; however, since the second season was to have been set in the world outside the Village and to have opened with 'Do Not Forsake Me Oh My Darling', 'Once Upon a Time' evidently went into limbo and 'Many Happy Returns' was instead adopted as the first-season finale. All of this was further confused when the series' length was then changed from two 13-episode seasons to a single 17-episode season, and 'Once Upon a Time' then reached its final position as the penultimate episode.

Many fans have closely scrutinised the dates that occasionally appear briefly in the series (such as the postmark on the envelope in 'Do Not Forsake Me Oh My Darling') with a view to matching up the episodes with real-world chronology and thus providing a rough guide to their order. However, as noted in *The Prisoner of Portmeirion,* the results of this endeavour have proved inconclusive (most likely because none of the written dates were intended to be seen by the audience, and indeed they are usually discernible only by using the freeze-frame and/or zoom function on the DVD player), and so these cannot be taken as a reliable guide to the production team's intentions with regards to the episodes' chronology either.

A key piece of evidence confirming that the crew had no real idea of a definite order of episodes comes from a conversation between author Max Hora and series writer Vincent Tilsley in 1981, which Hora reports in *The Prisoner of Portmeirion*. Tilsley said that, as part of the commissioning process, he had been told by Markstein about the premise for the series and shown a copy of the script for 'Arrival', and had written the script for 'The Chimes of Big Ben' based simply on these. However, we know that Anthony Skene was commissioned to write 'Dance of the Dead' at roughly the same time, while Gerald Kelsey was also writing 'Checkmate' and Patrick McGoohan, 'Free for All'. Hora thus concludes that, in fact, these four stories were *all* written as the second episode of the series: 'Each of them would fit into the second slot perfectly well – if it wasn't for the other three!' The stories were not written to show a general progression over time, but developed in parallel on the basis of the initial script for the first episode.

Moreover, the placing of the episodes in the initial broadcast order strongly suggests that they were deliberately sorted so as to intersperse location-heavy with studio-heavy episodes, much as, in the second series of *Danger Man*, the first three filmed episodes were interspersed throughout the series so as to hide the fact that a number of ideas used in those episodes (for example McGoohan's adoption of a mid-Atlantic accent) were subsequently dropped. Furthermore, the apparent progression in the episodes is largely down to the development of the rift between McGoohan and Markstein, and the latter's departure from the series: after the introductory episodes, Markstein's ethos initially dominates, but is then superseded by McGoohan's, suggesting a progression from the Prisoner arriving in the Village, then gradually learning how the Village works, and finally departing in a psychedelic blaze of envelope-pushing stories (although, significantly, this effect is lessened if the episodes are viewed in the American broadcast order, which interspersed the more conventional and the more psychedelic episodes). The problems that arose during *The Prisoner*'s production, as well as what appears to be an attempt to disguise a preponderance of studio-heavy episodes at certain points in the production block by interspersing them with more location-focused ones, thus means that one cannot point to a definitive episode order that the production crew had in mind.

Furthermore, the surreal nature of the series allows for the acceptance of apparent contradictions within the story order. For instance, although many people cite the fact that the Prisoner confesses that he has 'never seen a night' in 'Dance of the Dead' as proof that this episode must take place very early in his stay in the Village, authors Thomas M Disch, in *I Am Not a Number!*, and Blum and Booth, in *The Prisoner's Dilemma*, suggest that the Prisoner is being perpetually mind-conditioned (or, indeed, that time in the Village runs differently from in the outside world), and as such he might well believe that he is new to the Village when in fact he has been there for years; a suggestion upheld by such stories as 'The Schizoid Man'.

As such, then, it is impossible to claim any kind of definite progression or order to the stories, beyond that 'Arrival' must be first and 'Once Upon a Time' and 'Fall Out' must be last, and otherwise any attempt to impose one is purely arbitrary. Fans of *The Prisoner* can therefore enjoy the stories in any order that makes sense to them, and take the inherent contradictions between them as part of the series' overall surrealism and atmosphere of timeless disorientation.

Episode 5:
The Schizoid Man

First UK Transmission Date: Friday 27 October 1967: ATV Midlands/Grampian, 7.30 pm – 8.30 pm
Writer: Terence Feely
Director: Pat Jackson
Credited Cast: Patrick McGoohan (The Prisoner); Jane Merrow (Alison); Anton Rogers (Number Two); Angelo Muscat (The Butler); Earl Cameron (Supervisor); Gay Cameron (Number Thirty-Six); David Nettheim (Doctor); Pat Keen (Nurse); Gerry Crampton (1st Guardian); Dinney Powell (2nd Guardian)[10]
Known Uncredited Cast: Patrick McGoohan (Number 12); Frank Maher (Double for Patrick McGoohan/Number Twelve)

SYNOPSIS: The Prisoner has befriended a young woman, Alison, who practices her psychic abilities on him. One evening, she accidentally bruises his fingernail with a soda siphon while arranging to take a photograph of him. The Prisoner awakes, apparently the next morning, in a strange room, and with a new identity: his hair colour has changed, he is sporting a moustache and (as he later realises) he has become left-handed. Number Two greets him as a friend and tells him that he is to impersonate the Prisoner; he gives him a codeword, 'Gemini', with which to identify himself. Now designated as 'Twelve', the Prisoner encounters his double, who bests him in a variety of

---

10 Normally credited as 'Dinny Powell'.

competitions. The pair are brought before Number Two, and the Prisoner urges him to have Alison try to read their minds; Alison, however, cannot read the Prisoner's mind, suggesting that his double is in fact the genuine article and causing the Prisoner to doubt himself. That night, however, the Prisoner finds the photograph that Alison took, and realises that the bruise on his fingernail is now further up the nail than it is in the photograph; the Prisoner remembers his conditioning, and how he was trained into becoming left-handed with electroshock techniques. The Prisoner returns himself to normal by giving himself an electric shock, and confronts his double, Curtis; he fights him and extracts his codeword, 'Schizoid Man'. Rover arrives, and when the Prisoner gives it Curtis's codeword, it kills Curtis. The Prisoner endeavours to escape the Village by impersonating Curtis, but is exposed when he accidentally reveals that he did not know that Curtis's wife Susan was dead.

ANALYSIS: 'The Schizoid Man' is one of the most visually enjoyable and thought-provoking episodes of the series, bolstered by clever direction and excellent performances from all of the leads (particularly McGoohan, forced to play opposite himself for most of the story), taking the doppelgänger imagery of earlier episodes to its logical extreme as well as acknowledging the roots of the series.

Terence Feely, a well-established writer, had worked with George Markstein on *Armchair Theatre*, and was invited to submit a story for *The Prisoner* due to Markstein having been impressed with his surreal 1964 stage play 'Don't Let Summer Come'; he was allegedly inspired to write 'The Schizoid Man' upon discovering that he himself had a doppelgänger living in Germany. Feely would also be assistant producer on the first series of *Callan* (ABC 1967), and, in a return to his surrealistic roots, would pen two of the more psychedelic episodes of Gerry Anderson's *UFO* (a series heavily indebted to *The Prisoner*, notably because of David Tomblin's involvement in its latter half). Although a number of scenes were deleted or radically altered during the drafting process (the more interesting ones of which will be discussed in detail below), McGoohan was sufficiently impressed by 'The Schizoid Man' that he asked Feely to join him and Tomblin in partnership on Everyman Films.

DIDN'T YOU KILL MY BROTHER? DOUBLES AND SPIES

While doubles and doppelgängers have been a recurring theme of the series so far, 'The Schizoid Man' makes them the focus of the story. After the hints in 'Arrival', 'The Chimes of Big Ben' and 'Free for All' that the Prisoner has at least one double within the Village, and the dream-doubles of 'A, B and C', here we have a real, living and breathing double of the Prisoner. The 'doppelgänger'/'evil twin' episode is a stock feature, practically a cliché, of telefantasy, and particularly of spy-thriller television (at least two episodes of *The Avengers*, for instance, openly revolve around the apparent duplication of the central characters). 'The Schizoid Man' has a number of links to such stories: the Prisoner's range of skills (shooting, fencing etc) is very much in keeping with the secret-agent character, for instance – one might note that the double suggests Olympic boxing, and a boxing sequence features later in the spy send-up episode 'The Girl Who Was Death'. The gas gun that Curtis points at the Prisoner is similar to one later used in 'Do Not Forsake Me Oh My Darling'. A Mini Moke race between the doubles was also to have featured, but was ultimately cut, according to Fairclough in *The Original Scripts vol. 1*, because location footage had largely been filmed by that point and, as the episode was being shot in the winter, it would have been more than usually difficult to stage a car chase in Portmeirion (which has the additional hazard of narrow lanes and paths); it is also worth mentioning that it may have been difficult to find and hire stunt drivers capable of performing such a sequence under the stated conditions. We also see a slight misuse of technological terminology, as repeatedly seen in *The Avengers*, when the 'infrared' shot of the Prisoner that Number Two orders is quite clearly, to modern eyes, no such thing; and an instance of the use of cutting-edge '60s technology in that Alison/Number Twenty Four possesses an early Polaroid camera, which later becomes a significant plot point. The story thus has roots in 1960s spy and spy-spoof television plays.

However, as always with *The Prisoner*, this story has an extra layer. While in the abovementioned telefantasy/spy-thriller plays the duplicated protagonist always retains a sense of his own identity and must strive to convince others that he is the original, in 'The Schizoid Man' the duplicated character has been conditioned so as to lose his familiar habits, attributes, tastes and even body markings, so that the Prisoner himself begins to doubt that he is who he thinks he is. This is further complicated by the usual Prisoner imagery, in particular third-person flashbacks, which is a common television convention but one that, as before, suggests the Prisoner viewing and/or directing himself.

It has been suggested in a number of other publications that originally both the Prisoner and Curtis were to wear the same jacket, but that this was abandoned – with Curtis instead wearing a 'negative' of the Prisoner's familiar jacket – as it would be too confusing. Apparently supporting this, there is a production photograph of both McGoohan and Frank Maher (McGoohan's usual double, who was particularly in demand during this episode as, while most of it was shot on split-screen, some sequences required a double) both wearing the familiar white-piped jacket. However, the script specifically states that the Prisoner and Curtis wear contrasting black and white jackets during the fencing sequence, and there could be any number of alternative explanations for why McGoohan and Maher are wearing the same jacket in the picture (Maher having just finished doubling for the Prisoner but not yet changed into his jacket to play Curtis, for instance). The Prisoner is also specifically stated in the script to be wearing different pyjamas when he wakes up as Number Twelve than when he went to sleep as Number Six (where his original pyjamas are light blue, the alternate pyjamas are dark blue with white piping, reflecting the Prisoner's own trademark jacket perhaps; these are not solely associated with his role as Number Twelve, as he wears an identical set of pyjamas in other episodes, for instance 'A, B and C'). The idea that the production team would shoot footage of the two men wearing the same jacket, and then go to the trouble of commissioning a 'negative' jacket and reshooting the sequences with Curtis wearing this, does seem rather implausible. From a production point of view, also, the 'negative' jacket caused a number of headaches, with there being some confusion as to who was to be wearing which blazer at which point in the filming, and it seems unlikely that the team would go from an easier to a more difficult option.

BE SEEING YOU: PSYCHICS AND PSYCHOLOGY

The existence of psychic powers, the other main concept of the episode, is another near-cliché of telefantasy and spy-thriller series, suggesting that Terence Feely might have been having a kind of metatextual dig at the genre – taking two familiar plot ideas and standing them, as it were, on their heads. One interesting thing about Alison's psychic powers is that, although she says people in the Village don't believe her when she tells them she is psychic, the Prisoner, Curtis and Number Two all accept her skill as genuine, and don't seem to regard it as anything more phenomenal than, say, the ability to play the piano by ear or to work out square roots in one's head (the fact that she reads Curtis' cards correctly in Number Two's office, despite the fact that she is unlikely to have the same mental link with Curtis as with the Prisoner, suggests either that the sequence has been prearranged beforehand, or that she has a generalised psychic ability rather than an exclusive link with one man). Interestingly, given the restrictions elsewhere on the use of the number seven, Alison's scores are very seven-heavy: she scores 17 out of 25, and 73 out of 100 over four runs. While the sequence of the zenner card test (the standard test used for mind-reading abilities) was introduced principally because McGoohan objected to Feely's original idea of having Alison identify the 'real' Six by kissing him (while their dialogue early on could be played as romantic, McGoohan keeps it on a very avuncular level instead), the simple shapes on the zenner deck fit oddly well with the established symbolism of the series: a circle, a square (relating to the round-peg-square-hole images in 'Arrival' and 'Free for All'), three wavy lines (representing the sea), a star (representing the universe) and a cross (X for the unknown, or, possibly, Christianity). The circular light focusing on Curtis's forehead, between the eyes, echoes the 'third eye' imagery of 'Free for All'.

The Prisoner's brainwashing recalls a related concern of the 1960s espionage world. The CIA's mind control experiments, earlier suggested by the events of 'A, B and C', revolved partly around the belief of some psychologists at the time that severe mental illnesses could be treated by, effectively, brainwashing the patient's mind clean and rewriting a new, healthy personality into it. While these experiments ultimately proved unsuccessful, we do see here the use of aversion therapy and hypnosis to change the Prisoner's preferences and identity: he ultimately brings himself out of conditioning by practising a crude form of electroshock therapy. In the original script, the mental-conditioning sequence was much more extended, involving the Prisoner learning to use his left hand to get a drink of water and (bringing in another piece of recurring *The Prisoner* imagery) play chess, and doctors adulterating his food and cigars so that only certain ones taste acceptable (referenced later when the Prisoner breaks a cigar to discover that it has been tampered with). This sequence also appears to have been inserted into the original draft, and then removed at a later date – presumably this was at least partly for time reasons.

The Prisoner's conversation with Curtis about his dreams of resigning from his job also returns us to the Freudian themes of 'A, B and C', and Curtis's responses ('Why did you resign? … In your dream') recall the kind that a therapist might make when treating a patient who is externalising a traumatic event. The 'pulsator' lamp first seen in 'Free for All' again appears in this episode as a kind of mind control agent, as does the powerful and apparently paralysing overhead light; there may be a connection between the two, as both are associated with sound and both have a physical effect on those subjected to them. While it is possible to interpret the Prisoner's use of his left hand as symbolic (the left being, literally, 'sinister'), this may be reading too much into it, since the Prisoner's clumsiness at being forced to change hands is one of the key ways in which he is encouraged to believe that he is literally not himself.

In a chilling sense, also, Number Two actually wins on one level in 'The Schizoid Man', since the efforts of the Villagers have succeeded in getting the Prisoner actually to call himself Number Six. While he has responded to the number elsewhere, it has always been in the context of it being his house number or telephone number – indeed, earlier in the episode he refers to 'your Number Six' – and he has never taken the number as part of his personal identity. However, Curtis always identifies himself as Number Six, and by the time Curtis is interrogated, the Prisoner has actually started to refer to himself by that number (in a continuation of the playing with numbers seen in 'Free for All', Number Two comments that by the time they are done, he won't know if he is Six or the cube root of infinity). The Prisoner also wears a '6' badge voluntarily for the only time in the series, when he puts Curtis's badge on his own jacket. It is also worth noting that, early on, the Prisoner's response to Alison's suggestion that he and she are 'sympatico' is to say that he believes there is more to it than that; but that, when his identity is put to the test, he backs her idea unreservedly, indicating how people can be forced to adopt a perspective they would not willingly otherwise adopt through putting them in a confrontational position.

TIME FOR A CHANGE:
THE VILLAGE AND TIME DISTORTION

The Village once again contains some of the recurring imagery that we have seen in the series so far. The Supervisor for this episode is Haitian (specified as 'African' in the script – since he self-identifies as Haitian, this appears to be shorthand for ethnicity rather than nationality), which, as well as relating to the internationalisation seen earlier with the brief presence of a turbaned Indian (again, specified as such in the script), brings up the idea of zombies and unquiet spirits. There is a popular belief regarding doubles and doppelgängers that if one sees one's double, it means that one is doomed. When Number Two says to the Prisoner to give his regards to Susan, who is dead, it could be read with the implication that the Prisoner is going where she is; he is blindfolded in the helicopter, like a man about to be executed. While the chess game may have been removed from the conditioning sequence, game imagery recurs when Alison photographs the Prisoner with a hand of cards spread out and obscuring his face, like a gambler bluffing his opponent, and recalling his earlier remark about playing it according to Hoyle in 'Free for All'. Following on from the hint in 'A, B and C' that the Prisoner is able to get into the caves without being detected, a cut scene in the night sequence indicates that he knows where the cameras are in the Village and is able to deliberately avoid them.

While the Village does not appear to undergo physical or

structural disruption in this story (although the bulk of it was shot in the studio or on the MGM back lot, this is impeccably done, such that for the most part one only notices if one knows what to look for; a significant exception is the Alouette helicopter seen in the final sequence, which changes colour from black to silver and acquires a set of pontoons upon becoming airborne), time distortion again becomes a plot element. The original script gives the actual dates for the period that the Prisoner's conditioning takes place (10 February through 10 March), but this is removed in the filmed episode, making it ambiguous how long he has been out for (although the four-week period remains as a bit of a subtext: the beard and nail growth seen in the story suggests that he has been out of commission for at least three weeks). The removal of the dates, however, brings us back to the idea that time in the Village is non-linear: the Prisoner does not appear to find it strange that he goes to sleep on 10 February and wakes up, to all intents and purposes, on exactly the same date; the Villagers that we meet also act as if the 10 February date is unproblematic, possibly also indicating again that the whole Village is either being run exclusively for the Prisoner's benefit, or exists only in his mind (as does the fact that the set-up with Alison's psychic powers is a long-term and complicated one).

The copy of *Tally Ho* seen in Two's office visibly has the same date and headline as the one we see in 'A, B and C'. Since 'The Schizoid Man' was made before 'A, B and C' as the seventh episode in production, and since the script specifies that the newspaper must have the 10 February date, the *Tally Ho* prop must have been made specifically for 'The Schizoid Man', with the text questioning Two's suitability for a further term having been added simply as a kind of generic headline such as one might see on a newspaper anywhere in the world. The headline acquires a greater significance only due to its subsequent use in a story in which Number Two is visibly on the skids, in another case of something that would be taken as a coincidence or a continuity error in any other series becoming surreal and symbolic in *The Prisoner* (see also the novel *The Prisoner's Dilemma*). The use of the zoom function on the DVD of this episode reveals that the text of the *Tally Ho* is a jumble of unrelated sentences (some legible lines appear to relate to a London council meeting, a warriors' initiation ritual, and woodsmanship, which reportedly also formed part of the text of the different *Tally Ho* prop seen in 'Hammer into Anvil'). While again this is simply a function of prop design, it's oddly appropriate that a Village newspaper would not have anything literal to say, and to be a jumble of thoughts and ideas from around the world. The fact that a newspaper with the same headline appears in two episodes, as well as relating to the time-distortion and doppelgänger themes (if 'A, B and C' does actually take place on the same day, then there may well be *three* Prisoners in the Village), seems like a comment on the banality of journalism, and the lack of real 'news' in a political setting.

THE CUBE ROOT OF INFINITY: TWO AND SIX

Anton Rogers' performance in the role of Number Two is also worth mentioning (again, only the Prisoner, Curtis, Number Two and Alison receive anything approaching character development in the story). Although he is best known to modern viewers for his distinctly different role as an ageing solicitor in the sitcom *May to December*, Rogers was at the time mainly playing supporting roles in ITC/independent television spy series (he was another *Danger Man* alumnus, like Jane Morrow, who had appeared three times in the earlier series). Particularly noteworthy from a performance point of view is the scene in which the Prisoner suggests bringing Alison in to test which of the pair is the real Number Six, and Number Two looks distinctly worried. There are three different ways of reading Number Two's reaction: first, that he is worried that the Prisoner has found a way of proving that he is the correct Six; second, that he is bluffing, knowing that Alison is on his side but wanting the Prisoner to believe that he is afraid she will expose the deception, or, thirdly, that he is worried that Number Twelve has just done something that will prove conclusively that he is *not* Six, which is how he plays it afterwards, berating the Prisoner and yet placing all the blame squarely on a technician (in a nice comment on how the powerful frequently blame those lower down the chain of command for their own failings). The true nature of the sequence is made clear to the audience only after the test has failed. Elsewhere, there is a similar double meaning in Alison's final conversation with the

Prisoner, in that she knows that he is really the Prisoner rather than Curtis, but they are both pretending that it is the other way around. On a character level, Number Two's use of the word 'masters' suggests either that Number Two does not in fact report directly to Number One, but that there are people between him and the top, or alternatively that Number One is not in fact at the top of the Village command chain.

Finally, McGoohan's performance as Curtis is identical to the one he gives as the Prisoner in such 'baiting Number Two' episodes as 'Hammer into Anvil' and 'A, B and C': cocky, confident and acting as if he has rumbled some game of Number Two's. His cheeky remark about being 'summoned by the headmaster' when Rover comes to bring them in also fits in with the childhood imagery seen elsewhere. By contrast, his performance as the Prisoner waking up as a 'new man' is hunched, uncertain, without the sense of authority and self-possession that he normally displays. In another reference back to *Danger Man*, Curtis's normal clothes (which the Prisoner dons at the end of the story) resemble those that McGoohan wears in the publicity still from the earlier series repeatedly seen throughout *The Prisoner*. In a character point, it might be worth noting that the Prisoner's cottage has a battery of copper pans, which, as the items that appear in his London residence have been duplicated in his Village domicile, would indicate that, although we never see the Prisoner himself do any cooking more sophisticated than boiling an egg, he is a good hobby cook, since copper pans are so expensive that only those with a serious interest in cooking are likely to invest in a set; an idea that would be explored in the series of tie-in novels.

'The Schizoid Man' thus not only serves to disconcert the viewer, but also has a similar effect on the Prisoner himself, to the point where we see an initial crack appearing in his armour against Village manipulation.

Episode 6:
The General

First UK Transmission Date: Friday 3 November 1967: ATV Midlands/Grampian, 7.30 pm – 8.30 pm
Writer: Joshua Adam (pseudonym for Lewis Greifer)
Director: Peter Graham Scott
Credited Cast: Patrick McGoohan (The Prisoner); Colin Gordon (Number Two); John Castle (Number Twelve); Peter Howell (Professor); Angelo Muscat (The Butler); Al Mancini (Announcer); Betty McDowall (Professor's Wife); Peter Swanwick (Supervisor); Conrad Phillips (Doctor); Michael Miller (Man in Buggy); Keith Pyott (Waiter); Ian Fleming (Man at Café and First Top Hat); Norman Mitchell (Mechanic); Peter Bourne (Projection Operator); George Leech (First Corridor Guard); Jackie Cooper (Second Corridor Guard)
Known Uncredited Cast: Al Mancini (Loudspeaker Voice); Robert Rietty (Other Voices); Frank Maher (Double for Patrick McGoohan); Fred Coutoure (Double for Peter Howell); Robert Rietty (Additional Voicework)

SYNOPSIS: The Village is consumed by a craze for a new educational technique, Speedlearn, invented by the Professor and supported by the General, which purports to give its students the equivalent of a university degree in three minutes. In the Village café, the Prisoner is contacted by a young man, Number Twelve, who ostensibly works for Number Two; he suggests that the Prisoner take the course and implies that he wishes to help the

Prisoner escape. The Professor attempts to flee the Village, but is recaptured by the Villagers; the Prisoner finds a tape recorder dropped by the Professor, which contains a recording of the Professor asserting that the General must be destroyed. The Prisoner returns to his house and receives a Speedlearn lesson through his television set; he feels no different, but discovers in subsequent conversation with Number Two that he can recite facts about European history eidetically. He contacts the Professor's wife and, when she proves unresponsive, breaks into their house to find a roomful of busts; confronted by her and Number Two, he goes into the Professor's bedroom and destroys the figure he finds in the bed, revealing it to be a wax model. Number Twelve contacts the Prisoner under cover of an electrical fault and offers to help get the Professor's real lecture played; he gives the Prisoner a set of passes and tells him to meet him the next day. Using his pass, the Prisoner enters the Town Hall during a Lecture Approval Session, breaks into the Projection Room, overpowers the man he finds there, cutting himself in the process, and substitutes the new tape for the lecture tape. However, Number Two, observing the blood on the Prisoner's hand and realising that he is not the projectionist, has him apprehended. It is revealed that the Professor is simply a front for the General, who is in fact a computer. The Prisoner breaks the computer by feeding it the simple question 'WHY?'

ANALYSIS: Lewis Greifer, a scriptwriter for independent television since the late 1950s and a friend of Markstein's (apparently he was the one who introduced Markstein to McGoohan), famously wrote this story as a critique of rote learning, as he was frustrated by the way creativity and imagination seemed to be discouraged in his children's schooling in favour of memorisation of facts (his pseudonym for this story, Joshua Adam, which was reportedly adopted for contractual reasons due to the fact that he was then working as story editor on ATV's *Love Story* anthology series, was drawn from the first names of his sons). While the sentiment is admirable, and very much in keeping with the general feeling of the time, it does leave the modern viewer slightly uncomfortable in light of the damage done to the British educational system by the reaction against rote learning methods in the 1970s, in which too much emphasis on 'encouraging creativity' led to a generation of functionally illiterate and innumerate students in certain parts of the country. In the same vein, the slogan 'University for All in Three Minutes' ties in to the focus at the time of making higher education more accessible to people of all backgrounds, due to a rejection of the snobbish and unmeritocratic university culture satirised in Kingsley Amis's *Lucky Jim*. Ironically, given Greifer's stated dislike of the traditional education system, the Prisoner seems to come down in the end on the side of restricting university education, implying that a 'three-minute degree' is one so heavily devalued that there is no real point in having done the course.

BACK TO SCHOOL SPECIAL: KNOWLEDGE AND LEARNING

On a deeper level, the story focuses on the tyranny of meaningless facts, and what educational theorist Paul Ramsden refers to as the relation between 'deep learning' and 'surface learning': the latter involves rote, repetition and memorisation, the former involves actually understanding, internalising, and drawing conclusions from the memorised knowledge. While arguably one must know the date of the Treaty of Adrianople in order to have an opinion on it, it is another thing to be able to understand its significance and apply it to a debate about 19th Century history. When Number Twelve asks the Prisoner 'What is the Treaty of Adrianople,' and the Prisoner unthinkingly responds with *when* it was, we see that the Speedlearn process has enabled him to recite facts, but not to contextualise or rationalise.

However, the learning of facts can provide a false sense of knowledge: facts can be easy to memorise and reel off, and the process of doing so allows one to feel terribly clever, but if one can do nothing with the facts beyond recite them, one is effectively powerless. This is highlighted in the scenes in which the Villagers playfully ask each other questions and are delighted when they receive correct answers, while ignoring the fact that they can't use the information as anything other than an amusing party game. The Villagers who use Speedlearn also don't just take university courses, but act like university students: school references abound, and the students stage an apparently spontaneous Hallowe'en party and wield hand-lettered signs; however, crucially, those signs and events are in favour of Speedlearn, rather than protests against authority. Buried within the story is also an apparent critique of the 1960s arts movement: Madame Professor's students may tear up books and stand on their heads, but in the end they do not accomplish or challenge anything, any more than the Professor's students do. It is thus fitting that the question the Prisoner uses to finally defeat the General is simply 'Why?'; as he notes, the unanswerable question, and one that cannot be silenced with a simple fact.

On a more sinister level, the way the facts are presented controls how they are perceived: one memorised 'fact' within the story is 'Bismarck wanted war' (ironically given the themes of the story, the name 'Bismarck' is misspelled in the original script), which might not necessarily have been the case, or might have been part of a more complicated situation. By prioritising the memorisation of 'facts,' one can convince people that the interpretations concealed within them are not open for dispute or question. This is reflected in the way the examiners are dressed as undertakers: although top hats were established as a symbol of authority within the Village in 'Free for All', here it could also be taken as symbolising the death of independent thought, bolstered by the fact that the guards' uniforms are reminiscent of those worn by American military policemen (with connotations of censorship and repression in the then-current era of anti-Vietnam protests). All of this leads one to the conclusion that, if the Prisoner had succeeded in broadcasting the Professor's suppressed lecture, it would actually have done no good: the students would just have absorbed what the Professor said and repeated it back, without thinking about the implications for them of the Professor's critique of the system.

The themes within the story also point to a little-discussed influence on the series, Aldous Huxley's 1932 science fiction novel *Brave New World*. In this, the citizens of a future Earth learn painlessly in their sleep through the 'hypnopaedia' method, which is used at the same time to control their thoughts and beliefs. The way in which the Villagers reel off facts but do not understand them seems to be a direct reference to an early scene in *Brave New World* in which a prototypical form of hypnopaedia causes children to learn facts by rote but to be incapable of internalising and collating them. Orwell and Kafka are usually cited as the main literary antecedents of *The Prisoner*, and certainly the series' Orwellian aspects are almost blatant in the décor of this story, with pictures of the Professor atop meaningless slogans recalling the BBC's celebrated 1954 production of *Nineteen Eighty-Four* starring Peter Cushing (so much so that the obviousness of it rapidly becomes irritating to the viewer), and, as Big Brother in the novel proves to be a fiction, so the frequently-anthropomorphised General turns out not to be a person at all. 'The General' also deals briefly with the use of television for social control and for education (as well as presenting an ironic teleplay-within-a-teleplay, as the examiners watch the studios go through a studio check prior to broadcast). However, it can be argued that Huxley is a greater influence, because, leaving aside his novel's focus on drugs and cloning, rather than presenting totalitarianism and bureaucracy as squalid, terrifying and suppressing through fear, he focused on social control through enjoyment and pleasure: in his novel, no-one challenges the system, because they are happy, which seems to be reflected in the Village's carnival atmosphere, the mindlessly repeated catchphrases and slogans, and the insistence that the Prisoner participate in frivolous leisure pursuits.

MISTER AND MISSUS: THE PROFESSOR AND HIS WIFE

The character of the Professor deserves examination in this light as well. One of the less obvious themes of the story is that of the dangers of the cult of the celebrity academic. The 1960s was a time when a number of scientists and philosophers – Carl Sagan, Margaret Mead, Marshall McLuhan, Noam Chomsky and so forth – were receiving a lot of media attention, and were sometimes bemused, if not upset, at the way in which their works were consequently treated as authoritative and used outside their critical context. In the Village, there is very much a similar cult of the Professor: his image is everywhere (although, fortunately perhaps, the potentially misconstruable slogan 'Up the Professor', which the script states is on the students' rosettes, is difficult to make out, if indeed it remains at all). The students appear to love him: the scenes with the Professor being pursued along the beach seem oddly playful compared with the aggressive encounters of earlier stories, resembling nothing so much as the sequences in *A Hard Day's Night* and *Help!* in which the Beatles are chased by crowds of adoring fans, as Villagers of all ages cheer and laugh as they run the Professor down, as if this were some sort of affectionate student prank.

This leads to the interesting implication in the later part of the story that, in fact, the Professor is not the one writing the lectures, but simply a front for the machine. Number Twelve states, for instance, 'Speedlearn is the outcome of the General's prolific knowledge. Its basis is the student's confidence in a tried and trusted professor and the professor's confidence in science ...' – which could be read as meaning that the Professor's information is stored in the General and thereby transmitted to students, but alternatively that the General is the one with the knowledge, and the Professor, with his pictures of Napoleonic soldiers and office full of books, is simply there to encourage student identification, and induce them not to challenge the information they receive. Later, Number Two says of the Professor: 'Lovely fellow. People love him. They'll take anything from him. It's the image that's important, you see.' This might also explain the Professor's ambivalence about what he is doing, and why he tries to contradict the work he is being made to do.

However, this theme is undermined by a sense of confusion regarding the scene in which the Professor is taken out of the room by the Doctor and the Nurse in the middle of typing his lecture notes: if the General needs the Professor's knowledge, then the fact that he is interrupted before finishing will surely make for an incomplete lecture (causing one to picture Villagers wandering around saying to each other 'The Treaty of Versailles was signed in 19 – was signed in 19 – was signed in 19 –' due to the unfinished note); but if the General does not need the Professor's knowledge, why have him write notes at all? This clearly cannot be a kind of deception whereby the Professor is being made to feel that he contributes meaningfully to the system (which is also, peculiarly, suggested by the fact that he is taken out of the room before the Doctor feeds the lecture into the card machine), as the Professor is subsequently revealed to have invented the General himself (making him something of a polymath), and to be perfectly aware of the system, later making his notes into computer cards himself.

Elsewhere, Speedlearn is described as 'A brilliantly devised course delivered by a leading teacher … checked and corrected by an infallible authority,' a statement that leaves it unclear which one is the Professor and which the General. At times, the General (the appearance of which, though dated by modern standards, is not problematic, and indeed is rather sweet) is spoken of as if it has a mind of its own: the books on the shelves in the Professor's office are stated by Number Two as being 'all available to the General … There is no question … that the General cannot answer', which is in keeping with the '60s fear of technology taking over people's lives, but slightly at odds with the General's presentation elsewhere as a mere machine. It's also worth mentioning that the idea of a computer blowing up after being given an insoluble question is a well-worn cliché of 1960s telefantasy. The story could thus be taken as a critique of the way academics are presented in popular culture, but unfortunately undermines its own argument through inconsistency.

Madame Professor is also an interesting figure. She is clearly colluding with the Village in keeping her husband in line, and Number Two implies that she is willing to compromise because she loves her husband and is willing to sacrifice idealism to keep him (and herself) alive, although the Prisoner also implies that they are getting privileges for cooperating (and Madame Professor acknowledges this). She is specified in the script as wearing non-Village clothing, and she and her husband are the first people we have encountered in the Village so far, aside from the Butler, not to have numbers. It is suggested, also, that she might be involved more deeply in Village activities: one of the busts that she has made resembles one of the Romanesque busts used for surveillance at the edge of the Village, and there is also a bust of Leo McKern's Number Two previously seen in 'The Chimes of Big Ben', implying that she may have been involved in the arts competition in that story. It is not insignificant that she is an artist while her husband is a scientist, indicating that both fields of study are equally subject to corruption and collusion. Again we see an ambiguity over who are the prisoners and who are the warders: the Professor and his wife are both trapped by their circumstances and richly rewarded, at once colluding with the Village and wanting to resist its control.

The storyline involving Madame Professor is slightly

undermined by a confusing moment when the Prisoner shatters the head of the dummy Professor in the bed. While this scene makes slightly more sense in the original script, in which it is stated that Madame Professor's busts are wax portraits, and while it serves on a symbolic level to indicate the shattering of mute and hollow authority, one still has to ask why she and Number Two want to put it in bed and pretend it's the real thing, and why she reacts when the Prisoner attacks it as if he had attacked her real husband.

BRIEF ENCOUNTERS:
HOMOEROTICISM AND INTERNATIONALISM

'The General' appears to owe a partial debt to 'A, B and C', not only in the fact that the sets for Madame Engadine's house and garden have been reused as the Professor's house and garden and that the conga music from the 'dreamy party' recurs in the sequence where the Village students stage what appears to be a Hallowe'en celebration, but also in the fact that we again have a male character who adds a homoerotic subtext to his scenes. As with A in 'A, B and C', Number Twelve's lines are not inherently homoerotic, and McGoohan's performance of the scenes is very neutral. John Castle, however, plays up the homoerotic subtext to the idea of two men with something to hide meeting in a café, carefully making eye contact with the Prisoner, eyeing him up and down, and standing very close to him when they meet in front of the poster of the Professor. Later, the scenes between them are informed by the fact that the Prisoner knows that Number Twelve (who shares his number with Curtis, the Prisoner's symbolic 'twin', from the preceding story) has a secret he does not wish Number Two to find out. While none of this should be at all taken to suggest that the central character of the series – or, indeed, Number Twelve himself – is gay or bisexual, it is unsurprising that parallels can be drawn between the experience of homosexuals at the time and that of the central figure of a series about a man who is prosecuted by an unsympathetic small-scale society for making choices then considered socially unacceptable.

On the internationalism front, Fenella Fielding is replaced for the episode by Al Mancini, whose appearances in *UFO* and *The Dirty*

Dozen provide yet another set of connections between those series/films and *The Prisoner*, as the first male tannoy as well as the TV Announcer and the roving reporter (although, given what we've seen so far in the series, he could be playing several separate people). Given that the series has already featured Estonian and Chinese characters, it is surprising that this is the first time we have seen an American in the Village, in that most ITC programmes of the period were being made with one eye on the American market, and a lot of the social critique in *The Prisoner* is explicitly aimed at the American/Soviet standoff of the time. Other voice-overs in the story are supplied by Robert Rietty, who is so ubiquitous in the series that one might be forgiven for wondering if he will turn out to be Number One. With regard to women in the Village taking important roles, the script explicitly states that the General's attendant should be female. Themes of death briefly appear in the students' Hallowe'en party, when we see skull and devil masks being worn (as well as an ape mask, foreshadowing developments in 'Fall Out'). The scene in the projection room is noteworthy for being unusually gory for a TV spy series; these tend to shy away from showing much blood – presumably as it takes the injury out of the realm of 'fantasy violence' – but here the Prisoner's blood continues to flow quite graphically for some time after he is stabbed, and soaks through the bandage after his arm is bound up.

WHO TEACHES THE TEACHERS?
THE VILLAGE IN 'THE GENERAL'

As noted in the analysis for 'A, B and C', Colin Gordon returns in this story as Number Two; although he's still a milk addict (the original script had him drinking coffee, so the milk idea was presumably carried forward from the earlier story), he is more confident and self-assured, and seems less concerned about what his superiors will think. In the Council Chamber, he sits at the table, rather than, as in 'Free for All', in the raised chair in front of the chair with the eye. Significantly, the red telephone that he uses is normal-sized, further indicating that the distorted and enlarged telephone of 'A, B and C' is a symbolic, even Expressionist, exaggeration of his fear and sense of loss of control. It has been suggested that Number Two was originally to have been killed off in 'The General' and that the ending was rewritten once Colin Gordon took on the role; however, Fairclough's script book does not indicate that there were any drastic changes made to it (indeed, perhaps because Greifer was so close to both McGoohan and Markstein, there were very few changes between the script and the transmitted episode at all), and, as the ending features the Prisoner cryptically explaining to Number Two what happened to the computer, it would have needed some serious rewriting was Number Two not originally to have taken part. At one point, it is clearly indicated that Number Two has taken Speedlearn himself, further blurring the boundaries between prisoner and warder. The General itself was actually referenced in the earlier episode 'The Schizoid Man', in the line 'Report to the General? That's a new one.' We also see the return of the empty chair with the blue eye from 'Free for All', and yet another globe appears, in the Professor's house. The Prisoner's remark about the Speedlearn system producing 'cabbages' recalls his earlier description of the Villagers as such in 'Free for All'.

Elsewhere in the Village, the currency is again being referred to as 'credit units', and we learn that two of these will buy a cup of coffee. Although the Prisoner is described in the script as paying with a 'credit card', this seems to be less like modern credit cards (or indeed the card seen in 'Arrival'), and more like a ration coupon that the waiter punches to indicate the Prisoner's purchase. The story is openly dated to the 20th Century at one point. The disguised Prisoner's number is 56, meaning that he goes by the number Six even when incognito.

The 'Bandit Box' toy seen as the Examiners enter the town hall was included at McGoohan's request; as it is mentioned in the original script, the request must have been made very early on. Another thing that McGoohan got his way on in this story was the choice of director: he sacked the original director, Robert Lynn, and insisted that Peter Graham Scott should replace him, apparently pulling strings to release Scott from his responsibilities on *The Troubleshooters*. However, the story did run into some problems on its international release, as the French distributors felt that the name 'The General' might be taken to refer to de Gaulle, and so, in an oddly Prisoneresque moment of censorship, both story and computer were renamed *'Le Cerveau'* ('The Brain') for French release.

'The General' is a story that addresses contemporary themes of the time in a way that is still relevant to modern educators and students. However, a few key flaws make it difficult to pronounce it as an out-and-out classic.

Episode 7:
Many Happy Returns

First UK Transmission Date: Friday 10 November 1967: ATV Midlands/Grampian,7.30 pm – 8.30 pm
Writer: Anthony Skene
Director: Joseph Serf (pseudonym for Patrick McGoohan)
Credited Cast: Patrick McGoohan (The Prisoner); Donald Sinden (The Colonel); Patrick Cargill (Thorpe); Georgina Cookson (Mrs Butterworth); Brian Worth (Group Captain); Richard Caldicott (Commander); Dennis Chinnery (Gunther); Jon Laurimore (Ernst); Nike Arrighi (Gypsy Girl) Grace Arnold (Maid); Larry Taylor (Gypsy Man)
Known Uncredited Cast: George Markstein ('M'); Angelo Muscat (The Butler); Frank Maher, Brian Axworthy, Douglas Williams (Doubles for Patrick McGoohan); Robert Rietty (Additional Voicework); Tammy (Black Cat)

SYNOPSIS: The Prisoner awakes to find the Village apparently deserted apart from a black cat. He takes photographs of the area, constructs a raft and sails out to sea. After 25 days, his raft is picked up by a smugglers' boat and he is left for dead; climbing onto the boat, he fights with the men on board, swims to the nearest coastline, encounters a party of gypsies, discovers that he is back in England, and smuggles himself aboard a lorry to London. He returns to his house to find it inhabited by a lady named Mrs Butterworth, who appears sympathetic, feeding and clothing him and, upon learning that it is his birthday the next day, offering to bake him a cake. The Prisoner meets with his ex-colleagues Thorpe and the Colonel, who are suspicious of his story but agree to help locate the Village. The Prisoner goes to the Village's purported location in a plane; upon arrival, he is ejected by the pilot and stranded in the Village. Mrs Butterworth comes to his cottage, bearing the promised cake; she reveals that she is Number Two, and wishes the Prisoner 'Many happy returns'.

ANALYSIS: Seemingly less deep than the episodes around it, 'Many Happy Returns' is arguably the weakest of Anthony Skene's three scripts for *The Prisoner* (although, according to Steven Ricks in *In the Village* Issue 22, spring 1999, the original idea came from David Tomblin, who was interested in doing an episode with no dialogue until after the first act; indeed, the first English words are not heard until almost the end of Act Two). However, coupled with McGoohan's direction, it becomes an episode that expands upon the already-established idea of connections between the Village and the rest of the world.

'Many Happy Returns' was filmed as the last story of the first season (thirteenth in filming order), with the general intention that it would be the season finale, and that the second series would take the focus out into the wider world, with the Prisoner discovering that, in fact, the world is the Village and vice versa. Consequently, the story has a number of deliberate parallels to 'Arrival'. These include the use of the helicopter (specified in the original script for 'Many Happy Returns'; this sequence actually got as far as being filmed, and part of it appears in 'Fall Out', in the medium-shot of a helicopter slowly lifting off in a field near a Mini Moke) and the Prisoner's exploration of the deserted Village, including a visit to the café and the Stone Boat and a climb up the bell tower (the statue, which was mentioned as present in the script for 'Many Happy Returns', is now absent, suggesting that even the statuary has departed with the residents), where his tolling of the bell does not coincide with the appearance of the Villagers as before. A cut sequence in the hospital (probably removed as it would have required extensive rebuilding of sets) would also have seen the Prisoner observing the deserted Group Therapy Room, with empty straitjackets lining the walls. There are clear connections to 'The Chimes of Big Ben', in that both stories involve a seeming escape from the Village in a homemade boat (followed by the discovery that the escape was an illusion), and both identify a specific location for the Village. The sequence beginning when the Prisoner chops down trees to make a raft has the same music as the 'Escape' construction sequence in 'The Chimes of Big Ben', 'Tropical Forest'. Unlike in 'The Chimes of Big Ben', however, when the Prisoner flees the Village only to discover that his supposed exodus has in fact led him back to where he started, here he does actually flee, only to learn that the world is, in fact, the Village, before being brought back against his will.

ROVER'S RETURN: THE VILLAGE AND THE WORLD

The idea that the Village is the wider world is highlighted throughout the story. The two smugglers whom the Prisoner encounters eat beans and corned beef out of Village Foods tins (which aren't mentioned in the original script, where the implication is that the Prisoner has run out of food before encountering the boat); the obvious inference is that they are eating the food they found on the Prisoner's raft, but on the other hand, the symbolic connection between them and the Village has been made. Similarly, the Prisoner's London house causes a sense of deja vu, since the front room is identical to the front part of his cottage in the Village, and the whole residence is full of curves and bright colours, meaning that his life in London reflects his life in the Village; it is literally as if he never left. Mrs Butterworth – who is, unbeknownst to the Prisoner, actually a Village official – is the type of strong, unconventionally beautiful older woman whom we repeatedly encounter in the Village, and who dresses in a way that, while fashionable for the 1960s, is not dissimilar to what we have seen women wearing in the Village up until now. By a lucky coincidence, the pavement on which the Prisoner walks when he crosses Stag Place in London is in a checkerboard pattern of dark and light squares, echoing his walk across the chessboard-patterned lawn in 'Arrival' as well as picking up on the recurring chess metaphor associated with the Village. The original script also features an extensive cut scene in which the driver of a Mini on the highway spots the Prisoner and alerts nearby policemen to his presence, the Prisoner cuts through a hedge and runs across a deeply ploughed field, and the police at the roadblock are showing drivers a photograph that the Prisoner presumes is of himself; although the Colonel later claims that this was a hunt for an escaped convict, and nothing to do with the Prisoner at all, the implication still stands that the wider world is in league with the Village authorities.

As with the polyglot nature of the Village, we hear foreign languages in this episode: the smugglers speak German (rather badly), and the first people whom the Prisoner encounters are Romany-speaking Gypsies, an ethnic group found all over Europe and North America, so until we actually see the helmeted policeman, the Prisoner could have come to ground in any number of places. The original script specifies that the smugglers' radio would be playing an Albanian broadcast, which, as well as bringing an even more international flavour to the proceedings (since the script is also clear that the smugglers are speaking German and that their newspaper is German), suggests a Balkan setting ironically congruent with the Village location given in 'The Chimes of Big Ben'. However, the idea in the original script that the Gypsies were to speak in broad Cockney tones when the Prisoner approaches them and tells them that he wants to get to England, in keeping with the language-play in Skene's original script for 'A, B and C', would have damaged the feeling of placelessness of the finished version. The library where we meet the Colonel is, appropriately enough, a recycled set from 'The General', and contains yet another globe. Again, parallels are drawn between the Prisoner and McGoohan himself (they share the same birthday; the cake that Number Two presents to him has six candles); and, in light of future events, it might be worth noting that the Prisoner's London address is Number One Buckingham Place.

As mentioned above, this is also the second story to give a definite location for the Village: in this case, a possible island somewhere off the cost of Morocco, south-west of Portugal and Spain. If one takes the cut scenes from 'The Chimes of Big Ben' at face value, this suggests that the Village has actually changed physical location: its general position in 'Many Happy Returns' is determined by a Naval Commander and an RAF Group Captain, which lends it some authority, and it is while the Prisoner is conducting an aerial search of this region that the Village is located. The original script also initially suggests that the Village is situated on a particular volcanic island (thus providing a practical reason for its desertion), but this is dismissed by the Commander on the grounds that the trees described by the Prisoner are older than the island itself. The original story was actually rather more vague on the location of the Village, so one can only assume that the shifting location was intentional.

Considering the dreamlike nature of the Village, it is also appropriate that the whole adventure should take on hallucinatory qualities. For instance, when the Prisoner returns to the Village at the end of the story, the cat is still sitting beside the broken crockery as if no time has passed, although he has been away for nearly a month; the Villagers vanish and reappear without explanation, again, like in a dream. The Prisoner cryptically describes the Village as housing 'people who know too much or too little.' The Prisoner makes a journey that directly echoes his resignation trip, down to finding Markstein behind the desk, crockery unbroken beside him, much as he keeps reliving his resignation in his dreams in Skene's earlier script 'A, B and C'. In a related area, Georgina Cookson previously appeared as a party guest in one of the dream sequences in 'A, B and C'; while this could imply that 'Many Happy Returns' should be viewed before 'A, B and C' (as it would make sense for the Prisoner to remember an earlier Number Two in his dreams), it could equally be taken to indicate that the Village is *all* part of a dream, or an after-death experience, or a similar sort of psychic phenomenon. The sequence in which the cat apparently breaks a teacup and saucer also makes more sense as dream logic than a real event: it seems odd that the cat could have broken the cup and saucer in that way, as it appears to have shattered into pieces of its own accord rather than being knocked over, but it is worth noticing that it breaks at the exact point at which the Prisoner leaves the Village, in parallel with the way in which he shatters the crockery on Markstein's desk in the title sequence when he resigns. A cut sequence in 'Many Happy Returns' involves the Prisoner falling asleep in the truck and dreaming that the truck is riding through an alien landscape (we do not see him asleep until after we see an exterior shot of the truck in the landscape, leaving it ambiguous as to whether this is a dream or not, as well as suggesting that the

Village includes not just the world, but the whole universe), then he wakes (with a thick head, as if he had just woken up, meaning that to see the Prisoner apparently waking up does not mean that he is not still dreaming) to find that he is still in the Village, and is being pursued by a Mini Moke; he then leaps out of the truck in his dream, to find himself leaping out of the real truck into the real Piccadilly Circus, in another moment which blurs the boundaries between dream and reality for the Prisoner and the audience.

RANDOM QUEST: SYMBOLISM AND NARRATIVE

We also return obliquely to the idea of doubles or doppelgängers. Mrs Butterworth is something of a female double of the Prisoner: she lives in his house, drives his Lotus 7[11], and is first seen pulling up in front of his house in it, much as the Prisoner does in the title sequence: she also has a maid (a kind of female parallel to the silent butler), where the Prisoner repeatedly refuses maid service in the Village. Elsewhere, Patrick Cargill, who plays the sadistic Number Two in 'Hammer into Anvil' appears here as Thorpe; as 'Hammer into Anvil' was filmed beforehand, and Cargill was asked, on the strength of his performance in it, to stay on and play Thorpe, this turn of events is rather puzzling, unless the one was intended to be a double of the other (and the Prisoner at no point in either of the two stories draws any connection between the two characters). We again have a military type, the Colonel, with a title but no actual first name (paralleling Colonel J in 'The Chimes of Big Ben' as well as the various Admirals and Generals in the Village). A scene cut from the original script contains an exchange between Thorpe and the Colonel in which they discuss the Prisoner's story in such a way as to suggest either that the Colonel is not in fact one of those 'in the know,' or else that the Colonel is putting on a show for the benefit of Thorpe.

Death symbolism is associated with the Village here, highlighted in its wintry and desolate appearance. When explaining the Village, the Prisoner says that those who break are allowed a pleasant

---

11 This would be the last time that the original car, a Lotus demonstrator, as seen in the title sequence, was used in the series; those seen subsequently in 'Do Not Forsake Me Oh My Darling' and 'Fall Out' would be look-alikes.

retirement in the old age home, but that for those who try to escape, the Village also has an impressive graveyard, implying that the only way out for anyone is through death. The Prisoner himself collapses from exhaustion on the raft, and is assumed to be dead by the two smugglers. His name is not on the lease when he checks up on the history of his house, meaning that he has been erased in identity terms outside of the Village (the next episode, also written by Skene, will revolve around the 'death' on paper of a living individual). In the original script, a cut scene has the Prisoner discovering that, in the Village hospital, the inmates' beds are unmade as if they have all left in a hurry, perhaps suggesting fundamentalist Christian beliefs about the Rapture of the faithful. In the original ending of the story, Number Two was to give the Prisoner a present (a cartridge of film of pictures of the Village, that, in the original script, the Prisoner had hidden in a coin locker in the London Underground) wrapped in a copy of the *Tally Ho* bearing the headline 'Plane lost over sea. No hope of survivors.' She tells him to 'give in and enjoy being dead'; the Prisoner screws up the paper and replies 'I'll die first.'

The story has been likened by some commentators to a mythic quest. Although McGoohan cut most of the scenes that could bolster this argument (for instance, one in which the Prisoner succumbs to hunger and thirst like the Ancient Mariner, and is found by smugglers lashed to the mast like Odysseus), that which remains does have the common mythic structure of separation of the hero from society, followed by a 'liminal' period of isolation, and then a return, which is common to initiations and funeral rituals as well as mythology. The scenes McGoohan cut were principally those indicating that the Prisoner has a human and/or vulnerable side; ironically, the end result was to make the sequences on the raft less believably harrowing, and to cause it to resemble a children's adventure more than anything else.

In terms of references to childhood and children, the whole story, seen one way, resembles a colossal birthday prank, with everyone hiding and then, when the Prisoner returns, leaping out and presenting him with a birthday cake. Mrs Butterworth, although there is an understated sexual element to the character's relationship with the Prisoner, is also a motherly figure, plying him with sandwiches and offering to help him out; originally, she was to have been a scared and aggressive little old lady, and the clothes she lends to the Prisoner were to have been her son's rather than her late husband's. Perhaps surprisingly, considering McGoohan's normal avoidance of sexuality in *The Prisoner*, the idea of having Mrs Butterworth being an attractive and glamourous middle-aged woman seems to have come from him. The story of the Prisoner escaping on a raft, although the sail is more convincing and the boat more seaworthy than the one seen in 'The Chimes of Big Ben', is still, as Thorpe notes when he likens the Prisoner's story to 'a fairy tale', a little like something out of a children's adventure; his journal is described as 'a schoolboy log on the back of a newspaper.'

Mention must be made of the symbolism surrounding the village cat, which makes its first appearance in the broadcast episode order here, although its first filmed story was 'Dance of the Dead'. The cat was played in both stories by a local feline named Tammy, after a cat brought in from London refused to perform (no doubt insisting on more tuna and a three-day working week). Considering that black cats are associated with witches, it may be significant that the cat appears only in the two episodes that feature an older female Number Two, particularly as it is sometimes assumed to belong to Number Two.

The story also continues the comment on society and bureaucracy of earlier episodes. The copy of the *Tally Ho* that the Prisoner uses as writing paper sports the brilliantly meaningless headline 'What are facts behind Town Hall?', leaving it unclear whether this refers to a decision made by Town Hall or to a discussion of the personalities on the Council, or is simply questioning what facts are in general. It is stated that the Village holds town council elections every year (although it is left uncertain whether or not this is the same sort of event seen in 'Free for All'). There is also a possible reference to 'The General' in the original script, when it is revealed that Thorpe and the Colonel have access to a supercomputer named 'Edgar', which they use when trying to pinpoint the Village's exact location. The original script contained a long sequence (which got as far as the storyboard stage before being cut) in which the Prisoner goes to the Village hospital and releases the lab rats that he finds there, but, like the Villagers in 'Free for All', the rats are not grateful to be liberated, and simply sit around grooming themselves.

THE CAT COMES BACK:
CHARACTER DEVELOPMENT AND PRODUCTION

'Many Happy Returns' continues to develop the character of the Prisoner himself. He is here given for the first time a name (Peter Smith), although the context suggests this may be a pseudonym. He describes himself to Mrs Butterworth as 'an exile', though what he means by this is unknown: an exile from the Village, an exile from society, an exile from his former employers? The script also highlights the fact that the Prisoner's rejection of society goes hand in hand with an unrealised dependence on it, when it describes him as being 'irritated' by the lack of water, fresh milk and so forth in the deserted Village. A cut scene had the Prisoner waking up, going outside and discovering that his morning pint of milk has not been delivered – tying in with the fact that he himself is later delivered by the milkman (in that a man disguised as a milkman takes over from the first plane pilot), further indicating that he has not left the Village. In the original script, the Prisoner ejects himself from the plane, rather than being ejected by the pilot. He also signs his IOU with a number six, but adds a question mark (and the final sum on the IOU was changed in the transmitted version from 974 to 964). In the script, his London home is a flat within a building, rather than a house. The original script strongly implies, in keeping with activities seen earlier in the Village, that the Prisoner has been heavily drugged before the start of the story – he is said to wake with a nasty taste in his mouth and a sore head – which does not come across in the final version.

On the production front, this is the last story that Markstein had any involvement with, although it is on record that he thought very highly of the episode, and admired McGoohan's direction. Markstein's character is identified as 'M' in the original script, in both a James Bond reference and an inside joke; the character is also doing *The Times* crossword, in a reference to one of Markstein's hobbies. McGoohan took over as director, credited under the pseudonym Joseph Serf, when Michael Truman, who had been lined up to direct this episode, fell ill. The story underwent quite a bit of editing from shooting script to transmitted version, and is much the better for it (for instance, the original had the smugglers, rather unbelievably, imprisoning the Prisoner rather than leaving him for dead). This episode involved more location filming than usual, in the Irish Sea, off the coast of Dover (with the raft at one point nearly sinking the boat that was towing it, and having to be cut free) and on the A1 near Borehamwood. The boat used as the smugglers' motor-yacht, the *Breda*, had been used as the *Polotska* in 'Checkmate', filmed earlier but screened later. The Prisoner sports a new set of striped pyjamas early in the story, as well as a fetching new blue silk dressing gown with no stripes at all. The London scenes appear to have been shot fairly early in the morning, to judge by the angle of the shadows. We can also partially date the series from the Gloster Meteor aircraft used in this story: T7 1/2 Trainer WA638 was retired from service in 1977, meaning that the story can take place no later than that. Dennis Chinnery, who played Gunther, recalls having been vigorously throttled by McGoohan in the original take of their fight sequence, to the point where he thought he was going to pass out. This is, notably, the first episode in which the identity of the new Number Two is not revealed during the opening credits, with the voiceover being provided by the ubiquitous Robert Rietty and a shot of Rover being substituted where Number Two's face would normally have appeared.

'Many Happy Returns' is a deeply symbolic and surreal story, with the first dialogue not occurring until 23 minutes into the episode, picking up on images of fantasy, identity and death, in ways similar to 'Dance of the Dead', which follows it in the original UK transmission order.

Episode 8:
Dance of the Dead

First UK Transmission Date: Friday 17 November 1967: ATV Midlands/Grampian, 7.30 pm – 8.30 pm
Writer: Anthony Skene
Director: Don Chaffey
Credited Cast: Patrick McGoohan (The Prisoner); Mary Morris (Number Two); Duncan MacRae (The Doctor); Norma West (Girl Bo-Peep); Angelo Muscat (The Butler); Aubrey Morris (Town Crier); Bee Duffell (Psychiatrist); Camilla Hasse (Day Supervisor); Alan White (Dutton); Michael Nightingale (Night Supervisor); Patsy Smart (Night Maid); Denise Buckley (Maid); George Merritt (Postman); John Frawley (Flower Man); Lucy Griffiths (Lady in Corridor); William Lyon Brown (2nd Psychiatrist)
Known Uncredited Cast: Fenella Fielding (Loudspeaker Voice); Frank Maher (Double for Patrick McGoohan); Ray Cannon (Dead Man/Man in Photograph); Jill Hennessy (Girl in Photograph); Robert Rietty (Additional Voicework); Heulwen Vaughn-Hatcher (Double for Mary Morris); Tammy (Black Cat)

SYNOPSIS: The Prisoner undergoes a brutal interrogation, which is halted by Number Two, who advocates subtler methods. Subsequently, he receives an invitation to the Village Carnival the next day. Number Two tries to interest him in the young women of the Village, but warns him off a particular woman, whom he promptly tries to talk to, with little success; it turns out that she is his Observer, set to watch him. The Prisoner resists the Village's attempts to hypnotise him to sleep at night, and goes to the beach; when he wakes in the morning, he discovers the body of a man washed up on the shore, bearing a wallet and a transistor radio. He listens to the radio, but learns nothing useful before Number Two appropriates it. He writes a message outlining his situation, wraps it, together with a hand-drawn map and a photo of himself, in a plastic bag, attaches it to the body and sends it out to sea. After he has done this, he encounters Dutton, a former colleague who has been broken by his interrogation in the Village. That night, the Prisoner attends the carnival ball, dressed in the outfit he has been given – a tuxedo. Under cover of the celebration, he sneaks into a restricted area, where he finds the corpse and learns from Number Two that it is to be made to resemble him and given his identification, so that the outside world will believe him dead. Number Two stages a kangaroo court against the Prisoner, ending by condemning him to death; he flees through the Town Hall, pursued by Villagers, until being informed by Number Two that he cannot be killed, as he is, officially, already dead.

ANALYSIS: 'Dance of the Dead' very nearly did not see the light of day, as McGoohan did not like it and it was only the intervention of film editor John S Smith, who was so impressed with the reels that he viewed that he prepared a transmittable version of the episode from the material available, that saved it. It is the viewer's good luck that he did so, as it is one of the great surrealist triumphs of the series.

Although the episode order has been changed and changed again to the point where there probably is no 'right order', 'Dance of the Dead', which was filmed fourth and one of the first stories to be commissioned, does give explicit indications within the text of being an earlier story rather than a later one. The Prisoner, for instance, describes himself as 'new here' and claims that he has never seen a night (although he has, in 'The Chimes of Big Ben', 'Free for All', 'The Schizoid Man' and 'Checkmate'). He does not seem to realise that his house is bugged, as otherwise he would not test out the transistor radio so openly; he does not appear to understand how certain aspects of the Village work, running into the Town Hall without realising that he will be barred by a force field; and he experiments with putting a pillow over his television, suggesting that he has not come to accept its presence yet and that he isn't sure how to deal with it. Number Two explains to him about 'our traditions' as if she doesn't expect him to know anything about them; the Prisoner asks how the milk, food and so forth are delivered, when in other episodes he seems just to accept their presence.

Skene, who was involved with the series from a very early stage (he has said that McGoohan and Markstein did not even have any production notes at the time when he was asked to contribute), imbued this story with filmic and literary references, setting a precedent for subsequently-written stories' artistic self-awareness. Skene acknowledges as influences Jean Cocteau's *Orphée* (the hero lost among the dead, the two-way mirror in the Town Hall, and the nonsensical radio transmission, which in Cocteau's story was a reference to the coded messages sent to the French Resistance, hence the mention of 'wartime memoirs' towards the end of the broadcast), the works of Franz Kafka (it is worth noting that this is the only story in which the Prisoner is actually named as 'The Prisoner', in the trial sequence) and *The Devil and Daniel Webster* (in which villainous characters from American history put the protagonist on trial). J M Barrie and Lewis Carroll seem to be less overt sources. Skene also refers to the room with the filing cabinets (recalling the title sequence) in the Town Hall as being 'a Germanic horror,' which inspired director Don Chaffey to try for a German Expressionist feel for the sequence. Skene also foreshadows his own script 'Many Happy Returns' when the Colonel is name-checked as the Prisoner's superior. Orwell is again referenced heavily in the sequence where the Prisoner meets Dutton in the cave, in particular the sequence in *Nineteen Eighty-Four* in which a broken Winston Smith is set free by his tormentors to serve as a kind of lesson to potential future dissidents, knowing that he could be brought in and killed at any minute. Like Smith in *Nineteen Eighty-Four*, Dutton has given his captors everything he can, but still they want more, even though he is clearly broken: in Orwell's novel, the regime did not simply want confessions and information out of its political prisoners, but to gain absolute power over them. Similarly, within the Village, who is considered special and who isn't, who is allowed to be a rebel and who forced to conform, who is rewarded and who punished, seems to be totally arbitrary, suggesting the sadistic power games of the Oceanian regime.

The production of this story highlights early behind-the-scenes tensions, as McGoohan's refusal to film as scripted a final sequence in which the Prisoner dances with the Observer was reportedly another contribution to the growing rift with Don Chaffey, who left the series after completing work on 'The Chimes of Big Ben'. Precisely why McGoohan baulked at filming the sequence is unknown, as it was to have been a formation dance with several other Villagers, including Napoleon/the Doctor, Julius Caesar/the Town Crier, and Elizabeth I/the Maid, rather than an intimate dance between the Prisoner and the Observer, so his objection cannot have been the usual one regarding the depiction of overt sexuality in the series. It is worth noting that the Prisoner refuses to dance earlier in the story when instructed to do so by Number Two, walking backwards with his arms folded while the Observer dances (in fact, this was due to McGoohan's refusal to have the Prisoner and the Observer dance in the close manner required by the script), and so there seems to be no reason why the later dance sequence could not have been filmed in a similarly amended form. There is a slight production flaw in that the light reflecting off the sea causes the picture to darken briefly in response at a couple of points, and a minor continuity error that is, unusually, difficult to excuse even by *The Prisoner* standards (the confrontation between Number Two and the Prisoner over the radio was originally to have taken place in the bell tower and was moved to the Rotunda, but is still referred to as having taken place in the bell tower in the trial sequence); however, neither of these would have been sufficient justification to abandon the story after filming had been essentially completed. The exact reason for the initial shelving of the story thus remains a mystery.

DESERTS OF THE HEART: WOMEN AND NUMBER TWO

One of the most striking things about this episode is that it is female-dominated. Not only do we have the first female Number Two who is explicitly so for the whole story (Rachel Herbert in 'Free for All' took over at the end of the episode, and Georgina Cookson in 'Many Happy Returns' concealed her true identity throughout), but the Prisoner's Observer is female, the Day Supervisor is female, and even the cat, apparently, is female (and a spy). The workers painting the Stone Boat are supervised by a Welsh woman (rather than an 'Indian

Lady', as in the original script); and the maid, at the party, dresses as Elizabeth I, famously a powerful and masculine woman who never married.

Mary Morris, whose main previous telefantasy role had been as Professor Madeleine Dawnay in *A for Andromeda* (1961) and *The Andromeda Breakthrough* (1962), may have been responsible for the eventual choice of a Peter Pan costume for Number Two, as she had once played a version of Peter Pan as a volatile Gypsy child in a 1946 stage performance, an interpretation still viewed as controversial in the 1960s. Uniquely in the series, this Number Two acknowledges openly that the Prisoner knows what they are doing to him, and is seemingly almost amused by it (as, for instance, when he asks her 'Did I sleep well?' and she responds in the positive, acknowledging that they both know that the Village is attempting to manipulate him in his sleep). It is tempting to infer from the fact that Number Two, rather than trying to trick or break the Prisoner, is content to let his own actions bring him to the point where he accepts his role as Village inmate, that this story is a comment on male versus female approaches to problems and strategy; however, since this is present in the original script, in which Number Two is described as male, this may involve reading too much into it. Perhaps because Number Two was originally supposed to be male, and perhaps because of the boyish way in which Mary Morris plays the character, there are a few hints of a lesbian subtext here.

Whereas Skene's previously-screened story had emphasised the maternal attributes of its female lead, sexual jealousy instead forms a strong theme of this episode, with themes of infantilisation being largely limited to Number Two's comparison of the Prisoner to a fractious child. The Prisoner's maid flirts openly with him, and seems jealous of the attention he gives the cat (when he asks where it is, she says impudently 'Gone. And I didn't make it'). There appears to be jealousy between the Observer and the Supervisor over their respective relationships with the Prisoner (and this is made even clearer in a sequence cut from the final version). Number Two's treatment of the Observer in the trial scene could also be seen as an expression of jealousy, forcing the Observer to attack him so as to break up the relationship between them. Although the relationship in question is, as usual, understated and platonic, one of the effects of McGoohan's insistence that there be no overt sexual relationships within the series is to lend greater significance to understated cues of behaviour. This sequence could also, equally, be part of a larger pattern of psychological manipulation: Number Two's efforts to warn the Prisoner off the Observer early on could be seen as a kind of reverse psychology to get him interested, allowing her then to break the relationship violently when the pair become closer.

WHAT NOT TO WEAR: COSTUME AND IDENTITY

Costume and identity form another strong theme of this episode. Throughout, the story plays with the idea of people's costumes determining who they are, starting when the maid turns up at the Prisoner's door in period dress: since all the other maids are wearing these outfits, they cease to become costumes, and become uniforms. Later, in a postmodern twist, the same maid is seen dressed in a maid's uniform, which causes the viewer to question which outfit can be considered a costume and which a uniform. When the maid, the Town Crier and the Doctor don their costumes, as Elizabeth I, Julius Caesar and Napoleon respectively, they are treated as if they were genuine world leaders; they are deferred to by Number Two, and served by the Butler. Similarly, the Town Crier/Caesar addresses the Day Supervisor/Cleopatra as 'Your Majesty', implying again that in dressing as Cleopatra, the Supervisor has become the Egyptian queen in question. It is worth noting in this light that none of the Villagers wears numbers at the carnival, indicating that they have abandoned their Village identities and become their costumed characters; even the central figure is referred to not as Number Six, but as 'The Prisoner'.

The roles of the characters in the story are also symbolised by certain of their costumes. The Observer becomes Bo-Peep, symbolising innocence, but also referencing the decadent foolishness of Marie Antoinette (who was known for her fondness for dressing up as a shepherdess) and *The Manchurian Candidate* (in which, as Fairclough notes in *The Prisoner Companion*, the assassin's controller wears such a costume) and, as the Prisoner observes, suggesting an uncertain control over her 'sheep'; Number Two, as noted, dresses as Peter Pan, a traditional 'breeches role' for women. Dutton's Fool costume, which is in the same colours as his Village jumper, highlights both that his mind has now completely gone, and also that Two and the Doctor regard him as a foolish expendable. This theme gives greater significance to the maid's flippant remark about how the costumes are selected by other people for the participants: although she says 'It's a game,' it means in practice that one's identity is being chosen by someone else, and that one must conform to this externally applied identity.

The 'costume' worn by the Prisoner deserves some exploration in this light. As he has been given '[his] own suit' to wear, he interprets it as meaning that he is still himself (tying in with the symbolic connections between McGoohan and his fictional alter ego); we have certainly seen him wearing a similar suit before, in 'A, B and C'. There are, however, other interpretations. Number Two says that it indicates that he doesn't exist, as having no costume means that, symbolically, he has no identity. Equally, it sets him apart from the rest of the Villagers, whose costumes are all either fictional characters, long-dead historical figures, or archetypes such as Mandarins and flappers. Because it is an identity that he has been given, again, it could also indicate that he is allowed to 'be himself' only through the grace of others. It could further indicate that, where the other Villagers are capable of experiencing different lives through dressing in different ways (picking up on the role-reversal aspects of Carnival in general – which are also highlighted in the fact that, by implication, real alcohol is served at the event), the Prisoner himself is one-note, incapable of further identity development. Finally, it could indicate that the Prisoner himself is a historical figure (note that the story ends with him discovering that he is 'dead') and/or a fictional character/archetype: since the tuxedo is stereotypically associated with secret agents, it could mean that he is actually dressed up as John Drake.

NIGHT OF THE LIVING DEAD: CARNIVALS, DEATH AND PSYCHOANALYSIS

This brings us to the themes of death, real, symbolic and social, within the story. Carnival is also associated with the Mexican Day of the Dead (a name very close to the story's actual title), when the dead are said to rise and take part in worldly affairs; like the Day of the Dead, the Village Carnival is said to take place once a year, although, as with the elections in 'Free for All', it is doubtful how much weight to place on this. Correspondingly, none of the carnival-goers is dressed as a contemporary figure: there are no Beatles, Clint Eastwoods, Marx Brothers or Diana Dorses. The male Number Two was, according to *The Prisoner in Portmeirion*, originally supposed to have dressed as Old Father Time; other rejected ideas for his costume included Hitler and Jack the Ripper. Taken one way, the title could be seen as meaning that everyone in the story who dances is actually dead. In a cut scene in the original script, the text of the letter that the Prisoner has written and put on the corpse of the young man, accuses the Prisoner himself of having killed him, includes a photograph of the Prisoner, and urges the discoverer of the corpse to find him and bring him to justice. The dichotomous nature of the celebration can also be seen in the contrast between the cheering soundtrack and the grim faces of the Villagers when Carnival is announced.

Throughout the story, the symbolic killing of the Prisoner himself is enacted, culminating in a trial in which he is sentenced to death: but, as the dead man on the beach has taken his identity, he is already dead and, as Number Two points out, he cannot therefore be killed. We again see the black cat, with its connotations of bad luck and witchcraft; at one point, the Butler approaches the cat as the crowd moves off following the announcement of Carnival, almost as if the two are conspiring together. The Prisoner again goes underground and into a system of caves, where he meets Dutton, who is socially dead at the start of the story, and who will receive a physical termination order at the end of it. A cut scene has the Prisoner meeting two gravediggers at a freshly-filled grave in the woods, implying that someone has died, anonymously, off-screen, as well as foreshadowing the 'death' of the Prisoner (and referencing the fates of the anonymous young man and Dutton). The unshot sequence with which the story was originally to have ended featured the Prisoner acknowledging his death to the outside world, observing that death has its advantages and smashing the telex before joining in the abovementioned dance; this sequence, however, does not mention the Prisoner ripping the wiring out of the telex machine, followed by the machine starting up again despite the extensive damage, as happens in the final version, suggesting that the sequence we have is actually an alternate version of what was scripted (it is unlikely to have been filmed later as an insert, as that would involve reconstructing an elaborate set).

Perhaps surprisingly, given the association of doppelgängers with death, the theme of doubles is fairly understated within the story. The Prisoner gets yet another double in the form of the dead body that, according to Number Two, will take over his identity and make the outside world believe him dead, and the cat appears to have a double in that we see it on the bed in the Prisoner's house and then again in the Green Dome despite it not having had enough time to make it over by then. Patsy Smart, who previously appeared in 'Arrival' as the Waitress, reappears here with a completely altered identity (playing a much older woman with a different number and a different job). Elsewhere, William Lyon Brown, who appears as one of the medical staff, plays one of the undertakers in the title sequence, Bee Duffell, the other, is reprising her role from 'Checkmate' (made prior to 'Dance of the Dead'), and Robert Rietty again contributes a voice-over when he revoices the Flower Man at the end of Act One (the actor himself, John Frawley, also appears in 'Free for All' as the Man with Bass Drum). Lucy Griffiths, who plays the lady who hands the Prisoner the termination order for Dutton, also appeared in 'The Chimes of Big Ben' as a judge; there is no reason why these two should not be the same character. The fact that 'Dance of the Dead' was originally intended to precede 'The Chimes of Big Ben' in the episode order could explain why the woman does not appear to recognise the Prisoner when she meets him in the Town Hall corridor.

Themes of psychoanalysis are also present. The Doctor tries a kind of electroshock therapy to disorientate the Prisoner, which Number Two vetoes on the grounds that it will damage his mind, in a criticism reminiscent of the doubts being raised at the time about the actual validity of such methods as psychological treatment. Later, the Doctor dresses as Napoleon, recalling the stereotype of mad people dressing as the French Emperor, and he sits on a kangaroo court with a Roman Emperor (specified in the script as Julius Caesar, but also having associations with Nero, Caligula, Tiberius and so forth; in a cut line, Number Two states that the Doctor should be dressed as Jack the Ripper). Although a woman dressed as Elizabeth I is also there, the mad frequently try to associate themselves with the powerful. Finally, the notion that this is all happening in the Prisoner's mind is again referenced in his exchange with Number Two: 'So, to the outside world –' 'Which you only dream about.' This calls into question whether he is in the world and the Village is a dream or vice versa.

WAKING THE DEAD: METATEXTUALITY AND POLITICS

This story, like 'A, B and C' by the same scriptwriter, contains metatextual comments on the series itself. There is, for instance, a postmodern recognition of the televisual nature of the programme in the sequence where we see the Prisoner in his house and then, when Number Two swings her chair around, realise that she has been watching him along with us: we then, as it were, observe the observer. Number Two's later comment 'Observers of life should never get involved' could also be taken as a comment on the viewers themselves, and the way they are invited to actively become involved in the interpretation process rather than passively observe the series. The Prisoner's illicit radio also ties into this theme: he receives what sounds first like a broadcast in Russian and secondly a broadcast in English that alternates between commenting on the view, exhorting the listener to pay attention, and spouting political phrases, which is then seemingly contextualised by a female announcer explaining that this has been a typing exercise, although it is dubious whether or not we should take this at face value. As such, the broadcast resembles the text of the *Tally Ho* prop in being a series of random sentences put together. Like the programme itself, the radio broadcast is a random and surreal word jumble that could be a coded message, a political statement, or simply a lesson in typing; but it is left to the listener to decide which interpretation fits best.

There are again comments on politics and international connections. The failings of democracy are flagged up when Number Two states that the Village administration do what the majority want, invoking the common political dodge of using the concept of majority rule to ignore or overrule dissenters. At the party, Number Two comments more overtly on the limitations of democratic politics, revealing that the Village has done away with the presence of an opposition, and saying 'Even its best friends agree that democracy is remarkably inefficient.' The question of which 'side' runs the Village is again raised, as it could be taken from the events of the story that the Villagers are not members of the 'other side' trying to break the Prisoner, or of his 'own side' trying to find out why he resigned, but possibly members of his 'own side' trying to break him, through psychological mind-games, in order to have a hold on him. The Village administration do not appear to wish to divine a general reason for his resignation here, but to know the exact file, project or activity that was the last straw for the Prisoner. The fact that Elizabeth I, in the party sequence, is symbolically allied with the French and the Italians, again flags up the international connections within the Village; the script makes the connection between the three judges at the kangaroo court and the fact that French Revolutionary tribunals consisted of three judges and no jury. When the Prisoner asks Number Two 'Are you English?' she does not respond, much as the General refused to answer questions about his nationality in 'The Chimes of Big Ben', again suggesting that the Village is either multinational or beyond nationality. Finally, the sequence where the Prisoner finds the telex could be taken to imply that Number One is in fact some kind of machine or system of machines (perhaps involving the telex itself), an idea later picked up on by the independent novels based on the series.

'Dance of the Dead', although coming eighth in screening order, is one of the seminal episodes of the series, and clearly had a strong influence on the themes and imagery that turn up in later-scripted episodes.

Essay 3: The Black Queen's Pawn: Gender, Sexuality And Ethnicity In *The Prisoner*

The Prisoner is an unusual series for its time, not only in the obvious ways regarding its surrealism and innovation, but also in its treatment of women, gays and lesbians, and non-White characters, which is far more progressive than normally seen in 1960s television (it is also, incidentally, unusual for the large number of older actors that it employed). This may go some way towards explaining its continued resonance with modern audiences, where other series of the time can seem embarrassing in terms of their expressed social mores.

WOMEN

One of the particularly unusual aspects of *The Prisoner* for its time is that women frequently appear as scientists, agents and administrators, without this being seen as in any way unusual. The fact that Number Fourteen in 'A, B and C' is a scientist is casually portrayed – it is not flagged up as 'cute', or 'progressive', or as a warning against women being allowed to become scientists; she is simply treated as another professional in the Village. Although a line exists in the alternate print of 'Arrival' in which the Prisoner observes that driving a taxi is an unusual job for 'a girl', this was cut in the final version, presumably because it contradicts the fairly gender-egalitarian set-up seen elsewhere; the De Agostini publications also point out that the Prisoner's seeming misogyny in 'Dance of the Dead' (where he says 'Never trust a woman') is likely to be an attempt to conceal a possible weakness from his captors, which is supported by the sympathy and trust he displays towards female characters in many other episodes. Also, although domestic labour appears to be gendered in the Village – the men working as gardeners, the women as maids – there does not appear to be a category of 'housewives' who do unpaid domestic labour in exchange for support by a husband (although see the Analysis for the unmade story 'The Outsider'), but simply a battalion of maids who do domestic service throughout the Village in a kind of Socialist-style professionalisation of household labour. The main exception to the egalitarian set-up appears to be found in 'A Change of Mind', with its all-male Committee and all-female volunteer group (thus inherently trivialising female activities), and overtly sexist Number Two; however, this appears to be a deliberate reversal, highlighting the artificial, and, as Number Two learns, ultimately destructive, nature of repression and prejudice.

Moreover, *The Prisoner* also eschews the celebration of conventional female beauty, for the most part. The women with whom the Prisoner forms associations are often not conventionally attractive, are sometimes middle-aged, and are largely not the sort of posh women in their mid-twenties that populated the spy series of the day (including *Danger Man*). Even the Prisoner's fiancée, Janet, is somewhat outside the mould of tall, blonde, long-lashed beauties of the late '60s. While the script for 'Arrival' describes Virginia Maskell's character as young and attractive (suggesting that what the writers had in mind was a spy-series dolly-bird of this sort), she was finally portrayed by a 32-year-old actress, and, while she is attractive, it is not in a particularly conventional way. The women who fit the spy-series model best are Alison in 'The Schizoid Man' and the watchmaker's daughter in 'It's Your Funeral'; however, although both are young and pretty, neither is portrayed as remotely glamourous, and they are treated almost as children in some ways, rather than potential love-interests.

The Queen in 'Checkmate' is particularly worthy of note here. Although many series might have played for laughs the idea of a decidedly middle-aged and not conventionally attractive woman becoming enamoured of the handsome male protagonist, making the character seem ridiculous, here her love for him, although hypnotically induced, is treated sensitively: it is as if he *could* have a relationship with her, if he were not suspicious about where her sudden interest in him is coming from. Furthermore, we have an interesting gender reversal in 'Do Not Forsake Me Oh My Darling', in that it seems that the Prisoner has been remaining faithful to Janet, rather than expecting Janet to remain faithful to him, in contradiction of the conventional expectation that the woman should 'save herself' for her male lover rather than vice-versa. McGoohan himself has spoken out against what he sees as the exploitation of sexuality in advertising, calling it 'terrible dishonesty' in the Goodman interview, perhaps explaining why gender and female sexuality are treated with sensitivity in *The Prisoner*, rather than exploited to sell the programme. Gender and romance in *The Prisoner* are thus generally egalitarian in all respects.

HOMOSEXUALITY

As (real or implied) homosexuality has been connected with Cold War spying activities at least since the 1950s, it is not particularly surprising that the Prisoner features two male characters, and one female, whose sexuality can be read as ambiguous (the book *The Prisoner's Dilemma*, published in 2005, picks up on this in its implication that Number One Hundred and One is really the gay mathematician Alan Turing). What is somewhat more surprising, considering that male homosexuality was decriminalised only in 1967, is that these characters are portrayed as no worse than anyone else in the series, and might even be seen as positive.

A in 'A, B and C' and Number Twelve in 'The General' are both characters with homoerotic aspects to their portrayal. This is significant in that gay/bisexual men, or even simply 'camp' or effeminate men, are traditionally portrayed as traitors or fifth-columnists in British film, theatre and television; even a decade later, the science fiction series *Blake's 7*, which had several bisexual characters, portrayed none as anything other than sinister, manipulative and/or collusive. In *The Prisoner*, by contrast, while A may fall into the stereotype of the duplicitous homo- or bisexual man, Number Twelve is a positive character, risking his career, and possibly his life, to help the Prisoner resist and expose Speedlearn. Some critics have even argued that the Village is a metaphor for 1960s gay life in general, particularly pre-decriminalisation, with people generally giving the impression of being happy members of society, but some of them hiding a secret, which they conceal from the authorities, and meeting with each other to plot ways of escaping the repression they face. *The Prisoner* thus can be read as a metaphor for the gay experience as well as having some characters who could be read as gay.

A slightly less positive portrayal, however, is Mary Morris's interpretation of Number Two in 'Dance of the Dead', who has several lesbian aspects (the actress was, in fact, a lesbian herself). Originally supposed to have been male, this Number Two has cropped hair and a playful, boyish attitude; she dresses as Peter Pan for the costume ball, a pantomime role traditionally played by a woman in drag (making this costume more or less equivalent to a male character showing up dressed as Widow Twankey), the Prisoner addresses her as 'Mister Peter Pan', and she has a staff dominated by women. However, according to this reading, the scene in which she warns the Prisoner not to go to Carnival with the Observer (describing her as 'quite unsuitable' for the Prisoner, but offering no explanation as to why) has strong overtones of sexual jealousy and obsession, like the lesbian relationships in the 1968 film (based on a 1964 stage play) *The Killing of Sister George*: she is seen as having a controlling relationship with the Observer, and dismisses her for getting 'involved' (with connotations of sexual as well as social closeness) with the Prisoner. While the portrayal of homosexuality may be more sympathetic than in many other series, even later ones, this does have its limitations.

ETHNIC MINORITIES

The Village is distinct in having an explicitly multicultural setup, with a number of non-White performers being seen, and foreign languages regularly being heard. Non-White characters are also not negatively portrayed (or at any rate, no more negatively than White characters), in contrast to their treatment in many contemporary series (including, occasionally, *Danger Man*), nor, for the most part, subject to stereotyping: it is significant that the one proposed script that explicitly flagged up racial issues was rejected (see 'Eric Mival's Unmade Stories'). *The Prisoner* is also unusual in that none of the non-White characters is played by a White actor in make-up: while this might not seem strange to modern eyes, it is worth remembering that *The Black and White Minstrel Show* was considered a bastion of mainstream entertainment in Britain at the time, and such respectable series as *Doctor Who* and *Danger Man* saw nothing wrong with having 'blacked-up' White actors playing Black, Asian or Chinese characters (in fact, the unmade *The Prisoner* story 'Friend or Foe' was to have featured a White man passing as Black through wearing a rubber mask, which may be one of the reasons for its rejection). *The Prisoner* is thus more in line with modern thinking on the portrayal of ethnicity and multiculturalism than many of its contemporaries.

However, it is worth noting that none of the non-White characters in *The Prisoner* is particularly well-rounded, or has a major role (although the novel *The Prisoner's Dilemma* does feature a major Black character, Number Fifty Four, it was written nearly 40 years after the series). We never see a non-White Number Two or love interest (whereas non-White women were at least occasionally held up as potential love-interest figures on *Danger Man*, and non-White men were often seen in positions of authority); while some of the Prisoner's antagonists may be foreign, they are always White. The Chinese and (apparently) South American man in the Social Group sequence of 'A Change of Mind' are allegories of diametrically-opposed political systems: the Chinese man, representing Communism, accuses the Prisoner of being a 'reactionary', while the South American, representing right-wing totalitarianism, accuses him of being a 'radical,' making their ethnic origins representative of nominally different, yet ideologically similar, political systems. The closest the series comes to having a major non-White character is in 'The Schizoid Man', in which we meet the Haitian Supervisor: however, his origins are explicitly used in the script as an allegory of the story's themes of doppelgängers and soul theft, and thus could be seen as verging on the stereotypical. While the Village is visibly diverse, then, this diversity does not really extend towards giving non-White characters significant roles beyond the allegorical.

Overall, *The Prisoner* seems unusually modern in terms of its ethnic diversity, and treatment of women and alternative sexuality. However, it has to be said that it is still of its time in some ways, and is more progressive in terms of its portrayal of women than of either gay men and lesbians, or non-White characters.

Episode 9:
Checkmate

First UK Transmission Date: Friday 24 November 1967: ATV Midlands/Grampian,7.30 pm – 8.30 pm
Writer: Gerald Kelsey
Director: Don Chaffey
Credited Cast: Patrick McGoohan (The Prisoner); Ronald Radd (Rook); Patricia Jassel (1st Psychiatrist); Peter Wyngarde (Number Two); Rosalie Crutchley (Queen); George Coulouris (Man with the Stick); Angelo Muscat (The Butler); Bee Duffell (2nd Psychiatrist); Basil Dignam (Supervisor); Danvers Walker (Painter); Denis Shaw (Shopkeeper); Victor Platt (Assistant Supervisor); Shivaun O'Casey (Nurse); Geoffrey Reed (Skipper); Terence Donovan (Sailor); Joe Dunne (1st Tower Guard); Romo Gorrara (2nd Tower Guard)
Known Uncredited Cast: Frank Maher (Double for Patrick McGoohan); Fenella Fielding (Loudspeaker Voice); John O'Connor (Flower Bed Man); Jimmy Millar (Conspirator); Robert Rietty (Additional Voicework)

SYNOPSIS: At the request of the woman representing the White Queen, the Prisoner takes part in a human chess game played by an ageing aristocrat. During the game, the man representing the Rook makes an illegal move and is removed to the hospital. Making contact with the chess player, the Rook and a painter, the Prisoner explains his method for telling the prisoners from the guardians; that prisoners exhibit a subservient attitude while guardians are assertive. Number Two has the Queen hypnotised into believing

171

that she is in love with the Prisoner, and gives her a locket with a small homing device inside it; she follows the Prisoner, who is carrying out an escape plan with his accomplices, but he discovers and disarms the locket. The men contact a nearby ship, the MS *Polotska*, by radio, invade the dome and take Number Two prisoner. Reaching the *Polotska*, the Prisoner discovers that she is owned by the Village. He is returned to the Village, while the Rook convinces the others to give up the escape attempt. The Prisoner learns that the flaw in his plan was that, using his own scheme, the Rook identified the Prisoner as a guardian, and acted accordingly.

ANALYSIS: 'Checkmate' is one of the more visually iconic stories of the series, with the image of the Prisoner as a pawn on a chessboard being a particular favourite to illustrate guidebooks and articles on it, due not only to its striking appearance but also to what it suggests about the Prisoner's relationship to the Village. The episode itself generally delivers on this promise, providing insights into game-playing, psychology, leadership and romance in the Village.

Gerald Kelsey, a veteran of various police and detective series including the long-running BBC series *Dixon of Dock Green*, was one of the first writers contracted to work on *The Prisoner* – indeed, the story was one of the first few to be written -- and Markstein and McGoohan were both effusively delighted with the script. McGoohan, in fact, directed the interiors at MGM/Borehamwood (although Don Chaffey wound up with the sole directorial credit on the story, probably because the location footage was so extensive: as a rule, if an individual has directed 51% or more of a story, s/he gets sole directorial credit, no matter who else directs the remaining portion). The ending in the original script was somewhat different from that in the finished version, featuring the Prisoner boarding the MS *Polotska* with the Queen and discovering Number Two aboard rather than their confrontation taking place over the airwaves. 'Checkmate' was the third episode in production, back-to-back with 'Dance of the Dead', which wound up preceding it in the transmission order.

There are a few hints in the story that this takes place early in the Prisoner's time in the Village, as the Man with the Stick remarks 'You must be new here' and as the Prisoner is still trying

172

to sort out the captives from their guardians, rather than, as he does later, recognising the complexity of the Village set-up and concentrating on playing the system to his own advantage rather than identifying allies. The Prisoner, as in 'Dance of the Dead', also seems slightly unfamiliar with the Village; he shows no suspicion that the television is not the only surveillance device on the boat, and he drinks the chocolate that the Queen makes for him without reservation, despite his suspicions about her motivations (in contrast to other episodes in which he either shows awareness, or suspicion, that his evening drinks are being doctored).

PAWNS AND PLAYERS: THE THEME OF CHESS

The chess theme that has featured in earlier episodes comes explicitly to the fore in 'Checkmate' (much like how the theme of doubles was similarly highlighted in 'The Schizoid Man'). This episode takes the Admiral's metaphorical remark 'We're all pawns here' from 'Arrival' literally, employing chess games as a sustained metaphor for life in the Village (reminiscent not only of *Through The Looking-Glass*'s mirroring of the real world in Alice's dream of a chess game in which she plays the White Queen's Pawn, but also of Middleton's Jacobean political allegory *A Game at Chesse*). Throughout, the chess game and the lives of the Villagers are conflated: the Queen (Number Eight) and the Rook (Number Fifty Eight) are referred to by their chess piece names in the story as well as in the credits, and when Number Two and the Supervisor discuss what they see on the screen, it's hard to say whether they are commenting on the game (the threatened pawn could be protected by the queen, but it's more likely that the pawn will be sacrificed instead) or the Prisoner's relationship with the Queen (the Prisoner is putting himself in danger, and, although the woman seems friendly, he cannot count on her support). The Rook's castellated icon ironically foreshadows his being taken to the Village hospital (housed in the castle-shaped Castel Deudraeth). Carrazé and Oswald, in *The Prisoner: a Televisionary Masterpiece*, observe that the stark division between black and white on the chessboard also reflects the Prisoner's own Manichean view of the Village as divided into prisoners and warders (although one might add that the fact that the standards they carry are mixed black and white suggests a deeper ambiguity). The chess game thus serves as a symbol of the events of the episode.

There is also a conflation of the game and life in the Village. The chess players' orders are sometimes played out over the tannoy like Village announcements (when the white-haired player calls for a substitute, the transmitted version – though not the original script – has the call going out over the Village loudspeakers, symbolically connecting the players with the Village administration), and when, at the end, Number Two says that the Villagers will all be 'back on the chessboard' in the morning, there is a deliberate ambiguity as to whether he means they will be literally playing human chess, or simply that they will be returning to their usual roles in the Village. The Butler mirrors the chess games on a small board, obviously to allow players to check moves, but also as a symbolic indication that the Village is mirrored in the chess game. The Prisoner expresses his rebellion in this episode by announcing that he is not a chessman. This then, of course, begs the question: if the chess game represents human life, who do the players represent? Gods? Social forces? The Village administration? Number One?

Although this question is not answered in the broad sense, in the narrow sense we do see a number of characters who play with, and manipulate, other people without the others being aware of their actions, much like chess players. As well as Number Two, the Prisoner himself engages in manipulative activities: while the Queen offers to let the Prisoner be her pawn (and indeed the working title of the story was 'The Queen's Pawn'), if anything she eventually becomes his pawn. The Prisoner's escape plan is formulated as a chess game, with the conspirators using chess moves as a code; the signal for escape, for instance, is 'Rook to queen's pawn [i.e., the Prisoner], check.' Although the Prisoner might not see himself as a chessman (witness his exchange with the Queen: 'It's impossible to escape.' 'For chessmen, not for me'), his actions, and choice of code, reveal that this is exactly what he is.

ALL PAWNS? PLANS, PEOPLE AND PSYCHOLOGY

The Prisoner's plan, as well as falling into the chess imagery permeating the story, is based on a simple psychological idea – too simple, as it turns out. Following on, in narrative terms, from his assertion in 'Free for All' that he intends to find out who are the prisoners and who are the warders, he has concluded that the best way to do this is through observing people's behaviour: the warders, or guardians, are unconsciously arrogant, and the prisoners are unconsciously subservient. However, the plan fails because he does not take into account the complexity inherent in any situation such as this: that, for instance, there are more dominant prisoners (such as himself) and more subservient warders (for example Number Two in 'A, B and C'), meaning that the Rook, applying the Prisoner's own formula to the situation, decides that the Prisoner must himself be a warder. Similarly, the plan fails to consider nuances and shifts in social interaction: that a warder might act subservient to fool people (as Number Fifty Eight does in 'Free for All'), or that a prisoner might, like the Rook, be willing to betray his or her collaborators to the authorities. The Butler may appear to be in control of the chess pieces as he moves them about the board, but in reality he has no more independence than the players. As both the Prisoner and the Rook learn, it can be impossible to tell the prisoners from the warders – and indeed, since the Prisoner has inadvertently managed to get a number of anti-authoritarian elements into one group and reveal their identities to Number Two, he could be seen as acting here more on the side of the Village administration than of the resistance.

The story also raises questions about individuality and authority. At the start, the Man with the Stick (played by George Coulouris, who also appeared in the final episode of *Danger Man*) keeps walking when all the other Villagers, bar the Prisoner, have frozen at the sound of Rover. This could indicate that he is an individualist like the Prisoner, but could also indicate that he has high enough social status that he considers himself above the Village rules; not only is he a chess player rather than a chess piece, but the dialogue suggests that he is a former count (Kelsey based the human-chess scene at least partly on a story he had heard about a castle in Germany where the baron in question used his retainers as chess pieces in gigantic games, an activity subsequently associated with the Man with the Stick).

The Prisoner himself is, it comes out in the story, something of a natural leader as well. 'Checkmate' thus raises the question: how much of individualism is down to natural inclination, and how much is due to, through accident of birth, the opportunities one has to express it? This is also tacitly highlighted in the chess metaphor: while the pawns are all the same, the pieces further back are allowed a degree of individual identity (as queens, bishops, knights etc). Roger Langley points out that the Prisoner's position in Village society is analogous to the status of the King, who can be captured but never taken, highlighting at a stroke the Prisoner's social power, and the fact that he cannot escape the metaphorical chess game being enacted in the Village. The Prisoner's plan itself is based on the idea that people further up the social ladder have the freedom to display more ego in public; while in this case they are egotistical on behalf of the collective, rather than for themselves, the ultimate fate of the Prisoner's plan suggests that it is not merely that some are more inclined to resist than others, but that some, through opportunity, natural charisma, or social position, have more freedom to do so.

This is also picked up on in the case of the Rook. His explanation of how he wound up in the Village in the first place – that he decided to provide information about a defence system he had invented to both sides in the Cold War – suggests that, as the defence system promptly wound up being stolen due to a bureaucratic error anyway, it was not so much for inventing the defence system, nor for trying to give it to the other side, that he was imprisoned, but for taking the initiative rather than handing it over to his masters to do with what they thought best. Similarly, in the chess game, it is not the fact that he has made an illegal move that concerns the Village authorities so much as the fact that he moved without orders, and his placing the king in check through his move (thereby allowing his player to win the game) does not mitigate the severity of his treatment.

Psychology and its failings come to the fore elsewhere in the story than simply the Prisoner's own doomed forays in this direction. Once again the series reflects '60s concerns about interventionist psychology in the way that the Rook's individualism is spoken of as a treatable condition, with Two suggesting to him that he should inform someone straight away if he has another 'attack of egotism,' and his subsequent subjection to a kind of crude therapy that resembles both Pavlov's experiments and the anticipatory-avoidance experiments of R L Solomon and L C Wynne in 1953. However, the First Psychiatrist's assertion that the Rook will show no more signs of initiative after his treatment proves to be as false as the Prisoner's own simplistic views of human psychology, as the Rook clearly spends a lot of time thinking through and second-guessing the Prisoner, and then acts on his conclusions without prompting or consultation. His treatment seems not to have dampened his initiative, but merely to have increased his distrust of authority. The Village itself is also cast as a kind of gigantic therapy system, with the Man with the Stick asserting that the chess game is supposed to be a therapeutic means whereby the desire to control other people is satisfied. The uses and abuses of psychology are thus probed, not merely within a clinical setting, but in the wider context.

Also interesting is the word-association therapy scene, in which the use of a Jungian technique supposed to probe the unconscious reveals a few interesting details about the Prisoner himself. We learn that he likes sports and used to have a favourite pub, and he makes quick and complex puns on the subject of 'love', associating it with 'game' (referring on one level to tennis, but also to the idea of his relationships with women in general being psychological games, as well as to the specific fact that a woman is then and there playing mind games with him). He also, seemingly unconsciously, turns the tables on his interrogator and starts playing mental games with her. His association of the phrase '... for all' with the word 'free' not only recalls the episode of this title, but perhaps also how the phrase 'free for all' emerged, seemingly as a kind of word association itself, out of one of his surreal 'political speeches' in that episode. Death is once again associated with escape in this episode, highlighting the possibility that the Prisoner might be in some kind of afterlife.

We also see numerous references to childhood and infantile behaviour. The Rook's conditioning has an element of extreme pedagogy to it, as children gradually learn to participate in society through a combination of positive and negative stimuli. We again see adults playing children's games on the beach (as there are no fewer than three similar shots of two old men playing with boats and sandcastles, and another similar shot in 'The Chimes of Big Ben', it seems that the production team simply took a certain amount of footage of adults playing on the beach for use as establishing shots). The same doll that appears in 'Arrival' holding the 'Welcome' sign is here seen being placed in a window together with a brief musical reference to 'Arrival' in the score, referencing both childishness and (as it is a Victorian toy) technology and timelessness. We also hear 'Boys and Girls, Come out to Play' in the hospital again, and the Queen sings 'Pop goes the Weasel' as she prepares the hot chocolate – an action that seems almost metatextual, in that the song has appeared on the soundtrack earlier (albeit not in a scene with her in), and so it almost suggests that the Queen is actually aware that this is a piece of incidental music used in the episode (in other words, taking a piece of non-diagetic music and making it diagetic, a neat subversive trick reminiscent of French new wave). In that same scene, the Queen appears to have regressed to a kind of playful childishness, talking in an infantile way as she prepares the chocolate (traditionally a children's drink), bursting into tears when the Prisoner shows anger and cheering up instantly, like a child, when he relents. Childhood and childishness thus come in at key points in the action.

ANYONE CAN PLAY: THE CHARACTERS AND THE VILLAGE

The character of the Queen is ironically named, as she more than anyone is a pawn of the Village's activities, but the name also picks up on the theme of queens in 'Dance of the Dead' (featuring not only Elizabeth I and Cleopatra, but a female cat – a 'queen' in cat breeders' terms). She is also Number Eight, flagging up the fact that eights and twelves tend to crop up a lot among the people with whom the Prisoner associates (although it may be reading too much into it to point out that Alison in 'The Schizoid Man' is Number Twenty-Four, and thus has a number divisible by eight, six and twelve). While the script calls for the Queen to be young and attractive, instead the role was given to Rosalie Crutchley, who was 46; as well as reflecting the series' penchant for love-interest figures who are not conventionally attractive, this decision makes the Prisoner's relenting at the sight of her tears perhaps more understandable, as an older woman might seem less likely to attempt to manipulate him through judicious displays of emotion than a young, conventionally attractive woman like the maid in 'Arrival'. Her misguided feelings for the Prisoner – which appear to be at least partly there from the outset, since she invites him to join the chess game, and follows him around, before she is brainwashed at the Hospital – are treated sensitively within the story rather than played for laughs or as the desperate fantasies of an unattractive woman. Poignantly, we never find out what happens to her at the end of the story, leaving her situation unresolved.

The scene in which the Prisoner steals a taxi and the Queen, consumed by her desire not to let him get away, steals another and follows him, also suggests interesting things about love and affection. Earlier in the story it is implied that love is destructive, when the Village psychiatrists state that the Queen would betray the Prisoner if she thought it would protect him; and although the stealing of the taxi might seem to suggest that her love has driven her to acts of criminality, what we see is that, instead, her love liberates her, allows her to disobey the system and associate with notorious dissenters. Although her love is a cynical, artificially-enhanced condition, even as such it has positive effects for the Queen.

The Village also once again appears to be fairly egalitarian, with both the psychiatrists being female, and this not being directly remarked upon or deemed significant in any way within the text (although the fact that the original script specified that the First Psychiatrist should be male, and that the psychiatrist doing the word association therapy should be female, means that gender was to some extent on the writer's mind). Number Nineteen, the Second Psychiatrist, is played by Bee Duffell, who also played a psychiatrist in 'Dance of the Dead', providing a rare bit of continuity (and there is another such case elsewhere in 'Checkmate', in that the shopkeeper from 'Arrival' reappears).

Number Two in this episode is played by Peter Wyngarde, who had not by this point appeared in the role for which he is best remembered: the camp, flamboyant crime-solving writer Jason King of the series *Department S* and *Jason King*. Although he does not yet sport his trademark moustache, Wyngarde's Number Two is well-turned-out and exuding a sinister campness, as well as sporting eye-liner. He practices karate and evidently takes it quite seriously, as an art form rather than simply a type of self-defence.

The Village set-up within the story explores its members' apparent love affair with chess: it is here treated as a significant sport, with Villagers discussing it as if it were football; the *Tally Ho* running chess problems; multiple games being carried out; and formal substitutes being designated, as for sports teams. The newspaper chess problem that we see is in a column that is slightly different in colour from the rest of the paper, with accompanying text that makes sense and relates to the problem. The numbers written on the Prisoner's chess problem appear to be random, and, when he sees Number Sixty-Two, he crosses off a penned-in '8', in another odd action (although Six and Two do add up to eight); either he is playing some private game or, more likely, he is keeping a deliberately complicated record of who he has approached recently. The chess poles are two-coloured, one side having the black half on the right and the other the reverse, foreshadowing the two-coloured carnival masks of 'Fall Out' as well as reflecting the shifting allegiances of 'Checkmate'.

The changes in the Village in this episode are fairly superficial. The curfew music is now some kind of light jazz (as opposed to the classical guitar heard in 'The Chimes of Big Ben'); the lighthouse is briefly seen in the background. The original script has the Prisoner paying for his air mattresses with banknotes, which would have been the only time this sort of payment was used in the Village, but in the filmed story we do not see how he pays. We again see a brief set of doubles, in that the white-haired old man who plays the chess game against the Man with the Stick appears in the very same game, even wearing the same clothes, representing a bishop. The Control Room screen at one point features a lava-lamp screensaver, like that seen in Number Two's office.

This episode features one or two minor errors. In the opening sequence, for instance, we briefly see the chess lawn, with no game on it, but when we see it again shortly thereafter, the game has already been set up (although it has to be said that an instantaneously-appearing chess game would not be the strangest thing that we have seen so far in the Village). More seriously, the

First Psychiatrist evidently expects the Queen to go swimming with the transistor/locket on, as she remarks that it could have fallen off in the water – but she fails to recognise that immersing electronics in water (particularly exposed wires, as in the transistor device that we see) would short them out anyway. On a less negative note, it is worth listening out for Robert Rietty in a number of voice-over roles, among other things redubbing the pawn who says he enjoys a game of chess as well as playing a number of announcer voices and the *Polotska* radio operator.

'Checkmate' does for chess what 'The Schizoid Man' did for doubles and 'A Change of Mind' will do for interventionist psychology, picking up on a running theme or metaphor and turning it into an interesting and clever episode, which would also be the last one to focus on an escape attempt until the series' final story, 'Fall Out'.

Episode 10:
Hammer into Anvil

First UK Transmission Date: Friday 1 December 1967: ATV Midlands/Grampian,7.30 pm – 8.30 pm
Writer: Roger Woddis
Director: Pat Jackson
Credited Cast: Patrick Patrick McGoohan (The Prisoner); Patrick Cargill (Number Two); Victor Maddern (Band Master); Basil Hoskins (Number Fourteen); Norman Scace (Psychiatric Director); Derek Aylward (New Supervisor); Angelo Muscat (The Butler); Hilary Dwyer (Number Seventy-Three); Arthur Gross (Control Room Operator); Peter Swanwick (Supervisor); Victor Woolf (Shop Assistant); Michael Segal (Laboratory Technician); Margo Andrew (Shop Kiosk Girl); Susan Sheers (Female Code Expert); Jackie Cooper (1st Guardian); Fred Haggerty (2nd Guardian); Eddie Powell (3rd Guardian); George Leach (4th Guardian)
Known Uncredited Cast: Frank Maher (Double for Patrick McGoohan); Fenella Fielding (Loudspeaker Voice); Robert Rietty (Additional Voicework)

SYNOPSIS: In the hospital, Number Two interrogates a woman who has attempted suicide; overcome, she throws herself out the window, killing herself. The Prisoner, who hears the woman's scream but is unable to save her, vows retribution against Number Two, who is contemptuous of the Prisoner but also evidences a deep fear of his superiors. Subsequently, the Prisoner begins to perform some strange, but seemingly purposeful, acts, such as listening to multiple identical recordings of 'L'Arlesienne', requesting that a message be read out on community radio to a deceased Villager, placing a cryptic personal advert in the *Tally Ho*, and sending a numerically-coded message via carrier pigeon, convincing Number Two and his henchman, Number Fourteen, that the Prisoner is an agent reporting on Number Two's behaviour and activities. As the Prisoner's campaign escalates, Number Two becomes increasingly paranoid, beginning to suspect his own subordinates of acting against him as well. Deserted by his supporters and driven half-mad by his own suspicious mind, Number Two is confronted by the Prisoner, who forces him to telephone his superiors and resign.

ANALYSIS: 'Hammer into Anvil' is an enjoyable story, which provides plenty of interest as we see the drama unfold from both the Prisoner's and Number Two's perspectives. As *The Prisoner* episodes go, however, it is not particularly deep, being more or less a straight allegory of surveillance-state paranoia, albeit with some clever literary referencing to enliven it.

The focus of the episode is Patrick Cargill's Number Two, who is an overtly sadistic bully, fundamentally insecure, and eventually given more than a taste of his own medicine. Although writer Chris Gregory suggests that his knowledge of Goethe and authoritarianism implies that he is an ex-Nazi, the character gives no evidence of being anything other than English (the Prisoner, after all, also recognises the Goethe quote), and thus firmly in the tradition of the English public-school sadist, as seen in, among many others, Thomas Hughes, and Willans' and Searle's *Molesworth* novels. At the end of the story, Number Two reverts to childhood, sobbing and clinging to the penny-farthing (possibly symbolising an unwillingness to let go of the past), and curling up in the foetal position to report himself. Number Two is fundamentally a well-read but puerile Village chairman who reverts to infantile behaviour when routed.

Fairclough suggests that the Goethe quotation, rather than being indicative of Number Two's politics, highlights the literary antecedents of the story. Like the titular character in Goethe's *Faust*, from which the quote derives, Number Two is an arrogant man whose own actions cause him to be brought low and lose his soul (although scriptwriter Roger Woddis, who was better known as a poet, critic, satirist and puzzle compiler, leaves out the redemptive finale of Goethe's version, favouring instead Marlowe's more downbeat ending). It is also worth noting that the central conflict of the plot is in fact based on Number Two making a common misinterpretation of the Goethe quotation, when he says that the Prisoner is the anvil and that he will 'hammer him': George Orwell notes in *Politics and the English Language* that 'in real life it is always the anvil that breaks the hammer,' and, indeed, this is the case in 'Hammer into Anvil'. Number Two also, as Fairclough notes, resembles Don Quixote, who is referenced in a significant quotation from Cervantes' novel of that name running through the story, rendered in the script as 'Hay mas mal en el aldea que se suena' and in the recorded version as 'Y mas mal in aldea que se suena' and translated as 'There is more harm in the Village than is dreamed of'. Number Two is thus likened to Quixote, famed for his adventures tilting at windmills under the impression that they are fairy-tale giants, with Number Fourteen in the Sancho Panza role of the faithful henchman who sees through his master's delusions. However, as Gregory notes, the Prisoner himself may equally be the subject of the Faustian metaphor, having lost his soul through his embracing of the Village's methods to destroy Number Two; his quest to remain an individual against pressure from the Village to conform also resembles Quixote's quest to uphold chivalry in an unchivalrous world. The most important literary parallel, however, is, as Fairclough notes, the one not directly referenced in the text: Shakespeare's *Othello*, with the Prisoner as a vengeful Iago and Number Two as an Othello figure (who even, like Othello, kills an innocent woman at a crucial point in the story). The literary quotations are, therefore, less about political allegories, and more hints as to the origins of the episode.

Classical music is also extensively used to good effect. Bizet's 'L'Arlesienne', as well as featuring explicitly twice within the story, is constantly referenced in the incidental music, reflecting Number Two's increasing paranoia. 'L'Arlesienne' is a theme from a play of the same name by Alphonse Daubet, which focused around a girl who influenced the action of the story despite never appearing on stage (clearly paralleled by Number Seventy Three in 'Hammer into Anvil', who dies early on but affects all the subsequent events of the story). The shopkeeper makes another reference to France, when he says that it takes a Frenchman to play Bizet well. The other significant use of classical music occurs when the Prisoner's fight with Number Fourteen takes place against a backdrop of peaceful Vivaldi, foreshadowing the infamous sequence in the 1971 film *A Clockwork Orange* in which a violent rape and assault are committed to the sound of 'Singin' in the Rain'.

A QUIET MIND: VILLAGE SOCIETY UNDER 'HAMMER INTO ANVIL''S NUMBER TWO.

Number Two's paranoia, desire for control and insecurity are reflected throughout the Village. Number Two's assistant, Number Fourteen, is similarly a fundamentally insecure bully; the people of the Village are now acting like people in a fascist state, reporting each other one minute and defensively protesting their innocence the next, as even the act of reporting someone else's behaviour to the authorities raises the question of why they should do so. The enlarged and curved red telephone from 'A, B and C' reappears, symbolising, in a German-expressionist-inspired way, that, despite his bluster, this Number Two is every bit as neurotic and frightened of authority as the Number Two in the earlier story.

Parallels are drawn with the Nazis, and also with the Chinese and Soviet Communist regimes (in which people reported each other to the authorities simply because it was assumed that those who didn't report their neighbours had something to hide themselves), and, on the other side of the political spectrum, the anti-Communist witch-hunts in 1950s America; the 21st Century viewer will also notice parallels with the neoconservative philosophy of controlling the populace through fear of a nebulous enemy. It is significant that, although the talk in the Village is continually of 'sides', it is never made clear who the other 'side' are, or whether the enemy is internal or external, or both. However, in *The Prisoner*, a fifth-column element is able to use the inherent paranoia of the regime against it. The timelessness of the system portrayed here thus suggests that such situations are unfortunately common – but the fate of Number Two also, more optimistically, suggests that they are vulnerable to their own methods.

Perhaps because of the banality of totalitarian regimes, the Village's set-up seems unusually conventional this episode, with bomb disposal squads, networks of informers, bunkers and beam weapons being deployed; Rover does not appear. The graveyard on the beach has now moved to a memorial garden, and the shopkeeper seen in previous episodes has been replaced (it is tempting to speculate that this is the result of the events of 'Checkmate', but, given the Village's surreal nature, this is by no means certain) and the currency is simply 'units' (rather than 'credit units' or 'work units'), deployed again on a kind of ration card. The *Tally Ho*, for once, displays a genuine article that relates to its headline ('No. 2 calls for increased vigilance') as opposed to random phrases. We also find out that there are at least two Village publications besides the *Tally Ho* (which has transformed itself into a folded, newspaper-style publication for this episode, as opposed to a broadsheet instantly printed by a mobile roller device as it is in other stories): *Village Journal* (which looks a bit like *Paris Match* and displays a photo of Tony Anholt, who would go on to find fame in *The Protectors*, *Space: 1999* and *Howard's Way*) and the slightly funky-and-alternative-looking *Village Weekly*.

Another significant point is that the Prisoner has now not only figured out how the Village works, but is also able to use it to his own advantage. He is clearly aware of the extent of surveillance; his tricks with the records in the Village shop, talking to Number Fourteen in a whisper in the café, and his behaviour in his house would not make sense from a strategic point of view if he didn't think that he was being perpetually monitored, even in his own home. When Number Fourteen confronts him, he quotes a Village slogan – 'Music makes a quiet mind' – back at him, further indicating that he has appropriated the Village's culture for his own use. He knows at least one code in common usage in the Village. More chillingly, however, this suggests that the Prisoner has become complicit with the Village's ethos: he uses its own methods to break down Number Two and, although he doesn't kill his opponent, takes an arguably sadistic pleasure in breaking him down, echoing the way in which he bullied the Rook in 'Checkmate', a story in which the Prisoner also successfully impersonated a Village guardian. The Prisoner actually refers to himself as Number Six, for only the second time in the series thus far, in his final confrontation with Number Two. However one justifies it, the Prisoner's use of Village methods appears to bring him closer to the Village mentality that he has hitherto been fighting to avoid.

'Hammer into Anvil' also features two unusual cases of doubles. First, Patrick Cargill returns, having previously played the similarly authoritative and arrogant Thorpe in 'Many Happy Returns', but the Prisoner clearly does not recognise him or call him by name, as he would if he identified him as Thorpe. It is possible to put this down to a memory wipe, as in 'The Schizoid Man', or to the generally surreal and dreamlike nature of the Village. Secondly, the Prisoner submits a message to be read out on radio ostensibly from Number One Hundred and Thirteen, who, it transpires, is dead; it is perhaps surprising that no new Number One Hundred and Thirteen has come in to replace her (although the fact that numbers are continually replaced might explain why the Supervisor sees nothing peculiar in the attribution of the message to a recently-deceased Villager; note that the number was previously taken by Harold Berens' character in 'Free for All'). There are also more hints of a connection to *Danger Man*, in that the listening booth in the Village shop is similar to those seen in the *Danger Man* episode 'Koroshi', and in that the Prisoner convinces Number Two that he is an agent with the codename D6 (for 'Drake' and 'Six', perhaps?). The way it is played leaves the possibility open that he might, in fact, be an agent working for the authorities (either unwittingly, or else playing a far more complicated game than anyone in the Village realises) – and, as in 'Checkmate', his actions, whatever their motivation, do aid the Village in getting rid of a weak leader.

Certain of the series' repeated motifs also recur in this episode. When Number Two is attempting to intimidate the Prisoner by waving a sword blade in front of his face, he ends by pressing its point into his forehead at the 'third eye' position featured in 'The Schizoid Man' and 'Free for All'. An orange-and-silver lava lamp is seen both in the Doctor's office and in the surveillance laboratory; the Village flag features the same penny-farthing motif as its badges. There is also another nod at the viewer's own interpretations in that one of the main messages of the story is that it is dangerous to read too much into things, particularly as it is easy to forget, as Number Two does, that our observations are necessarily influenced by our own prejudices and fears. We also see a new addition to Village culture: Kosho, arguably the most ludicrous-looking sport in the world outside of dwarf-tossing, which was apparently invented by McGoohan and adapted by stuntman and ex-paratrooper Frank Maher; as it was initially introduced in 'It's Your Funeral' (which wound up, in the way of *The Prisoner* stories, being screened after 'Hammer into Anvil'), we shall discuss it in more detail in our analysis of that story.

There were some key changes between the original script and the filmed version. The suicide of Number Seventy Three (the only character to have a seven in her number in the series) was originally to have been more dramatic, involving her smashing through a glass window rather than simply jumping to her death. Although the script had the Prisoner disguising his voice when he rings the Director of Psychiatrics, the filmed version does not, which actually makes for a better scene as, first, the Director does not recognise the Prisoner anyway, and, secondly, Number Two's use of the oscilloscope to prove that the voice is the Prisoner's makes it seem as if he is so paranoid as to not trust his own ears, or the word of others, without technological backup. The conversation between the Prisoner and Number Fourteen in the café was extensively rewritten; the original had the Prisoner, rather than talking about going for a walk on the beach, asking about the food: 'What's good? Sausages? Or did you try the fish-cakes?', and the only line common to both versions is 'Don't look now, but the waiter is watching you,' which led to a further change to the subsequent scene, when Number Fourteen explains to a disbelieving Number Two what they were talking about (i.e. the menu in the original script, walking on the beach in the final version). The intention in both versions – innocent conversation deliberately played so as to look suspicious – is, however, the same. One of the technicians in the sequence in which Number Two tries to figure out who the Prisoner is signalling to on the beach was specified as being an 'American girl' in the script, but became an English man in the final version, losing a brief moment of internationalisation and gender-egalitarianism in the Village. The final scenes were also somewhat changed; originally, a new Number Two was to have walked in to the office right after Cargill's character reports himself, greeting the Prisoner with 'Be seeing you,' which was probably left out because it didn't contribute enough to the story to justify the expense of hiring another speaking actor. The Prisoner was also originally to have visited Number Seventy Three's grave at the end, which was removed probably because it would imply too much of an emotional connection between the two characters, to the point where his feelings for her could have been interpreted as romantic.

There are also a number of errors and interesting things to watch out for in 'Hammer into Anvil'. In the scene in which the Prisoner approaches the Village shop, the banners with the music-related slogans are briefly swapped about between the studio and the location footage, and the message carried by the pigeon (which on the original insert shots read 'ZYPRSTVHIJPNRS', rather than a sequence of numbers), is written in thick black ink when it first appears, but in light blue ink when Number Two reads it. The newsstand where the Prisoner takes out his personal advert is selling contemporary 1960s postcards of Portmeirion. The actor who played the bandmaster, Victor Maddern, was an established character actor who accepted the brief role simply because he wanted to work on McGoohan's new series; he is doubled by a stand-in on location. Finally, in a lovely visual metaphor, the end of the story sees the Prisoner looming large in the foreground over a diminished Number Two.

'Hammer into Anvil', although it does give the viewer pause for thought about the nature of the central character, is sufficiently straightforward that there is little to analyse in its content which has not already been covered in other publications. The story, while not without merit, lacks the depth of most of its predecessors, a trend that will continue in the next episode.

Episode 11:
It's Your Funeral

First UK Transmission Date: Friday 8 December 1967: ATV Midlands/Grampian,7.30 pm – 8.30 pm
Writer: Michael Cramoy
Director: Robert Asher
Credited Cast: Patrick McGoohan (The Prisoner); Derren Nesbitt (New Number Two) Annette Andre (Watchmaker's Daughter); Mark Eden (Number One Hundred); Andre Van Gyseghem (Retiring Number Two); Martin Miller (Watchmaker); Wanda Ventham (Computer Attendant); Angelo Muscat (The Butler); Mark Burns (Number Two's Assistant); Peter Swanwick (Supervisor); Charles Lloyd Pack (Artist); Grace Arnold (Number Thirty Six); Arthur White (Stall-Holder); Michael Bilton (M C Councillor); Gerry Crampton (Kosho Opponent)
Known Uncredited Cast: Frank Maher (Double for Patrick McGoohan); Brian Axworthy (Waterskiing Double for Patrick McGoohan); Fenella Fielding (Loudspeaker Voice); Robert Rietty (Additional Voicework)

SYNOPSIS: A young woman, daughter of the Village watchmaker, enters the Prisoner's cottage, claiming that there is to be an assassination in the Village, but that no-one will believe her because she is a 'Jammer', one of a number of Villagers who lie persistently about plots and escape attempts so that plans for genuine attempts, should the authorities learn of them, will not be believed. It transpires that this has been arranged by the acting Number Two, who wishes the Prisoner to learn of the plot. He has his subordinate, Number One Hundred, replace the Prisoner's watch with a non-functioning duplicate, so that the Prisoner will go to the girl's father's shop. Once there, he learns that the old man has some explosives and a remote-control device; investigating further, he learns that the plan is to place explosives in a duplicate of the Village Great Seal of Office, which will be worn by the outgoing Number Two at a forthcoming Appreciation Ceremony, following which he will retire. The old Number Two having returned to the Village, the Prisoner attempts to make him aware of the plans, but the acting Number Two has faked a recording to suggest that the Prisoner is continually reporting assassination plots against Number Two where there are none. However, Number Two is made suspicious by the peculiar behaviour of his assistant (who knows about the plot but has misgivings). On the day of the ceremony, the Prisoner finds the old man about to carry out the plot and gets the transmitter away from him; he fights Number One Hundred until the ceremony is complete and the new Number Two is wearing the Seal of Office. The old Number Two is thus able to escape unmolested in a helicopter.

ANALYSIS: Chris Gregory's review of 'It's Your Funeral', the eighth story made in the series, in *Be Seeing You*, sums it up by calling it 'a highly conventional piece of television series "fodder", exploiting typical dramatic conventions by using fast cutting and dramatic music to build up to a "surprise" ending.' This description is, perhaps unfortunately, a rather apt one; like 'Hammer into Anvil', 'It's Your Funeral' can be entertaining to watch, but is, on the whole, not one of the deeper or more mind-blowing stories of the series.

FUNERAL GAMES:
THINGS THAT DON'T MAKE SENSE ABOUT THIS STORY

Michael Cramoy, the writer of 'It's Your Funeral', was – in contrast to Roger Woddis, writer of 'Hammer into Anvil' – well-versed in adventure shows for radio and television, both in the United States and in Britain; in particular, he had written for a number of ITC thrillers including *The Saint* and *The Baron*. He had been given a brief to write a story that made as much use of available stock location footage as possible (a technique most apparent in the sequence where a red blip representing the Prisoner is tracked across the Village; the intercut scenes of McGoohan, partly made up of footage shot during the filming of 'Arrival', show him wearing his dark suit in long shots, but his usual black jacket, turtleneck and beige trousers in the close-ups), about a political assassination that wasn't all that it appeared to be. As Fairclough notes, the result has predictably strong influences from *The Manchurian Candidate*, featuring as it does a parent/child team caught up in an assassination attempt, a plot to destabilise a society so that the plotters in question can gain power, and a protagonist who is manipulated into becoming part of a political assassination. At one point the script describes the Prisoner as sweeping the rooftops with his eyes like 'a presidential secret serviceman looking for potential snipers.' In the original script, the Watchmaker had been brainwashed, as with the assassin in *The Manchurian Candidate*, but this was largely cut from the final episode, with the term 'brainwashing' being used in a way that could refer to ordinary persuasion techniques as much as actual mind control. The resulting story is almost an inversion of 'Hammer into Anvil'; where the latter story has a solid plot but is thin on material for analysis, this one has interesting ideas, but a weak plot.

The concepts of the story contain a number of problematic elements. The plot revolves around the idea of 'Jammers,' which in and of itself is clever: if people who lie about everything do reveal the truth about a genuine escape attempt, they will not be believed by the authorities, thus keeping the plan safe. This also fits with the previous episode, which focused on a network of informers (as opposed to resistors), whose structure the Prisoner exploits with what can be described as 'jamming' activities. However, the idea does not really fit with the Village set-up we have seen before: in previous episodes, such as 'Checkmate', we have learned that those who exhibit even fairly minor rebellious behaviour are routinely carted off for mind alteration, so it seems unlikely that the Village would allow this sort of activity to continue (unless it is all a ploy on the part of the establishment, which does not seem to be the case here). This may be explained by the idea that the Village changes from story to story, with its rules as well as its names for things, nature and organisation transforming; the fact that the Prisoner seems to have a solidly established morning routine here does not contradict this, as we do not know if this routine is the same as in earlier stories, and the solidity thus may be an illusion.

It is harder, however, to justify the plot revolving around 'Plan Division Q'. The idea that, for some vaguely specified reason (possibly because they know too much), senior officials at the Village are killed when they hit retirement age poses problems at the outset, as, leaving aside the issue of where 'Free for All' would fit into this scenario, it begs the question of how the Village ever manages to recruit anyone for the job. Even if the killings were all done in ways that made them appear to be accidents, eventually people would begin to notice the trend – particularly if, as here, they involved such conspicuous events as explosions. The young Number Two is fully aware of the situation, making his eagerness to take the top job somewhat peculiar; although the Prisoner's remark at the Old People's Home suggests that the rank and file, not simply Number Twos, are disposed of in this manner. The scenario also begs the question of why, once he discovers the fake seal with the explosive centre in the Watchmaker's shop, the Prisoner does not just steal the apparatus and leave the plotters without any means of carrying out their ends.

The reason why the outgoing Number Two is to be assassinated is also obscure. The implication is that the Village authorities want a way of justifying retribution against the Jammers, possibly because if Villagers are punished in retaliation for a Jammer-planned assassination, the Villagers will turn against the practice and use social pressure to force the Jammers to conform (see the next screened episode, 'A Change of Mind'). There are visible parallels here with the assassination of top Nazi official Reinhard Heydrich in Prague in 1942, after which the Nazi regime executed all males over 16 in two Czech villages, Lidice and Ležáky, in retribution. While nobody knows precisely why the assassination was planned, one possibility that has been suggested is that it was to make the general population rise in rebellion, much as the Watchmaker (played by Martin Miller, who was a native of the part of the Austro-Hungarian Empire that later became Czechoslovakia, and who had previously played a doomed bomb-maker named Stavros in the Danger Man episode 'The Lovers') expects the Villagers to do here. That having been said, the Village is hardly Nazi-occupied Prague, being instead a facility in which a group of warders/interrogators are trying to get information out of prisoners (or, quite possibly, out of one prisoner), so the parallels aren't particularly readable.

In order to achieve the authorities' objective, the young Number Two plans to set up the Watchmaker, a Jammer, to assassinate the old Number Two. The Watchmaker believes that the assassination, and the retribution that will follow, will cause the Villagers to shake off their complacency and resist, much as the ringleader of the 1605 Gunpowder Plot, Robert Catesby, believed (erroneously, as it happened) that the assassination of James I and VI would cause Catholics in England and Scotland to rise up against the regime. While this makes sense as a plan, and is in keeping with the Village's use of psychological manipulation in earlier episodes, the fact that the level of resistance in the Village is evidently not high makes one wonder why the young Number Two is going to so much trouble, as it would surely be easier, and less volatile, to simply have his predecessor poisoned.

Beyond this, the young Number Two also plots to diminish the Prisoner's credibility, as he thinks that the only person in the Village whom the old Number Two will believe is the Prisoner himself. In order to do this, the young Number Two and his assistant, Number One Hundred, engage in a plan that is convoluted, but predicated on a precise knowledge of the Prisoner's psychology and how it interfaces with Village society as a whole – drugging Number Fifty, for example, so that the Prisoner will, first, see her as a victim and, secondly, believe that she cannot be complicit in the Village authorities' schemes. However, this makes sense only from the audience's point of view: the viewer knows that the Prisoner is a man of integrity, but the old Number Two has never met the Prisoner before (this appears to be the first time that we have seen the real Number Two, the others having been only acting-chairmen), and is reliant simply on Village files, which would undoubtedly reveal that the Prisoner is not above a spot of deception (in 'Checkmate', for instance, and 'Hammer into Anvil'). If the young Number Two had wanted to make certain the Prisoner wasn't believed, all he would have to do would be to indicate on the

Prisoner's file that he was a known Jammer (indeed, given the events of the previous two episodes, it seems strange that this has not already been done). Furthermore, the plan backfires, as it arouses the old Number Two's suspicions and engenders apparent misgivings in Number Twenty Two that cause him to give the game away to his superior. If the Village authorities can predict and manipulate the Prisoner's psychological reactions to the unbelievably precise degree seen here, then one wonders why they do not simply concentrate their efforts on getting the old Number Two to manoeuvre himself into a position where he can be killed in an undoubted accident instead.

Even the practical aspects of the assassination attempt make little sense. The idea of blowing the old Number Two up with a medallion is used purely for plot reasons, and is considerably more complicated than simply sending a man up to the bell tower with a rifle. The fact that the old man goes to the bell tower to detonate the device is also strange, as it would make more sense for him to position himself where he can dispose of the evidence and flee relatively quickly, as opposed to where he can be easily trapped and will have to throw the detonator away (in a way that will be quite visible to the crowd below) to get rid of it. Also, the young Number Two seems not to have considered the safety implications of standing within three feet of a man wearing a large amount of plastic explosive on his chest. All in all, the assassination plot is convoluted, cumbersome, and difficult to rationalise in the Village set-up, even if one takes the latter's continuously changing nature into account.

THE PRISONER PROGNOSIS: VIEWERS AND TELEVISION

One area in which the story does provide some clever moments is in its treatment of the boundary between television and viewers. Twice in this episode the audience are turned into voyeurs by sequences in which a piece of film is suddenly revealed to be a piece of surveillance footage: early in the story, for instance, the camera pulls out to reveal that our view of Number Fifty is in fact being shown on a screen, and that the person viewing it is the Supervisor (meaning that the viewers themselves have been briefly cast in the Supervisor's role). There is also a blurring of boundaries between the viewer and the action, since the story hinges on the premise that we have been watching the series for the past ten episodes, and also that we recognise the Prisoner as the hero of the series and a trustworthy man (also tying in with the theme of infantilisation, in which the Prisoner, like an infant, is the centre of attention, and/or with the idea that the Village is all in the Prisoner's mind, since he would naturally be the central figure of his own fantasy). This blurring of boundaries between viewer and programme is frequently flagged up in the directions in the script (for example, 'We blend into, and seemingly through, the screen …' followed by the next scene), implying that this might have been the author's intention.

The prognosis sequence also plays with television conventions. This involves a montage apparently made up of unused footage and alternate takes from 'Arrival', 'Many Happy Returns' and 'A Change of Mind' (the waterskiing sequence was in fact probably from 'Arrival', as one was apparently written into the original script), together with previously unseen shots of the Prisoner in the café, playing chess and so forth, overdubbed with a voiceover by Robert Rietty (who also overdubbed the clip of the Supervisor that begins the sequence, which was also taken from 'Arrival'). As the Computer Attendant watches the montage, she seems to be viewing pre-recorded sequences on a monitor up until the '7:30' point in the narrative, at which time the Prisoner's activity, a workout, occupies full screen. This appears to mark the moment at which we begin to view the actual prediction of the Prisoner's activities, since, to judge by the people in the background and their positions (which correlate with the real-time events we view later on, when the Prisoner buys the sweets for the old lady as the Computer Attendant and Number Two watch), the '9:00' prognosis of the Prisoner's encounter with the old lady at the kiosk is a projection of what will actually happen, and the portrait-painting sequence is also visibly a projection of a future activity; and yet, the Computer Attendant appears to be actually viewing the Prisoner's activities at this point in the story, as in the very next scene featuring the Prisoner, he is having his portrait painted. However, the fact that we subsequently have the sequence in which the Computer

EPISODE 11: IT'S YOUR FUNERAL

Attendant explains the prognosis to Number Two means that the order of the events in the story is different from the order in which we view them, since the positioning of the portrait-painting scene suggests that the events she is 'predicting' have now actually happened. The sequence blurs the boundaries between the observing character and the viewer by using a convention of television – the montage – in a way that cannot possibly work, except in the audience's minds.

The sequence was, however, a late addition to the story (the original script cut directly to the Prisoner's conversation with the artist), probably to prevent it from under-running, which explains the fact that the time sequencing does not work out. The earlier prognosis, for instance, does not match up with the later one: the first version has the Prisoner buying his newspaper after morning coffee, the second has him buying it on a 'daily stroll' through the Village sometime later. Consequently, although we have been told that he will have his encounter with the old lady between 9.00 and 9.20 am, then have his chess game and sit for his portrait, he apparently has the encounter after having his portrait painted, since the Computer Assistant and Number Two observe the event in real-time. While the sequence works as a narrative, attempts to analyse it as a logical sequence are futile.

Furthermore, although the prognosis sequence is entertaining – with the Prisoner's activities being accompanied by deadpan lines like 'It is possible that subject likes the view' (explaining why the Prisoner might climb the bell tower daily) and 'Subject cooling off' (accompanying an image of the Prisoner waterskiing) – it does beg a particularly difficult question. If the computer is sufficiently strong and well-programmed that it can not only predict the Prisoner's own movements, but figure out how the movements of others would affect his, how is it that the Prisoner can do anything remotely unpredictable in the series at all? How is it that the authorities are unable to identify all the Jammers and figure out when they are telling the truth and when they are lying? Finally, if the Village authorities (and/or their computer equipment) understand the Prisoner's mind so well that they can predict his movements, why are they incapable of breaking him down? While these problems are dealt with in detail in the original novel *The Prisoner's Dilemma*, the sequence as it stands in

'It's Your Funeral' drives a cart and horses through the series' premise.

TWO AND SIX-PENCE? THE CHARACTERS OF THE STORY

One thing often commented on by reviewers is the irony of the story's premise, in which the Prisoner is forced to protect Number Two, thus, perhaps, suggesting that, as in 'Hammer into Anvil', he is now adopting Village methods. However, that may be taking the idea a little too far; while he is protecting a member of the Village establishment, it is against another member of that establishment, and, in doing so, he is actually blocking what we are told is one of the standard practices of the Village. Everything else in the story suggests that the Prisoner's attitude is unchanged; his interrogation of Number Fifty resembles his usual interrogation of Number Two in the opening credits ('Who are you? What do you want?') with the inversion being that Number Fifty responds 'I'm a number' in direct contradiction of the Prisoner's own stated identity. The fact that he is suspected of being a Village guardian by the Watchmaker is also in keeping with the previous two episodes.

The 'portrait' of the Prisoner seen in this story is also revealing. It shows a circle and two rectangles interlinked, such that they are both inside and outside of each other, suggesting a number of possible readings: first, that the Prisoner is an abstract, an enigma onto which the viewer can read diverse meanings rather than being confined to a single interpretation; secondly, that the links form a kind of infinite loop, indicating both the nature of the Prisoner's life and his inability, thus far, to escape from the Village; and thirdly, that the pattern is an echo of the round-peg-in-square-hole metaphor from 'Arrival'. Although the script says that the Prisoner's response on being shown the picture should indicate that he is being polite to the painter rather than appreciating the painting (suggesting that this sequence is another dig at modern art), McGoohan actually plays the scene more ambiguously, leaving it open whether the Prisoner thinks the portrait is a good likeness or not.

One of the Prisoner's more inexplicable traits is his fondness for Kosho – which was introduced to the audience in the previous episode, but appears to have been intended to be seen for the first time in this story. The martial art's name translates as 'old book rare book', and bears no resemblance whatsoever to the obscure but genuine Japanese martial art Kosho-ryu. This time there is a fairly extended sequence that introduces the game and its premises. Other indications that this story might have best preceded 'Hammer into Anvil' include the fact that the Prisoner's ploy with the cuckoo-clock in 'Hammer into Anvil' would have had more resonance coming after an incident involving a watchmaker and a bomb, and that his mild involvement in Village politics here would have made aesthetic sense as a precedent to his deeper involvement in 'Hammer into Anvil'. However, in the current screening order, we still get a sense of the Prisoner playing God with the Village, destroying one Number Two but saving another, and/or of a child learning to master his environment (bluntly at first, then with more subtlety), a mental patient regaining control of his senses, and so forth.

Derren Nesbitt, appearing here as the Prisoner's main opponent, was a well-known British character actor who had appeared in three roles in *Danger Man*. He makes for a distinctly hip Number Two, looking like some kind of malevolent Gerry Anderson puppet; although the combination of blond hair (dyed that colour for Nesbitt's appearance in the film *The Naked Runner*; he offered to change it back to its natural dark brown for *The Prisoner*, but McGoohan reportedly declined the offer) and thick black-framed glasses is a decided nod at Michael Caine's appearance in *The Ipcress File*. While his having glasses is mentioned in the original script (because of the scene where he uses a microphone in them to communicate with Number One Hundred), they are described there as being horn-rims. Nesbitt displays great telephone-acting abilities here, pulling a series of amusing faces as he communicates with his superior/s; delivers the script's witty remarks with aplomb (on the computers' refusal to comment on the accuracy of the prognosis: 'They'll be wanting their own trade union next'); and appears to enjoy playing the slouching, laid-back youth, pressing control buttons with his feet and making an appearance in the Control Room clad in a dressing gown.

The fate of Number One Hundred, Number Two's assistant, is slightly different in the script than in the final version. In the original, the Prisoner gains control of Number One Hundred and frogmarches him off to make a public confession of the assassination attempt, but Number Two sends Rover to kill Number One Hundred, which it does, filling gruesomely with blood in the process. The scene was dropped, partly for time reasons and partly due to fears that it would be too graphic; however, the film of Mark Eden being smothered by Rover appears in 'Arrival'. McGoohan's enthusiasm during the final fight scene frightened Mark Eden, who thought he was taking it far too seriously.

Unfortunately, the other supporting roles are not quite so good. Australian-born Annette Andre (who would go on to find fame in *Randall and Hopkirk (Deceased)* as Jeannie Hopkirk) gives a fairly wooden performance as the Watchmaker's daughter, Number Fifty, possibly because of the tensions on the set at the time; she has spoken publicly about the discomfort she felt at the sacking of the story's original (and still credited) director, Robert Asher (who was a friend of McGoohan's, and had been asked to direct by him, but nonetheless became the first director to be replaced following a public dressing-down from the series' star, who went on to take over direction of the episode himself). Although Number Fifty and her father are interesting in being the only family to be featured in the televised Village, and in that the girl is a rare example of a Villager with a known first name (Monique), they are let down by some unbelievably clichéd dialogue. In their first scene alone, we get dire exchanges like: 'Oh, Father, you must give it up. I beg you. For my sake.' 'No, not again, I am sick of your begging and whining, you hear? There will be no more of it. No more.' One might also ask why the Village, a place in which time is arbitrary and the daily routine contingent on the needs of the moment, requires a watchmaker at all, although one might excuse that on surrealist grounds.

The Village still appears to be operating on a kind of ration-card system of currency (as in the previous episode), though the units are this time unnamed. However, it has now returned to more of an offbeat and satirical state than in 'Hammer into Anvil': the monument intended to show the Villagers' appreciation for their leaders, for instance, turns out, in a charmingly postmodern inversion of overblown memorials and monuments, to be a simple plaque reading 'Appreciation'. We see more lava-lamp 'screensavers' in the Green Dome (one red, one green, both speeded up) and a green and silver lamp in the computer room; the penny-farthing also appears on the badge of office. We get more death imagery in that the Village council members and Master of Ceremonies appear in top hats and undertaker suits, and a rare nod at the outside world when the Prisoner says to Number Two in the final scene, 'Fly now, pay later' (an old Pan American Airlines slogan). There are again hints at the importance of psychoanalysis, with the use of drugs for behaviour control and the prediction of the Prisoner's actions being deemed a 'patient prognosis'. Fairclough suggests that the computer's refusal to comment on the efficiency of the prognosis may be an early sign of artificial intelligence. An unfortunately cut announcement over the loudspeaker also provides a lovely comment on bureaucracy, as follows: 'Your Citizens' Council also wish to make it clear that attendance at this ceremony will not be compulsory. Special non-attendance licenses may be obtained at the Town Hall. Any citizen with a legally valid reason for not attending this spectacular event may purchase one of these licenses. They will be equally available to one and all.' Finally, we also get the surreal implication that the silent butler can in fact speak, when Number Two says to him: 'I already told you, I don't want to see anyone – tell him to go away.'

'It's Your Funeral', is, rather like the Kosho game that features in it, fun to watch and to figure out, but makes little sense. While it provides a neat counterpoint to the previous story in many ways, it does not stand up to extensive analytical attention.

Episode 12:
A Change of Mind

First UK Transmission Date: Friday 15 December 1967: ATV Midlands/Grampian,7.30 pm – 8.30 pm
Writer: Roger Parkes
Director: Joseph Serf (pseudonym for Patrick McGoohan)
Credited Cast: Patrick McGoohan (The Prisoner); Angela Browne (Number Eighty-Six); John Sharpe (Number Two)[12]; Angelo Muscat (The Butler); George Pravda (Doctor); Kathleen Breck (Number Forty-Two); Peter Swanwick (Supervisor); Thomas Heathcote (Lobo Man); Bartlett Mullins (Committee Chairman); Michael Miller (Number Ninety-Three); Joseph Cuby (1st Member of Social Group); Michael Chow (2nd Member of Social Group); June Ellis (Number Forty-Eight); John Hamblin (1st Woodland Man); Michael Billington (2nd Woodland Man)
Known Uncredited Cast: Frank Maher (Double for Patrick McGoohan); Fenella Fielding (Loudspeaker Voice); Robert Rietty (Additional Voicework)

SYNOPSIS: The Prisoner beats up two Village bullies who have come to disturb his early morning workout, and is referred to the Village committee, who determine that his case must be investigated further. He attends a 'social group' intended to help non-conforming Villagers to conform, but disrupts it through arguing about the validity of their arguments, and they accuse him

---

12 John Sharp's name was misspelled on the credits of this episode.

of being a 'disharmonious rebel' and a 'reactionary'. This is a diagnosis supported by the committee, who then classify him as 'unmutual'. As such, he is shunned by the rest of the Village until he is taken away for 'Instant Social Conversion,' a kind of ultra-sonic lobotomy. The Prisoner returns home, seemingly lobotomised and attended by Number Eighty Six, the woman who performed the surgery; however, he sees her putting drugs in his tea and, when he empties the cup without her knowledge, he finds that his mind is clearing, and that the lobotomy has been all a fake. Having tricked Number Eighty Six into drinking the drugged tea, he hypnotises her and learns the entire plot: to render him docile so that he will confess why he resigned. Pretending to be still under the influence, he goes to see Number Two and announces his desire to make a public confession; when Two complies and takes him to the Village Square, Eighty Six, under hypnotic suggestion, accuses Two of being unmutual, and he is pursued out of the square by a mob of angry Villagers.

ANALYSIS: 'A Change of Mind' was Roger Parkes's first professional script, written while he was in his late twenties; in an inversion of the normal pattern for *The Prisoner* scriptwriters, he went on to work on other, more conventional, ITC series such as *Man in a Suitcase* and *Strange Report*. Prior to this, he had been a trainee story editor on *Compact*, and a journalist, at one point being editor of *Farming Express* (which may explain the barnyard/rural metaphors that permeate 'A Change of Mind'). He has since written over 20 novels, and episodes of a number of highly regarded BBC series. He consulted his psychiatrist brother while writing 'A Change of Mind', and appears to have been generally interested in issues of mental illness and mind control; one of his episodes of *Blake's 7*, 'Voice from the Past', also deals with these themes.

Like 'Free for All,' this story is one that has a number of obvious points for analysis: the controversy surrounding the efficacy of lobotomies that raged in the 1960s; the connections with, among other things, *A Clockwork Orange*, *One Flew Over the Cuckoo's Nest* and *The Manchurian Candidate*; the Maoist and McCarthyite image of public confessions. However, there are other aspects to the story that frequently go unremarked: for instance, its position on non-invasive therapy techniques; its commentary on leadership; and its treatment of both creativity and gender.

OUR UNMUTUAL FRIEND:
THERAPY AND SOCIETY IN THE VILLAGE

One of the key points made by this story concerns the way supposedly 'non-invasive' therapy techniques can be as damaging as the more invasive procedures also seen in the episode, picking up on themes explored in such contemporary and near-contemporary satires of psychotherapy as the early films of Woody Allen, and Luke Rhinehart's novel *The Dice Man*. The drug-taking sequence, in which Number Eighty Six gleefully declares that she is higher than Number Two and gathers flowers, highlights how both the rebellious hippie movements and the professional therapists of the time were using exactly the same drugs to achieve their ends. Number Ninety Three's public confession is in line not only with those encouraged by totalitarian political regimes, but also with practices encouraged by 12-step programmes and therapy groups, in which members stand up, admit their problems and discuss their progress; the fact that the listening Villagers applaud him casts them in the role of therapy group members showing support for a fellow patient who has learned the 'correct' messages (in the original script, this parallel was less clear; as he made his confession, which was not prompted by the speaker, the Villagers in the antechamber edged away from him rather than applauded him, and he did not grow hysterical as he repeated 'Believe me').

The 'social group,' similarly, recalls group therapy, and the actions of the Appeals sub-committee resemble those of friends of a person with a substance abuse problem, staging interventions as needed. When the Prisoner is referred for further diagnosis, and later declared unmutual, the Villagers avoid him, following the therapeutic maxim of not acknowledging bad behaviour (as that will gratify an attention-seeker) but rewarding good behaviour (by, in this case, applause, attention and music). Number Forty Two's joining of the Appeals sub-committee recalls the way in which, in some cases, people who have undergone or are undergoing therapeutic treatment help out people who are less far along in their progress, and/or the fact that psychoanalysts must themselves undergo psychoanalysis as part of their training. It is fitting that this is one story in which the problem of finding out why the Prisoner resigned appears to be less of a priority for the Village; here, the Village instead resembles a kind of gigantic therapy group, in which the 'warders' become therapists to treat those deemed mentally ill and/or antisocial.

The case of Number Forty Two brings up a wider theme of this episode: the question of where the boundary line actually lies between creativity and insanity. It is well known that creative people can be misdiagnosed, or overdiagnosed, as mentally ill, particularly (as Roland Littlewood notes in his study of the British psychological establishment *Aliens and Alienists*) amongst women and ethnic minorities. Virginia Woolf and Charlotte Perkins Gilman, whose short story 'The Yellow Wallpaper' was partly informed by her experience, were both diagnosed as mentally ill, for example. The metaphorical and creative aspects of writing and art can cause what was intended as a flight of fancy to be interpreted as an insane delusion; and, as Littlewood notes, acceptable behaviour in one culture or subgroup might be considered insane in another. At the same time, it can be argued that in some cases, there is a direct connection between creativity and mental illness, as in the cases of Spike Milligan, John Lennon, Philip K Dick and Winston Churchill. Patrick McGoohan himself has said that he experienced 'three nervous breakdowns' as pressure mounted on *The Prisoner*. The story explores the question of whether or not a creative person should be forced to conform, if what makes him or her creative is also something that could be deemed by society as antisocial or a mental illness.

Taken further, one could read the story as painting the diagnosis and treatment of mental illness as a form of social control. Number Forty Two, for instance, need not be diagnosed as in need of treatment, just sympathy and friendship. Similarly, the Prisoner's behaviour in the story simply indicates a wish for privacy at times. But by deeming him mentally ill, or 'unmutual', the authorities place him in a category that gives society a measure of control over him (recalling how the Soviet regime frequently silenced political activists by having them put in mental asylums). Similarly, at the end, simply labelling Number Two as unmutual causes the Village to turn against him, regardless of the validity of the diagnosis or the man's power within the Village. This reflects how the label of 'mentally ill' can be one of the most damaging forms of stigma, as it represents something that is mysterious, unknown, not necessarily 'curable', and something that comes from within; we see this reflected in the treatment of the 'unmutual' Prisoner by the other Villagers, whereby he is unable to carry out normal social behaviour like having a cup of coffee in a café without incurring hostility. When a person's behaviour is stigmatised with a label, the person himself or herself is stigmatised, even pathologised. The story raises these important points about diagnosis, and the use of labels, as a form of social control.

Finally, 'A Change of Mind' touches on the way therapeutic techniques can influence politics, on the macro and the micro levels. Throughout the series, the use of brainwashing, coercion and other psychologically inspired methods to gain social and political consent is paramount, and here, as Chris Gregory notes, there are strong similarities between the Appeals sub-committee and Mary Whitehouse's media-focused lobby group, the National Viewers and Listeners Association. 'A Change of Mind', however, points out that the question of who are the prisoners and who are the warders is a redundant one in a therapy group; all it takes is one facilitator, and the group polices itself. Parkes, in his foreword to *The Prisoner: The Original Scripts vol. 2*, also points out that the lobotomy would make the Prisoner 'lose his aggressions and moral scruples,' acknowledging that the Village needs to make the Prisoner lose his sense of morality in order to get him to tell them his secrets. In this episode, we get insight into the informal social control aspects of the Village, and why it is harder for the Prisoner to organise an escape than he has at times believed.

THE MIND'S EYE: SURREALISM AND THE VILLAGE

This story, made right after 'It's Your Funeral', also had its original director, Roy Rossoti (whose impressive list of credits at the time included working as second unit director on *Doctor Zhivago*) replaced by Patrick McGoohan, after a single morning's work;

McGoohan's nom-de-plume of Joseph Serf[13] is credited as director for the first time (in production order, but not transmission order). Angela Browne, who played Number Eighty Six, recalled in an interview on The Unmutual website that despite his reputation for ferocity, and despite the fact that he appeared to her to be very much under pressure, McGoohan struck her as a very kind and considerate person to work with, even telling the crew to be quiet so that she could concentrate on a difficult piece of dialogue. As with 'Free for All', we can see surrealist and allegorical aspects in the way the story is filmed. This is particularly apparent in the sequences in which the Prisoner confronts the Town Council (with the Town Hall sporting a 'Council Chamber' sign for the occasion). Again we see the empty chair decorated with an eye, and blue lights; the dwarf butler, again, plays a curious role, opening and closing the committee circle and, at the end, appears in a sequence that leaves it ambiguous as to whether he is following Number Two, the crowd or the Prisoner, or just moving to some unknown purpose of his own.

There are some notable differences between the initial Council Chamber sequence as scripted and as filmed. In the script, the Prisoner is spoken to by three committee members, plus the Chairman; the voices of the committee members are always just behind him, so he is constantly turning to face them. The three voices are, in the finished version, replaced by a single, disembodied voice that appears to come from a kind of speaker/recording device (or, possibly, given its similarity with the tape-driven mechanism seen in 'The General', a computer), with the sense of disorientation provided by a turning camera and rapid, strange shots of the faces of the committee and the Prisoner. The fact that the camera keeps cutting to the recorder becomes surreally ambiguous, as the turning of the tape reels might suggest that the Prisoner is talking to a recording that has somehow anticipated his responses (as with the computer in the previous episode), but, also, as it is stated that the Prisoner's responses are being recorded, could imply that the machine is recording him instead. There is a peculiar

---

13 Given McGoohan's usual fondness for symbolism, it is worth pointing out that Joseph is Hebrew for 'Increaser', and 'Serf' a medieval word meaning a labourer or slave, suggesting that McGoohan is complaining about the increase in his workload incurred by taking over direction at short notice; his other nom-de-plume, 'Paddy Fitz', could be taken literally to mean 'Irish Bastard'.

juxtaposition early on, when we have a brief shot of the recorder in between a shot of the Prisoner going to the Council Chamber and a shot of him in the anteroom, which can be taken to suggest that there is a second recorder in the antechamber; however, the wide shots of the antechamber do not reveal such a device, meaning that the juxtaposition is intended merely to cause confusion. In the second Council Chamber sequence, the Prisoner speaks only with the Chairman (who, unlike in 'Free for All', is not Number Two, but a lesser number seated at the table with the others, leaving both Number Two's chair and the chair with the eye empty), in pitch blackness; and when the lights come up, the Chairman vanishes, like a hallucination. As in 'Free for All', the surreal touches of direction make the Village seem a weird, disorientating place.

Moreso than in the previous two episodes, the Village's almost exclusive focus on the Prisoner is highlighted here. Even the presence of other Villagers being 'helped' by therapy serves simply to highlight the Prisoner's own situation. The whole Village, not simply the doctors and psychiatrists, participates in the Prisoner's rehabilitation, and, when he is apparently rehabilitated, they all cheer. Tannoy announcements are made regarding the Prisoner, but not about any other Villager (though Number Ninety Three's rehabilitation makes it into the *Tally Ho*). Again, the focus is on the Prisoner, in a kind of infantilised situation, or an ego-focused dream or fantasy.

ONLY A WOMAN:
GENDER RELATIONS IN 'A CHANGE OF MIND'

Although the set-up is as international as ever, with Asian and South American Villagers joining the therapy group and an Eastern European (played by George Pravda) also turning up, unusually for the Village, we see discrimination against women in this episode (which is also a feature of the unmade script by Parkes's friend Moris Farhi; see the entry 'Unmade Stories 1: The Outsider'). While previously the Village institutions have normally been mixed, here the Council is all male, and the Appeals sub-committee all female, giving the men a diagnostic/powerful role and the women a therapeutic/volunteer role. The Kitchener-style posters of Number

Two, which are explicitly mentioned in the script, also suggest a paternalistic, authoritarian and old-fashioned regime. An earlier draft of the script, in fact, was considerably more sexist, including some decided prejudice from the Prisoner himself (for instance, during a deleted scene with Number Eighty Six, he has a line about not being able to stand deceit, 'least of all from girls in trousers'). Although much of this is toned down in the finished script, with the Prisoner being closer to his usual egalitarian self, and some of the more unbelievable moments (for instance, when the Prisoner impugns Number Eighty Six's tea-making skills, in the original she goes wide-eyed with humiliation and aims to slap him; rather hysterical and insecure behaviour from a professional brain surgeon) are deleted along with the (somewhat clunky) suggestion of a romance between the Prisoner and Number Eighty Six, enough remains to give the idea of a more–prejudiced-than-usual Village this episode.

One possible source for the Village's change in attitude might be Number Two. This episode's incumbent is something of a misogynist – he calls Number Eighty Six a 'stupid woman' and voices doubts that she can do her job properly – suggesting that prejudice at the top of an organisation can lead to negative attitudes further down. Since Number Eighty Six clearly has strong professional skills and is visibly more intelligent than Number Two – stating, while under the influence of drugs, that she is also 'higher' than him, which might refer to her value within the organisation as much as to her mental state at the time – this suggests that he resents her power and abilities. Number Two's description in the original script as a 'large, cattle auctioneer type' suggests that Parkes originally wanted Number Two's appearance to imply a traditional, rural person (making the decision to have the character speak with quite a posh accent rather odd, especially since actor John Sharp is a Yorkshireman and could have managed a regional one). Number Two's sexism also, however, highlights the subtext about labelling referred to above: give a group a negative label – 'stupid woman,' for instance – and one fails to recognise, and thus to capitalise, on its members' skills and abilities, making oneself vulnerable through the loss of an asset. Because Number Two is convinced that women are stupid, he fails to realise that Number Eighty Six has in fact been duped by the Prisoner, not made a mistake and drunk the wrong cup of tea, which means that he fails to realise that the Prisoner has discovered his plan and is about to make a move against him.

LOSING MY MIND? THE PRISONER AND PRODUCTION

In terms of the Prisoner himself, we once again see him posing as a warder rather than a prisoner (hypnotising Number Eighty Six into believing he is her superior, and pretending to be a reformed character at the end of the story). Although he refers to himself as 'Number Six', he does so while assuming the role of Number Eighty Six's superior, or when facetiously styling himself 'public enemy Number Six,' so it is not a case of adopting the numeral as a spontaneous self-description as in 'The Schizoid Man'. Although he appears fussy about how his tea is made, this is unlikely to be one of his normal character traits, as the fuss he makes serves a key function in his plan (i.e. ensuring that Number Eighty Six consumes the drug and he does not). Parkes, quoted in Fairclough's *The Prisoner: The Official Companion,* says that McGoohan's rationale for scotching the flirtatious element of the Prisoner's relationship with Number Eighty Six was probably that the Prisoner wouldn't really trust anyone. In a wonderfully telling, but unfortunately cut, line, when Number Two says 'The lamb returns to the fold,' the Prisoner was to have responded 'Like the month of March' (cleverly punning on the proverb that when March goes in like a lamb, it comes out like a lion; Number Two's response was to have been, 'Quite so, well, no more lions from now on, eh'). One does have to ask, however, where the Prisoner gets his support and credit units from if, as seems apparent, he does no work in the Village; is there an equivalent of the welfare system as well as of therapy groups?

Production-wise, this story featured another *Danger Man* veteran, as Angela Browne had guest-starred in the Series 1 episode 'The Girl in Pink Pyjamas'. The script suggested that she should speak with an assumed Swedish accent for her first scene (presumably relating to the international and surreal themes of the Village) and should make tea in a 'noxious Continental' manner, which would have suggested that the Prisoner's rejection of the drink was, on the first two occasions, due not to his suspicious, cunning nature, but simply to a dislike of the way she made the tea, and that it was only on the third occasion that he realised that he was being drugged, when he caught sight in a small mirror of her putting the pill in his cup (as opposed to observing her drugging his tea from the beginning in the final version). Elsewhere, Michael Billington, who played one of the Village heavies seen at the start of the story, was – according to Roger Langley in *Free for All*, Autumn 2004, Issue 12 – given the starring role on Gerry and Sylvia Anderson's *UFO*, for which he is now best known, entirely on the strength of his performance here. The original script, charmingly, refers to the *Tally Ho* mobile printing press as an 'instant newsstand'. A couple of scenes involving the Prisoner being attacked by Villagers after having been declared unmutual were cut; however, the fact that he has mussed hair and a hunted manner in the scene that was originally intended to come after the second attack, in which the Appeals sub-committee meet him following his shunning in the café, suggests that the second cut at least was made at a very late stage, possibly even after the scene was filmed. Also visibly apparent is that in the location footage comprising the final scene, Number Two is being played by a double (as he is thinner than actor John Sharp and has more hair); Sharp himself had an 'e' accidentally added to the end of his name in the credits, but this fact appears to have come to light only recently, meaning that a number of reference books on the series also contain the error.

'A Change of Mind' contains a number of interesting themes – frequently obscured behind more obvious messages about lobotomies and totalitarianism – exploring therapy, gender and the social role of psychology.

Episode 13:
Do Not Forsake Me
Oh My Darling

First UK Transmission Date: Friday 22 December 1967: ATV
Midlands/Grampian,7.30 pm – 8.30 pm
Writer: Vincent Tilsley
Director: Pat Jackson
Credited Cast: Patrick McGoohan (The Prisoner); Zena Walker
(Janet); Clifford Evans (Number Two); Nigel Stock (The Colonel);
Angelo Muscat (The Butler); Hugo Schuster (Seltzman); John
Wentworth (Sir Charles); James Bree (Villiers); Lloyd Lamble
(Stapleton); Patrick Jordan (Danvers); Lockwood West (Camera
Shop Manager); Frederic Abbott (Potter); Gertan Klauber (Café
Waiter); Henry Longhurst (Old Guest)*; Danvers Walker (First New
Man)*; John Nolan (Young Guest)
Known Uncredited Cast: Frank Maher (Double for Patrick
McGoohan); William Lyon Brown (Undertaker/Waiter)
*Not in finished episode

SYNOPSIS: In an unknown location, three men view a series of
photographic slides of various places; two of them discuss it but can
find no pattern. Meanwhile, in the Village, Number Two plans to
use the 'Seltzman Device' to swap the Prisoner's mind with that of a
man known as the Colonel. Waking up in London, believing it to be
the same day that he resigned (it is in fact a year later), the Prisoner
discovers with shock that he is in a different body. He is met briefly

by his fiancée, Janet, who turns up at his house hoping that he has returned. He goes to his department and confronts his superior, Sir Charles, who is also Janet's father, and who apparently refuses to believe his story. The Prisoner goes to Janet's birthday party and, claiming to be a friend of her fiancé's, inveigles a receipt for some photographic slides (which he had left with her a year ago) out of her. She realises his identity. The Prisoner retrieves the photographs, which turn out to be the same slides seen at the outset; using a predetermined code, he puts them together in order such that the name of a location appears on the screen: Kandersfeld, Austria. Driving to Kandersfeld, the Prisoner discovers Seltzman posing as the local barber; however, agents of the Village and the British government (or possibly both) have used the Prisoner to track Seltzman down and kidnap both of them to the Village. Seltzman apparently reverses the mind-swap process on the Prisoner and the Colonel, then collapses; the Colonel departs, and the Prisoner reveals that Seltzman put his own mind in the Colonel's body, allowing him to escape.

ANALYSIS: 'Do Not Forsake Me Oh My Darling' is a story about which virtually no-one has anything good to say. The characterisation is largely quite poor, and the plot, as well as being trite, contains a massive hole (as identified by Langley in *Free for All*, Winter 2005, Issue 13), as it never seems to occur to anyone that to reverse the operation, all that would need to be done would be to run the initial body-swap process a second time; Seltzman himself is not in fact needed at all. That having been said, the superficiality of the main plot does overlie some interesting comments on the series, the Village, the Cold War and psychology.

It is often remarked that this is the only *The Prisoner* story to feature a pre-credits scene, and yet this sequence demands further exploration. It involves three figures (later identified as Sir Charles Portland, Stapleton and, viewing silently, Villiers) looking at a set of slides and commenting, in part:

'Yet I'm convinced they contain the clue we want ... Extraordinary order of filming, isn't it? Loch Ness, the Yorkshire Moors, Dartmouth, the Eiffel Tower, Beachy Head. What's Number Six? Hopelessly overexposed.'

'Nine on the roll very overexposed, and as many under... I hate to mention this, Sir Charles, but it is possible that there is no clue to be found in these shots... Breaking a code or cipher is a finite problem. But as I said, with these, we don't know that there is a problem, and if there is, on what level of reasoning it is set.'

'We just haven't thought of it, and I don't accept that it is impossible to do so.'

This sequence can be interpreted in at least three ways. The first has to do with the nature of the Village: over the course of the previous 12 episodes, the Village has been said to be in a number of mutually exclusive locations; and, in the end, it will turn out to be a popular British holiday destination (like several of the places named in the pre-titles sequence; Beachy Head was even a filming location for *The Prisoner*, in 'Many Happy Returns' and 'The Girl Who Was Death'). As the figures examine the slides, it can almost seem as if they, too, are trying to figure out where it is, or else are indicating that it is, in fact, everywhere, in keeping with the idea that the second series would see the Prisoner go out into the world and discover that one cannot escape the Village. Secondly, the line about Number Six being hopelessly overexposed makes for an obvious pun, in that Six has been the focus of the story so far, and yet he is going to disappear for this episode, making someone else the focus of the series. Finally, the sequence could even be taken to relate to the act of interpreting the series itself: by looking at a sequence of filmed pictures, one may convince oneself that there are clues to its meaning, and yet it may be that there is no code or cipher there, but simply random images.

OUT IN THE WORLD:
THE VILLAGE AND THE OUTSIDE WORLD

One of the things most often commented about regarding 'Do Not Forsake Me Oh My Darling' is that it is the episode of *The Prisoner* that comes closest to being a conventional spy story: leaving aside the pre-titles scene (typical of normal ITC series), the body-swap motif had been used elsewhere, most notably in *The Avengers*. The Village, also, seems to revert to conventional spy-series mode, with talk about 'sides' and the forcible recruitment of Germanic scientists featuring prominently. However, this is one story that focuses strongly on the idea that the Village is the wider world, and vice versa, with Seltzman having lived at 20 Portmeirian (sic) Road, the Prisoner having apparently owned a diary with pages identical to those of his diary in the Village, and the Austrian waiter greeting the Prisoner with the phrase 'Welcome to the Village.' The Prisoner in his London house wears the same blue silk dressing gown he has previously been seen wearing in the Village, in 'Many Happy Returns'. Even Number Two's us-and-them talk could be interpreted more ambiguously; he remarks that 'we' can put a man into orbit around the moon (an oddly prescient phrase, since this would not happen until the Apollo 8 mission in December 1968, and the fact that the Prisoner's letter to Seltzman is postmarked May 1967 would date this episode to around May 1968[14]), but it is unclear whether he means NATO, the West, or humans in general. The idea of the Village being the world is again referenced in the story's iconography, most notably the large map of the world dominating the HQ office in London, and in the name of the camera shop, Walter's World Cameras Ltd (which was an actual shop in Shaftesbury Road at the time). This story, which was originally intended to be the first of the second series of *The Prisoner* and to establish as its premise the idea that the Prisoner would go out into the world (hence the lack of the 'Where am I?' sequence in the title credits), provides an interesting case of the ambiguity of the Village. Rather than changing from one episode to the next, here the Village embodies two contradictory principles in the same story: Cold War insularity and a universal embracing of all cultures.

This can also be seen in the use of surveillance in the story. The Prisoner is, throughout, followed by Potter, an agent who is reporting to Sir Charles, and also by a Village undertaker in a hearse (who can also be seen dressed as a waiter at Janet's party, in civilian clothes outside the camera shop, and finally in some kind of uniform, possibly a chauffeur's, in Austria). The question that arises, however, is whether the Prisoner is being tailed by agents, acting either separately or on behalf of the same power (with one

---

14 The date on the postmark could possibly be read as 'May 1961', but Peter Remell, writing in Max Hora's *The Prisoner of Portmeirion*, says that the stamp on the envelope is a fourpenny blue, which was not introduced until June 1961, meaning it must have been sent later.

being intended to distract from the other's presence), or whether the whole thing is just another metaphor (with the undertaker representing the fact that death follows all humans and ultimately catches up with them – an idea also referenced in the fact that, for Seltzman, 'escape' from the Village involves the literal death of his body). Throughout, ambiguity exists regarding the Village's relationship to the wider world.

At the same time, however, we have the surrealism that we have had for most of the series relating to the Village running throughout the story. Since scriptwriter Vincent Tilsley's previous contribution to *The Prisoner* was 'The Chimes of Big Ben', it is perhaps unsurprising that we encounter a character referred to simply as 'The Colonel,' recalling 'Colonel J' of that earlier episode as well as 'The Colonel' of 'Many Happy Returns' (while there is no reason why there should not be more than one colonel in the series, it is a notable continuation of the way titles and numbers, and the convention of referring to people by title rather than by name, keep recurring within the series). However, since Tilsley's original script had the character named 'Colonel Oscar,' this thematic referencing may well come from McGoohan or Tomblin instead. We also get yet another set of superiors for the Prisoner; while this is not an inherent contradiction of the set-ups we see in 'The Chimes of Big Ben' and 'Many Happy Returns' (as a man in his position would have to deal with a number of different people), it recalls the way the Village itself changes nature and set-up, suggesting that the Prisoner's situation in the outside world undergoes similar surreal changes. Duplicates are once again to the fore (albeit in reversed form, as it involves the Prisoner's mind being transferred to another person's body rather than identical bodies housing different minds), and are also thematically referenced in that the gas gun the undertaker uses is the same one seen in 'The Schizoid Man', and Seltzman's barber's chair appears to have a duplicate in the Village (while in the original script it is stated that it is the same chair in both cases and that it must play a part of the reversal process, this is more ambiguous in the finished version). The flashback montage, in which the Prisoner remembers who he is and his life in the Village, includes a sequence of his own mind-transfer process as seen on Number Two's viewscreen, which he could not possibly have witnessed (it also includes a shot of Number Two that has not previously appeared in the episode as transmitted). The episode thus references earlier, more surreal themes as well as looking out to more conventional political situations.

DOCTOR STRANGELOVE:
SELTZMAN AND COLD WAR SCIENCE

While the Professor Seltzman subplot relates directly to the use and misuse of science during the Cold War, once again the situation is much more complicated than that. Seltzman appears to have fled to Austria to avoid having his invention used for political ends, and compares himself to Rutherford, whose splitting of the atom led to the nuclear bomb. This parallels the real-life controversies surrounding many 19th- and 20th-Century inventors and scientists whose research was used for war-related purposes: some, like Einstein and Alfred Nobel, were dismayed by the uses to which their discoveries were put, but others, like the Wright Brothers and anthropologist Ruth Benedict, were pragmatic about this (with Benedict, who carried out a study of Japanese culture in the 1940s with the explicit understanding that it would be used by US intelligence services to help them understand their enemy, arguing that in wartime, one must put one's talents, whatever they may be, to the service of one's country).

However, Seltzman's motivations here are ambiguous. In the Cold War, German scientists in the West generally fell into two categories: Jews who had fled Nazi persecution in the 1930s, such as Einstein and mathematician Emmy Noether, and Nazis, or people willing to tolerate Nazi ideology, who had decided to collaborate rather than face trial after the war, including, most famously, Werner von Braun. The question thus arises as to which category Seltzman falls into. He bears a superficial resemblance to Einstein, and his first name, Jacob, is a fairly common one among European Jews. However, when Number Two mocks him by making a Nazi salute and saying 'Heil,' he does not react as one would expect of someone who had faced ethnic persecution (and, indeed, if he were Jewish, it would have been an unbelievably tactless thing for Number Two to have done). Also, for all Seltzman's protestations that he does not want to see his work misused, he has evidently been continuing his experiments (possibly in the large basement beneath the barber shop), as he has progressed beyond what both the Prisoner and Number Two expected; the Prisoner remarks at the end of the story that he is now free to continue his experiments. Whether Seltzman has continued his experiments because he wishes to profit from them, or because (as has sometimes been argued for von Braun) he is a man who is devoted to the pursuit of science to the point where he must work on his experiments regardless of the consequences for himself or others, is left ambiguous. The Prisoner also seems uncharacteristically angry and resentful when announcing that Seltzman has escaped, rather than triumphant that he has helped an innocent man to evade the Village's clutches. This casts doubt on the interpretation that many viewers have made, that the Prisoner resigned because of his feelings of anger over the exploitation of Seltzman's research, and suggests that the situation regarding Seltzman may be rather more complex. It may be that the Prisoner is aware that Seltzman is not simply a good, peaceful scientist being exploited by Cold War organizations, but a man with his own agenda, and one not totally honourable.

This also casts an ambiguous light on the Prisoner's own motivations. We see in this episode that the Prisoner was not only working for Sir Charles when he resigned, but was proposing to marry Sir Charles' daughter Janet (significantly, the only woman the Prisoner ever kisses in the series, and then only when he is in the body of another man), which raises the question of how he expected to maintain a personal *and* a professional relationship with Sir Charles, particularly as he wanted to resign from the secret service. The Prisoner's treatment of Seltzman is also rather selfish: it seems that, in order to get his mind back in its original body, he is quite willing to lead the Village agents to Seltzman and allow them to capture him.

DAMNIT JANET, I LOVE YOU: THE BODYSWAP PLOT

McGoohan was unavailable for the bulk of filming of this episode (being in Hollywood for the making of *Ice Station Zebra*), and so had his part largely taken by yet another *Danger Man* alumnus, Nigel Stock, aided by some stock footage – from 'Arrival', 'Free for All' and, curiously, 'Once Upon a Time', which had been filmed but not shown by then, making this an image from the Prisoner's future rather than his past – and occasionally rather obvious doubling (particularly in the sequence where the Village guardians drag him off). McGoohan also does not appear to be present in any scenes with other characters (note that his 'conversation' with Number Two consists of cutaway shots between them, casting doubt on whether the two actors were in the same room at the time, and the scenes of the Prisoner reclining on the operating couch are all in long shot with his face disguised by goggles, leading to the assumption that the man in question is most likely a stand-in), suggesting that his scenes were filmed with him on his own and then inserted into the action. While defenders of Stock argue that he is able to capture McGoohan's mannerisms with uncanny accuracy, we would argue that his performance makes it plain how much McGoohan is able to get away with through sheer charisma: phrases that would sound cocky and amusing from McGoohan sound arrogant and silly coming from Stock. Some of this may be down to problems of characterisation – the Colonel is described in the original script as seeming cold and arrogant, and certainly the Prisoner does seem more callous than usual here – but it is nonetheless difficult to resist quoting the rather interesting analysis of the situation given in the Canadian publication *The Prisoner Puzzle*: 'Our hero, deprived of his marvellously fit and attractive body, must resume his life in a new, unappetising shape... "Will [Janet] know me in this body? Will she know that inside this unsightly bulk I am really an athlete, a romantic hero?"... A real princess should know that under the mattress of fat is her true lover. Is this girl a real princess?' Lest one think that the reviewer is taking things too far, it is worth noting that the Prisoner himself remarks disparagingly at the end of the story that Seltzman undoubtedly does not look the way he wishes he looked. Stock's performance thus comes in for a lot of not-entirely-unjustified criticism from many quarters.

The body-swap plot also has the unfortunate effect of making the Prisoner seem hopelessly inane, even ditzy. As our impression, as viewers, has hitherto been that the Prisoner is an intelligent, cunning and cultured secret agent, it is rather disconcerting to learn that the man's inner monologue consists of banal waffle about his girlfriend's birthday, his car, handwriting, money and so forth, rather than ruminations on the international situation, the nature of existence and the ethics of resignation. Considering that he believes this to be the very day on which he was going to resign, furthermore, it seems odd that this fact features nowhere in his list of things to do that day. He also can't be a very reliable agent if he was supposed to be covering up Seltzman's disappearance, as it seems to be common knowledge. He displays a shamefully classist attitude towards Danvers, sneering at his Liverpudlian origins and amorous predilections, and his taste in girlfriends is perhaps a little surprising, as Janet looks far older than her years, dresses in outfits that are ten years out of date, and regards a sedate foxtrot as a good time, when the Prisoner has always given the impression of being fairly up-to-date and with-it. It is possible to read into the story (albeit that the implication is probably inadvertent) that Sir Charles thought the Prisoner a bit of a lunatic for wanting to marry his daughter, and/or that the Prisoner was sent to the Village as a means of preventing the marriage. Although the presence of Janet does explain why he has kept his Village relationships chaste, they do seem a fairly ill-matched couple.

The body-swap plot is also not very well-thought-through from a logistical point of view. We have to ask why the Prisoner does not immediately wonder what has happened to his arm when he wakes up and looks at his wristwatch, and his amnesia seems to be sporadic: while he appears to shake it off when he first looks in the mirror, a minute later he is talking with Janet in a way that indicates that he still thinks that her dress fitting was the previous day. The idea that he would have the same handwriting – and kissing style – whatever body he is in is problematic enough in itself (since it could be argued that this is as much a product of motor functions as of the mind) but also begs the question of why other physical quirks and characteristics, such as Seltzman's Austrian accent, do not also survive the body-swapping process. Moreover, Janet is really far too trusting if she would hand over an important piece of paper to someone who merely claims to be her fiancé's friend.

Finally, leaving aside the above-mentioned plot holes, the subplot regarding the photography shop is ridiculously overcomplicated. While ITC spy series of the time do frequently contain some fairly silly ideas, it is still hard to believe that the

Prisoner and Seltzman would have gone to all that trouble to work out a code, engineer the letters into the negatives, and left the slides at a particular shop where they would remain for an indefinite amount of time; suffice it to say that there would have been far easier ways of getting the message across. The story is thus simultaneously more conventional, and as such, ironically, less believable, than more surreal *Prisoner* stories.

BEHIND THE BODY-SWAP: THE TROUBLE WITH 'DO NOT FORSAKE ME OH MY DARLING'

The problems with this episode stem from the fact that it was conceived at a time when the series was, effectively, at a crossroads. The story, filmed as the first of the second production block, was originally intended to open a second 13-part series of *The Prisoner*; it was the first to be made after the departure of Markstein (although he remained in the title sequence, at least for the moment); McGoohan's behaviour was becoming increasingly eccentric; the series was over budget; and the whole team seemed uncertain what direction to take *The Prisoner* in. The story's genesis also marked a transition: there are indications that it was commissioned before Markstein left (although it is known that it was written specifically to cover McGoohan's absence during the filming of *Ice Station Zebra*), and the idea of taking the Prisoner out into the world is one often attributed to Markstein, but David Tomblin (who would be as big an influence on the second production block as Markstein had been on the first) claims that he came up with the body-swap concept (although Vincent Tilsley, in interviews, has also laid claim to having the initial idea). Tilsley has frequently voiced displeasure with the result, particularly noting that the body-swap plot is a 'very corny idea.' The series was somewhat undecided whether to go down a more conventional ITC spy series route, or to strike off in unknown directions.

'Do Not Forsake Me Oh My Darling' comes across as a worrying glimpse of what the future might have been for *The Prisoner*, being both overly conventional and filled with production-crew inside jokes. An example of the latter is that the title 'Do Not Forsake Me Oh My Darling' was moved from the Western-set episode 'Living in

Harmony', which it fitted better thematically, to this episode, apparently at least partly as a joke about McGoohan's absence. Similarly, the folk tune 'My Bonnie Lies Over the Ocean' is repeated throughout the incidental music, referring not only to the relationship between the Prisoner and Janet, but apparently also to McGoohan's presence in America at the time. The theme tune and title sequence are referenced when the Prisoner returns to the London HQ. In the original script, Number One is spoken of as if he were a kind of *Charlie's Angels*-style boss, absent but nonetheless demonstrably human and politically active; while this was largely removed by the final edit, the notion survives in the Colonel's dying remark that the Village must contact Number One and tell him that he did his duty. Another connection with *Danger Man* also appears, in that Potter happens to have the same name as Christopher Benjamin's character in 'Koroshi'. 'Do Not Forsake Me Oh My Darling' thus suggests that, had circumstances been different, *The Prisoner* might have become a much more conventional spy series, returning to its *Danger Man* roots.

To add to this, the constraints on the filming of the episode (as well as the shortcomings of the plot) have made for a production that has too many problematic aspects for these all to be put down to the general surrealism of the Village set-up. While Pat Jackson had previously done brilliant work on 'A, B and C', 'The Schizoid Man' and 'Hammer into Anvil', this story demonstrates that even a good director can fail under outside constraints. When the Prisoner sees himself in the mirror in his London house, for instance, the necessity of keeping the camera from showing up in the reflected background means that the angle of the third person shot is inconsistent with that of the one representing his point of view. The stock footage of the Prisoner's journey across Europe was clearly filmed from vehicles that were all taller than a Lotus 7, meaning that we have the impression at times that the Prisoner's car is floating between three and eight feet off the ground. In some of the long shots of the Prisoner driving in London, it is extremely obvious that it is McGoohan at the wheel of the car rather than Stock; and Stock's double is also noticeable in the long shots in the Green Dome and the fight sequence under the barber shop (as he appears to grow and lose hair from moment to moment). Stock is seen wearing a black suit, identical in style to the Prisoner's in 'Arrival' (although one would assume that it is not actually the same one, given the difference in size between the two men), when he goes to the London HQ, but apparently changes to a white shirt, dark tie and blazer to drive back to Buckingham Place, then dons the black suit again before actually parking his car and getting out. As the original car had been sold abroad, this episode featured a stand-in, hired from a local Borehamwood man. The World Backgrounds-supplied stock footage of London used in the sequence where the Prisoner is seen going to the camera shop features a number of suspiciously vintage-looking cars, suggesting that it was actually sourced from a period film; and the stock footage of Madame Engadine's party from 'A, B and C', the garden set from the same episode, and more of the set from *The Dirty Dozen* reappear during the birthday-party sequence.

'Do Not Forsake Me Oh My Darling' is something of a mess, due to the outside circumstances surrounding its production and the crew's uncertainty about the direction and future of the series. However, it is still possible to find at least one or two points of interest in the script, if only with regard to the Village's relationship to the wider world.

Essay 4: Putting A Different Face On Things: 'Face Unknown'

The story that ultimately finished up as 'Do Not Forsake Me Oh My Darling' began as a script by Vincent Tilsley entitled 'Face Unknown', which was to have been the opening episode of the second series of *The Prisoner*. Tilsley has gone on record as saying that he was very unhappy with the rewrite, which he puts down to McGoohan and Tomblin. There are also occasional reports, for instance in White and Ali's *The Official Prisoner Companion*, that McGoohan was unhappy with the version that he saw on his return from Hollywood and insisted on re-editing it, even shooting new scenes. While the narrative of the original is essentially the same as the finished version, there are enough changes to warrant some discussion here.

To begin with, great pains are taken within 'Face Unknown' to re-establish the central scenario of *The Prisoner*, in keeping with this being the opening story of a new series, and to also emphasise strongly that the events take place exactly a year to the day after the Prisoner's abduction to the Village: a specific date, 12 July, is mentioned in 'Face Unknown' but not in the final version. The dialogue from the titles sequence is also reiterated throughout the story: when the Prisoner wakes up in his London house, his inner monologue begins 'Where am I? … Home …' (although he suspects something is wrong from the outset), and the usual 'Where am I?' 'In the Village …' dialogue between the Prisoner and Number Two is repeated when the Prisoner reawakens in his own body. Seltzman is described as having 'defected from both sides,' to which the

Prisoner responds 'How honest can you get?', restating the central idea of the series regarding both 'sides' of the Cold War being equally untrustworthy. There are also a few inside jokes, particularly with the titles of a number of earlier episodes featuring in the dialogue: a male guest wishes Janet 'Many happy returns,' for instance, and Sir Charles's unseen companion (see below) says that if the released Prisoner does not go to find Seltzman, 'It's your funeral.' The line 'Welcome to the Village,' spoken by the waiter in Kandersfeld, is present in both the original and the finished version.

Another noteworthy difference is that in the original, Number One is explicitly referred to as an unseen character. While – as noted above – a remnant of this idea remains in the finished version in the Colonel's dying request that Number One be told that he did his duty, this one line could be put down to surrealism, or to the fancies of a dying man. In the original, however, we also have the following dialogue between the Colonel (whose name is given as Colonel Oscar here) and Number Two:

NUMBER TWO: Machines. We still think we're in control. Perhaps we've resigned and don't know it.
OSCAR: We control the machines.
NUMBER TWO: And Number One controls us.
OSCAR: Of course.
NUMBER TWO: Are we sure *he* isn't a machine?

As well as containing the only direct mention by a Village official of Number One being the Village controller, this exchange also carries the implication that Number One could be a machine; an idea that was implied in 'Dance of the Dead' and will feature later in Thomas M Disch's novel *I Am Not a Number!* At the end, Seltzman/Colonel Oscar says that Number One is waiting for him and implies that he has met him, an idea that Number Two accepts without question, and it is stated earlier that the Prisoner was kidnapped on Number One's orders. Around the end of the story, Number Two actually speaks to Number One on the phone. In this script, then, Number One is much more explicitly a real character, albeit one whose nature is not fully known.

The fate of failed Number Twos is also explicitly referenced in 'Face Unknown'. The second scene features a sequence in the Green

Dome in which Number Two (who is said to be on a diet and having a sparse breakfast as a result) talks to the Butler (referred to as 'Angelo' in the script), and says: 'Don't you ever wonder what happened to them? Your ex-masters? ... It's comforting to know that one won't be mourned. I would hate to cause you grief ... however, I don't intend to fail.' The first episode of the second series was thus originally to have made it more or less explicit that failure leads to death for a Village chairman.

The idea that there is collusion between the Prisoner's former employers and the Village, while still present (albeit ambiguously) in the final version, is also much more explicit in 'Face Unknown'. Principally, there are a number of cut scenes where Sir Charles observes the Prisoner from a darkened room via a one-way mirror, speaking with an unseen man (who, in shades of *The X-Files*, smokes throughout), which suggest that Sir Charles is in collusion with a third party that may well be the Village. At one point, Sir Charles and the unseen companion observe Janet's party on a TV screen, and the other man asks Sir Charles if he knows what side his daughter is on (dialogue between Oscar and Number Two elsewhere directly alludes to the conflict of interest inherent in the Prisoner's relationship with Janet, and suggests that he did not tell her why he resigned out of concern that she might tell her father). The Prisoner does not in fact encounter Janet until after he has seen her father; he tells her that his name is 'Robert Edward Turner'. A conversation between two male guests at Janet's party suggests that they know the Prisoner has been taken to the Village (the Prisoner then surprises them by greeting them by name, leaving them puzzled as to how an apparent stranger knows who they are). Seltzman (whose name is spelled 'Saltzman' in 'Face Unknown') asks the undertaker, regarding Potter, 'Are you on different sides or just different ministries?' to which the undertaker implies that they work for the same cause. Seltzman also claims that he invented the Village gas-pistol, suggesting that the Village authorities have had extensive access to his work before. One difference in the other direction, however, occurs where, in 'Face Unknown', the Prisoner is charged 30 shillings for the development of the slides; 'Do Not Forsake Me Oh My Darling' does not mention a price, blurring the boundaries between the Village (with its changing, surrealistic currency units) and the outside world moreso than the original.

The scene of the Prisoner waking up to discover himself in a new body is also slightly different in the original script. To begin with, somewhat more believably, the Prisoner's resignation is very much on his mind throughout the initial monologue (in fact, when he goes to tender his resignation to Villers later on, we discover that he has delivered an exact replica a year earlier, which is on his file). The whole sequence is specified to be shot either from the Prisoner's point of view or in such a way as to obscure his identity, from the moment when he wakes up until he reaches Danvers' office; it is there that, for the first time, he speaks in Oscar's voice (his inner monologue having been in McGoohan's voice) and sees himself in a mirror (which is slightly hard to believe, as it implies first of all that he prepares to go out without once checking his appearance, and secondly that he manages to drive to the office without once catching sight of his own reflection in the rear-view mirror), suggesting a gradual process whereby the character that we, and he, assume to be the Prisoner morphs slowly into Oscar, completing the process when we see the latter's face. Oscar is referred to as such in the scripts until he changes bodies with the Prisoner, after which he is referred to as 'O', much as the Prisoner is traditionally referred to as 'P' (as part of the 'morphing' process, he is 'P' in the stage directions up until the point at which he sees his face). Whereas in 'Do Not Forsake Me Oh My Darling' the Prisoner's amnesia lifts once he looks in the mirror, in 'Face Unknown' this does not happen until his mind has been transferred back, suggesting that he has returned to the Village afresh for the new series and allowing the central concepts to be re-established.

Another major set of differences comes with the treatment of the slides. 'Face Unknown' does not include the pre-titles scene that appears in the finished version (the occasional postmodern touches to the scene also rather suggest either McGoohan's or Tomblin's influence); the first appearance of the slides (which here are pictures of Seltzman rather than holiday snaps) comes instead when the Prisoner looks at them in his home, a scene paralleled by one of Number Two and Colonel Oscar (who is wearing the Prisoner's body at this point; the original featured a number of scenes with Colonel Oscar played by McGoohan, which were removed when the extent of McGoohan's Hollywood commitments became known) looking at the same slides, and Number Two observing that he cannot figure out the significance of them – particularly one that is totally black but for a single line near the bottom right-hand corner, which starts thickly and tapers away. The solution to the mystery is revealed when we discover the hidden image, which in 'Face Unknown' is a map of the Continent revealing Seltzman's location rather than a name. The map then reappears superimposed on the montage of the Prisoner driving to Kandersfeld, with an animated line tracing the route, and the slides taken away one by one to finish on an image of Seltzman, in a sequence that it would have been interesting to see televised.

The hearse and undertakers also feature more extensively in the original script. After the Prisoner's mind is transferred and his memory wiped, we see a shot of a toy balloon, which turns out to be held by a child outside the Prisoner's house in London, with the undertakers taking a coffin back through the front door. When the Prisoner returns later, the hearse is outside a house a few doors away, with an undertaker apparently waiting and observing him; as he goes into his own house, bearers are seen to carry a coffin out of the house a few doors away. The hearse was also to have made a brief appearance outside the house where Janet's party takes place, when Potter arrives. In the scene in the camera shop (which was called 'West End Camera Suppliers' in the script), the Prisoner was to have looked out and seen not just the disguised undertaker but an entire funeral procession, complete with hearse, going by. In the scene where the undertaker turns up in Kandersfeld clad in what appears to be a chauffeur's uniform, he was originally to have retained his undertaker's garb and hearse, and the gassed Prisoner and Seltzman were each to have been placed in a coffin for transport. Finally, the undertaker, clad in a white lab coat, was to have formed one of a party of scientists who observe the reversal process in the Village. The end was to have also featured a long and clunky explanation about what Seltzman had done to the Colonel, with the idea that the Prisoner and Seltzman had agreed on this plan between them, which was fortunately cut down in the final version.

It is difficult to claim either that 'Face Unknown' was a decent script ruined by its revision (since the original, somewhat contrived, idea is common to both, and the earlier script featured a much more prosaic treatment of the Village, Number One, and so forth), or that it was one that needed much improvement (since it does contain a few clever sequences and concepts that were omitted from, or appeared only in modified form in, the finished version). The comparison between the two, however, does give us some idea of how *The Prisoner*'s central concept might have been re-established for a second series, and of the somewhat more conventional spy-series direction that it was starting to take at the time that the script was written.

Episode 14:
Living in Harmony

First UK Transmission Date: Friday 29 December 1967: ATV Midlands/Grampian,7.30 pm – 8.30 pm
Writer: David Tomblin (from a story by David Tomblin and Ian L Rakoff)
Director: David Tomblin
Credited Cast: Patrick McGoohan (The Prisoner); Alexis Kanner (The Kid); David Bauer (The Judge); Valerie French (Kathy); Gordon Tanner (Town Elder); Gordon Sterne (Bystander); Michael Balfour (Will); Larry Taylor (Mexican Sam); Monti De Lyle (Town Dignitary); Douglas Jones (Horse Dealer); Bill Nick (First Gunman); Les Crawford (Second Gunman); Frank Maher (Third Gunman); Max Faulkner (First Horseman); Bill Cummings (Second Horseman); Eddie Eddon (Third Horseman)
Known Uncredited Cast: Frank Maher (Double for Patrick McGoohan); Peter Brace (Zeke); Peter Brayham (Cowboy Thug 1); Stephanie-Ann Maher (Little Girl); Gary Maher (Little Boy in Checked Shirt); Robert Rietty (Additional Voicework)

SYNOPSIS: In the Wild West, a nameless sheriff resigns his commission and turns in his badge and gun. He is then beaten up and taken to a mysterious small town named Harmony, ruled by the Judge, who urges him to become the town sheriff. He refuses, despite repeated hostility from the townsfolk, and despite witnessing the depredations of a sadistic young man called the Kid. He is helped to escape by a saloon girl named Kathy, but is recaptured. Kathy is put to trial, found guilty of aiding him, and imprisoned in the town jail under the guardianship of the Kid, who is unhealthily obsessed with her. The nameless man agrees to become town sheriff in order to protect Kathy, but refuses to carry a gun. He is attacked by a group of heavies but prevails, earning the respect of some of the townsfolk, who offer to help him clean up Harmony. The Judge's hired thugs, however, intimidate the townsfolk, and the sheriff decides to leave town again, this time with Kathy. The Judge gets word of this to the Kid, who kills Kathy in a jealous rage. The sheriff buries Kathy, then, removing his badge and taking up his gun, challenges the Kid to a duel and kills him. He goes to the saloon and takes on the Judge and three of his gunmen in a shootout, during which the nameless man is shot dead by the Judge.

The Prisoner wakes up in the Village, discovering himself to be on a Western set filled with cardboard cut-outs in the shape of the townsfolk (and, apparently, horses). He goes to the Green Dome to investigate, and we learn that he was subject to a reality-altering process invented by Number Eight, who played the Kid in the Western scenario, on behalf of Number Two, who played the Judge. This process has, however, affected the participating Villagers, and Number Eight returns to the set, where he kills Number Twenty Two, who played Kathy, and commits suicide, before the eyes of the Prisoner and Number Two.

ANALYSIS: 'Living in Harmony' is unusual even by the standards of *The Prisoner*, in that, while earlier episodes have played with the conventions of television and of spy drama, this one actively defies the conventions of genre, transforming the series, with no explanation until the end of the story, from a surreal spy drama into a seemingly-conventional Western. As such, it marks the point at which the series finally throws caution to the wind and becomes wildly experimental; an approach that will culminate in the mysterious and exuberant 'Fall Out'.

This story's genesis has been the subject of some controversy. It was the only successful submission to come out of an initiative by McGoohan and Tomblin to canvas the production staff for story ideas. Assistant film editor Ian Rakoff has stated (most notably in his memoir *Inside The Prisoner*) that he came up with the script, which Tomblin then appropriated wholesale, leaving him with a partial credit for the original story. However, it should be pointed out that McGoohan had apparently been keen to do a Western-inspired episode for some time (a cowboy, an Indian and a Mexican are clearly visible among the extras in "Dance of the Dead"). Stuntman Frank Maher, a Western fan who went on to write a number of Western novels, and who oversaw the authenticity aspect of 'Living in Harmony', also lays claim to having suggested the original idea. It was thus probably a case of a number of people all having similar ideas at the same time, although Rakoff has the best-substantiated claim to having come up with the specific elements of 'Living in Harmony' itself. Rakoff attributes the ideas behind the story (including the ironic use of the name 'Harmony' for a disharmonious village) to a number of Western comics he had read and films he had seen, as well as to his own feelings about the Vietnam War and his experiences as an anti-apartheid activist in South Africa, where he was discouraged from carrying a gun despite the obvious utility of arming oneself in such a situation.

Production-wise, the story was fraught with difficulty, reportedly taking five weeks to film where other episodes took around a fortnight.[15] The opening sequence includes a stock footage background of what may be the real American West (it is certainly not England, although there was some location work done on the Dunstable Downs in Bedfordshire), but most of the story was shot at the Borehamwood studios, which were also playing host to the production of *2001: A Space Odyssey* at the time, so that actor Alexis Kanner recalls having to share his dressing-room with a leopard that was being used for the film's famous 'Dawn of Man' sequence. Kanner also claims that there was a one-sixth of a second difference between his and McGoohan's quickdraws in the shootout sequence; he asserts that his was faster, but running the DVD on slow-motion suggests that McGoohan was the winner. Finally, upon first British transmission, certain sequences, particularly those involving hanging or strangulation, were cut and the episode consigned to a

---

15 Cameraman Len Harris, in an interview on The Unmutual website, has however claimed that it was 'only a normal ten-day shooting'.

post-10.00 pm slot in some areas, because of a then recent case in which a child had accidentally hanged himself while trying to imitate a lynching he had seen in (ironically) a TV Western.

ONCE UPON A TIME IN THE WEST:
GENRE-CROSSING IN 'LIVING IN HARMONY'

As noted, this story is mostly interesting for its premise: the entire set-up of *The Prisoner* is transposed across time, space and genre, even down to the title sequence (during the 1970s repeats, some ITV networks, fearing that this change might cause confusion, superimposed a *The Prisoner* caption slide over the opening scenes on first broadcast, against McGoohan's wishes). While this type of genre-crossing has since become a popular staple of telefantasy series (with shows as diverse as *Star Trek: The Next Generation*, *Buffy the Vampire Slayer* and *Xena: Warrior Princess* all featuring episodes in which the main characters are recast into historical or fictional settings), it was not only groundbreaking at the time, but also considerably more serious in tone than the modern examples, which have been generally framed as lightweight diversions from the series' usual fare. It seems counterintuitive, under the circumstances, that a spy story could survive such a transformation without becoming an effective pantomime, and yet it all fits perfectly into the Western genre. This flags up the idea that the story of the Prisoner and the Village is literally universal: not only is the Village the world, as we have seen before, but it is the world in all times and places. It also throws open other possibilities in the mind of the viewer. Could the Village be transposed to outer space? The court of Louis XV? Central Asia? The answer, according to this story, would appear to be yes, which is further borne out by the equally convention-defying next story in the UK transmission order, 'The Girl Who Was Death'.

It is, however, worth noting that the West portrayed here is not the historical American West, but a filmic West, complete with all the clichés of the genre (corrupt small town administration, comedy Mexican, tart with heart of gold, and so forth). This may shed light on why, although the actors playing the Judge and the Kid are American and Canadian respectively, they both (along with

Kathy/Number Twenty Two) assume English accents for their 'real world' scenes as Number Two and Number Eight, highlighting that their Harmony personae were simply roles rather than explicit avatars of their real selves. Indeed, one of the ways in which the audience is able to accept Number Eight's suicide at the end of the story (despite the fact that neither his real-life self, nor the Kid, has shown any tendencies along these lines before; in the original version of the script, Number Eight falls off the balcony accidentally, fleeing two ambulance attendants who have come to take him away) is that there is a tradition in Western and related stories of a character engaging in a suicidal act to avoid facing justice for his crimes. Unlike in other *The Prisoner* episodes, the set-up is not particularly multicultural, with the one ethnic minority character being the comedically stereotypical Mexican (who was originally to have been a Native American; he is played by the same performer who appeared as one of the Gypsy men in 'Many Happy Returns'). The use of cardboard cut-outs to represent the characters at the end of the sequence could perhaps be a nod to the two-dimensionality of characters in most genre fiction. In highlighting the fictionality of the set-up, the story also expands the Western out to the world, pointing up that Western stories are not only about the Wild West, but about bigger issues as well, and that the same applies to other sorts of genre fiction, including, of course, the spy story.

The parallels between the real Village and the fictional Harmony are drawn, visually and textually, throughout the episode. Like the Village, the jail contains various random posters and printed announcements. These include several 'wanted' posters and one for some kind of performance, plus the more enigmatic/Village-esque 'The Bishop is Coming!' The Stranger does not recognise Harmony at the outset, much as the Prisoner does not recognise the Village upon his arrival there. Harmony also mirrors the Village in having incidents of violence and coercion ironically juxtaposed with a seemingly peaceable exterior, most notably emphasised in the superimposition of the title 'Living in Harmony' over a scene of the Stranger being beaten up by thugs. The second time the phrase 'Living in Harmony' is used is right before a posse of villagers attempt to administer a similar beating. Certain aspects of the story also recall scenes in earlier episodes of *The Prisoner*: the angry reaction of the locals when the Stranger says Harmony isn't his kind of town parallels similar scenes of hostility in 'A Change of Mind', and the kangaroo court recalls the trial in 'Dance of the Dead' and also foreshadows 'Fall Out'. The parallels are therefore not only in terms of personnel and setting, but also in terms of the atmosphere of Harmony and of the story's connections to other episodes.

The question arises, though, of why the Western should be the genre chosen for this episode, rather than, say, the space opera, the war story or the medieval fantasy (the romance novel, given McGoohan's desire to steer away from this type of story, being obviously out of the question). While connections are frequently made between 'Living in Harmony' and the spaghetti Westerns of Sergio Leone (particularly those involving Clint Eastwood as the Man with No Name, whom the Stranger in 'Living in Harmony' clearly references; the lack of Native American characters in 'Harmony' may also, unconsciously, parallel a similar lack in Leone's Western films), it bears a closer resemblance to the subgenre of 'allegorical Westerns,' which frequently focus, like *The Prisoner*, on the legitimacy of the political system and the conflict between the individual and society. These include Leone's *Once Upon a Time in the West,* Fred Zinneman's *High Noon,* George Marshall's *Destry Rides Again* (which is a spiritual antecedent to 'Living in Harmony' in that it features a deputy sheriff who refuses to carry a gun, and earns the respect of the townspeople through using lateral thinking to defeat the local wrongdoers) and John Ford's *The Man Who Shot Liberty Valance*. The latter is particularly relevant to 'Living in Harmony', featuring as it does a plot in which James Stewart (who also appeared as the above-mentioned deputy sheriff in *Destry Rides Again*) plays a lawman who goes to a Western town where there is no law but vigilante justice, symbolised by a desperado named Liberty Valance. In order to get the townsfolk to accept the rule of law, he must persuade them to give up the liberty of anarchy, and accept instead the constraints (but also the safety and protection) of civilisation, symbolised by his quest to kill Liberty Valance. In the end, however, Liberty must be killed by another desperado, played by the ageing John Wayne, signifying that the sacrifice of liberty in favour of law and order must be performed willingly in order to have any legitimacy. 'Living in Harmony', similarly, features an allegorical distinction between vigilante justice and the rule of law (as the Stranger will not wear the gun and the sheriff's badge simultaneously; note the parallel with the Prisoner's own refusal to wear the Number Six badge in the Village), and a discussion on the freedom of the individual versus the needs of the community and the possible consequences of decisions made in that regard (as the Stranger refuses to take on the role of sheriff to please the Judge, but will do so for the sake of Kathy and other vulnerable villagers; although, in doing so, he also serves the Judge's interests). By using a genre that explores ideas of anarchy and justice, *The Prisoner* can cast new light on what are by now familiar themes within the series.

MADE IN AMERICA: THE VIETNAM CONTROVERSY

One consequence of the team's choice of genre and subject matter was the fact that the episode was banned in the USA on the series' initial broadcast. Although the ostensible reason was that it contained references to drugs, and while the real reason is often said to have been that it was seen as supporting draft-dodging and other forms of pacifist opposition to the Vietnam War, there are other, more complex, issues involved. As a genre, the Western is strongly bound up with American origin mythologies and sense of identity, and also with the American emphasis on the right to own and carry guns as a basic freedom, so a story, made by a British production team, about a man in the Wild West, at the symbolic founding of America, refusing to wear a gun, is bound to touch the occasional nerve.

More than this, however, the message of the story appears to be, in part, that the rule of law and the use of firearms are mutually exclusive. When the Stranger wears the badge, he refuses to carry the gun, and when he takes up the gun at the end of the sequence, he removes his badge. The Kid is good with a gun but loses when forced into a fistfight, again suggesting that the gun is inherently a weapon of cowards, favoured by gangsters and psychopaths. Despite his prowess as a sharpshooter, the Kid gets hit a lot, including by the Judge, and bitten by Kathy. The only fight he wins is when he strangles Kathy, suggesting that those who resort to guns can only win otherwise when they are fighting a weaker opponent. It's also worth noting that although the Stranger is physically attacked by Zeke and his gang when he goes out without his gun, this action still brings a number of townsfolk to his side, as they are impressed by his integrity and willingness to stand up for himself; and, had events not taken the turn they did, he might have succeeded in bringing order to a lawless town. The idea that you can't police people by killing them, but can win them over by acting with integrity, was probably not a message that went down well in a country that was engaged in a 'police action' of dubious legitimacy in South East Asia at the time that the episode was made and broadcast.

This also brings up the issue of involvement in politics. The focus in this episode is not on finding out why the Stranger resigned as sheriff, but on getting him to join the Judge's 'team', reflecting the way the Village in the wider series has gradually gone from simply trying to glean 'information' from the Prisoner in the earliest episodes, to the more subtle, and sinister, goal of trying to change his mindset entirely. The Judge was played by David Bauer, an American who, ironically, had come to England in order to escape the McCarthy witch-hunts. In this story, the Stranger has to compromise; rather than see people suffer, he must accept the badge, but doing so means that he also accepts a role within a corrupt system (although, since the Stranger's original rejection of the badge was a symbolic rejection of the system, it is significant that he takes off the badge when about to embark on his revenge for Kathy's death – indicating that he has again rejected the society and intends to destroy it). The corruption of the system was further highlighted in the original script by recurring sequences of the Judge playing an interminable game of poker with Harmony villagers (including at least one explicitly identified as a town elder), and cheating, which they are too afraid of him to challenge; most of these sequences are changed in the final version to the Judge playing patience, and although two poker games do survive, there is no suggestion that the Judge is cheating in them. This theme of political corruption reflects on the Prisoner's original fateful decision, suggesting that it may have been for similar reasons: does one resign, and allow a system one does not agree with to carry on, or does one stay in, try to change things, and ultimately become corrupted? In 'Living in Harmony', the Stranger's decision to compromise leads to the system putting more pressure on him to conform, with ultimately fatal results for both Kathy and himself.

The issue of taking sides is also reflected in the Harmony set-up. The Judge wants the Stranger on his side, as opposed to anybody else's, suggesting that again the Village's concern with the Prisoner's resignation is less about finding out the reason for it than about ensuring that he stays on the same 'side' (as emphasised in, for instance, 'A, B and C'). The Village authorities, like the Judge, fear the idea that one of their agents resigned because he had more sympathy for the other side, raising the possibility that the other side has more to offer, whereas the Prisoner's motivations, as seen in, for instance, 'Do Not Forsake Me Oh My Darling', seem more complex than simply a choice of sides. In order to survive in Harmony, however, the Stranger is forced to take sides, first accepting the badge, and then rejecting it and fighting the Kid. Taking sides ultimately proves detrimental to everyone in the story, and yet, as in the Cold War itself, it is impossible for the Stranger not to do so.

GETTING INVOLVED: THE KID, KATHY AND THE GAME

This story also deals with involvement in another sense: that of getting involved in fictions. In this, 'Harmony' foreshadows the cyberpunk genre of novels (and, to a lesser extent, films) of the 1970s and 80s, which frequently deal with the idea of virtual reality and its relationship to physical reality; another forerunner of the genre, the film *Westworld*, about a role-playing theme-park, also focused on Westerns and dealt with the problem of fiction blending into reality (when antagonistic robots designed to provide a sense of excitement without any real danger of injury suddenly become genuinely hostile, making the fiction no longer a pleasurable diversion but a very real adventure with the possibility of a tragic ending). In 'Harmony', the fiction becomes so powerful that it draws the players in without them realising it: Kathy/Number Twenty Two and the Kid/Number Eight cannot let go of their in-game personae and continue to act out the story afterwards (something made even more explicit in the original script, in which the final confrontation between Number Eight and Number Twenty

Two openly mirrors that between the Kid and Kathy, in that he kisses her, she bites his lip and he chokes her).

For the Prisoner himself, the game comes to an end not because he learns to differentiate fact from fantasy, but conversely because he becomes so involved in it that his fictional persona is actually killed. This could be seen as an allegory of the Prisoner becoming drawn into the Village despite himself: while he has tried to maintain an air of detachment, over the past few episodes we have seen him becoming repeatedly involved in the Village, and openly using its methods at least twice. In this story, too, we see him wandering around the Harmony set after the game has ended, perhaps indicating that he, too, was drawn into the story. McGoohan, at the time, was also becoming, in the opinion of Rakoff, a bit too involved in the series: 'The division between what he was, and what he was acting, was a slender line. There was a fight going on, and it was all inside of him. I felt that I'd hate to have been around if it should ever spill out' (*Inside The Prisoner*, p 26). The message of 'Living in Harmony' is thus that no-one is immune from being drawn into fantasy, but that it can have dangerous consequences.

Within the story, the character of the Kid (yet another Number Eight; an example of the way particular numbers seem to recur randomly amongst the main protagonists) deserves further exploration, as he represents three clashing principles: authority, death and infantilisation. The Kid wears a top hat, which in the Village is worn by two groups of people: the Village Council and the undertakers, representing authority and death respectively. In the Kid's role as a representative of authority, it is significant that he is a mute imbecile: the Village Council themselves are also imbeciles, parroting and deferring to the will of Number Two and/or mysterious tape recordings, or sometimes not speaking at all. Like the Council, the Kid is also subject to a higher power, the Judge. In the original story, the Kid was not mute; the decision to cut his lines, as well as sparing the audience a number of unfortunate clunkers (some examples: 'Maybe you don't know who I am. I'm the Kid.' 'I'm good. I'm the best. I'm the fastest'; to which the Prisoner responds, 'You're certainly the loudest.' 'I like to see a man's eyes when he dies.' 'And that goes for the rest of you. Stay away from her.') and giving a surreal, sinister edge to the character (who, being silent and obsessive, recalls a kind of psychopathic Harpo Marx with his top-hat and curls) and a parallel with the bowler-hatted but equally mute Butler, provides a comment on the lack of political voice of the people in a corrupt system like Harmony. His other top-hatted function, as a death-figure, comes to the fore in his role as murderer and ultimately suicide; in three episodes' time, Kanner will again return as a death-figure, wearing a top-hat and black suit and singing 'Dem Bones'. The story also involves a symbolic death for the Prisoner, as his exit from the role-playing game is rather like the symbolic death he went through when he went into the Village; the idea of death as escape will come to the fore strongly in the remaining episodes of the series.

The final major theme reflected in the Kid is that of infantilisation. Leaving aside the obvious connotations of the character's name, Kanner portrays him as a kind of mobile id: preverbal, staring and not vocalising, acting purely on base sexual and violent impulses, and throwing tantrums with little provocation. His attachment to Kathy has a quasi-maternal as well as sexual feeling to it: his shooting of the cowboy who gets fresh with her in the bar, suggesting that he is so unaware of his social environment that he can't differentiate between a genuine rival for Kathy's affections and a pathetic middle-aged man who is a little bit drunk, seems not only like a young child who has not yet learned to differentiate between self and environment, but also like a child who is jealous of rivals – sibling or paternal – for his mother's affection. The scene in which the Kid strikes gunfighter poses in the jail while the Stranger ignores him recalls a child aping its elders in a bid to get attention, and failing to receive it. It is worth noting that some aspects of the story also reflect psychoanalytic themes – the idea of role-playing as a form of therapy and of the Prisoner coming, through his role-play, to terms with the rest of the world and abandoning his delusions. The story thus deals with psychological problems and specifically their roots in childhood and infancy.

Arguably, this infantilisation is reflected in the rest of the story as well. In some ways, it could be characterised as the Village deciding to have a jolly game of Cowboys and Indians (a pastime more common for 1960s children than modern ones), particularly as it draws on the stylised conventions of the fictional West rather than real colonial history, as the children's games of Cowboys and Indians reflected the sanitised film and TV Westerns of the 1950s and 1960s rather than real life (although it must be said that, as only the Prisoner, Number Twenty Two, Number Eight and Number Two are seen wearing headsets at the end of the story, it seems likely that the other inhabitants of Harmony are projections rather than role-playing Villagers). For the first time, we actually see children in the series, these being Gary Maher, son of Frank Maher, clearly visible in a checked shirt, and two others, reportedly Gary's sister Stephanie-Ann and the son of assistant director Gino Marotta, in the background; Gary Maher apparently handed the Stranger his hat, *Shane*-style, during the recording, but it is uncertain whether or not this was spontaneous or, indeed, whether or not it was filmed. One can also see the Prisoner's awakening and going down into the Village afterwards as a maturing individual abandoning childish play and becoming more focused on adult concerns (much as *Peter Pan* can be read as children coming to the realisation that eternal childhood is not necessarily a good thing and accepting that they have to grow up). In that case, the fact that he is drawn back to the Harmony set might be a way of saying that adults are affected by their childhood experiences, and that people cannot totally abandon the things of childhood, nor should they do so.

Mention must be briefly made of Kathy. She is slightly older than the other saloon girls, reflecting the usual age trend for *The Prisoner* women, and played by Valerie French, who had also played a victim of strangulation in the Western movie *Jubal*, and would act in another Western, *Shalako*, after her stint on *The Prisoner*. Again, the suggestion that she and the Prisoner might have a romantic relationship was excised from the original script, and there is also a convincing reason here as to why their relationship might be close but not sexual, as the Stranger symbolically replaces her brother in the Harmony village set-up; her brother dies shortly after he arrives, as a result of the Stranger's arrival, and he forms an emotional bond with Kathy (whose name in the original script was spelt with a C) due to her unjust treatment by the Judge. In fact, the Stranger physically takes the brother's place in the county jail cell, and the hanging of the brother is partly shot from a first-person perspective. In the original script, we learn before Number Twenty Two dies that the Village has been holding her real brother hostage to ensure her cooperation; however, this could have been seen as another case of the fiction bleeding into her real life, and may have been cut as a consequence of this ambiguity.

'Living in Harmony' remains one of the most controversial and mould-breaking stories in the series to this point, exploring concepts of reality, fiction and the difference between the two, as well as political themes that, although more familiar, are on a level that, at the time, really began to excite controversy. Coming as it does after a number of relatively conventional stories, it marks a transition to much more surreal and challenging fare.

Episode 15:
The Girl Who Was Death

First UK Transmission Date: Friday 18 January 1968: Scottish, 7.30 pm – 8.30 pm
Writer: Terence Feely (From an idea by David Tomblin)
Director: David Tomblin
Credited Cast: Patrick McGoohan (The Prisoner); Kenneth Griffith (Schnipps); Justine Lord (Sonia); Christopher Benjamin (Potter); Michael Brennan (Killer Karminski); Harold Berens (Boxing M.C.); Sheena Marsh (Barmaid); Max Faulkner (Scots Napoleon); John Rees (Welsh Napoleon); Joe Gladwin (Yorkshire Napoleon); John Drake (Bowler); Gaynor Steward (Little Girl); Graham Steward (First Little Boy); Stephen Howe (Second Little Boy)
Known Uncredited Cast: Frank Maher (Double for Patrick McGoohan); Phyllis Bundy (Pretty Spectator); Alexis Kanner (Voice of Chief and Photographer); Jimmy Millar (Irish Napoleon)

SYNOPSIS: A man is killed by an exploding ball during a cricket game; an agent ('Mr X'), who looks like the Prisoner, is ordered to investigate. Mr X foils the plot, and a beautiful woman, Sonia, leaves him a message suggesting that they meet at his local pub, where she attempts to poison him. She then leads him on a chase through a Turkish baths, a boxing match, a fairground, and the ghost town of Witchwood, where she apparently kills him; however, he survives and, by clinging on to her helicopter, is able to follow her to a lighthouse. Her father, it transpires, is Schnipps, a mad scientist obsessed with Napoleon, planning to blow up London and take over the UK. Mr X attempts to foil their plans, but is caught and left tied up inside the lighthouse, which is really a rocket aimed at London. Mr X escapes by sliding the back off the chair to which he is tied and freeing his hands, sabotaging the console and tricking Sonia and Schnipps into blowing themselves up with stick grenades.

The whole story is then revealed to be a tale that the Prisoner is telling to some Village children before bed. As this innocent activity is also an attempt to catch him off guard, it is being observed by Number Two and his assistant. However, the ploy is unsuccessful, and the Prisoner bids his audience goodnight.

ANALYSIS: 'The Girl Who Was Death' was originally supposed to follow on from 'Hammer into Anvil' rather than 'Living in Harmony' (and indeed still does in the American broadcast order), presumably on the grounds that having two weird, genre-bending stories so close together might be problematic. However, the juxtaposition of the two merely reinforces the fact that *The Prisoner* has now taken a turn firmly into the realms of surreal and challenging television.

YOU HAVE JUST BEEN POISONED: 'THE GIRL WHO WAS DEATH' AND SPY STORIES

Although it can claim a number of other antecedents (including *Orphée*, which features a mysterious woman who literally is Death), this story is the one in which *The Prisoner's* debt to *Casino Royale* (which was first screened in April 1967, several months before 'The Girl Who Was Death' began filming) becomes most apparent. Leaving aside the fact that the Witchwood sequence was filmed on the same back lot as *Casino Royale*, both 'The Girl Who Was Death' and the film are spy spoofs with a psychedelic element to them, that poke fun at the James Bond film genre, particularly its gadgetry (David Niven's character in *Casino Royale* refers disparagingly to 'joke-shop spies'), cars and *femmes fatales*. There are even some aspects of 'The Girl Who Was Death' that appear to be conscious references to *Casino Royale*: both feature a car chase between an English gentleman-spy and a blonde girl dressed in white in a

Jaguar E-Type, and a gun that fires backwards; Peter Sellers dresses up as both Napoleon and Hitler in *Casino Royale* (for the significance of which see below); and O'Rourke, the Irish Marshal in 'The Girl Who Was Death', was originally named 'O'Toole', which was taken by actor Kenneth Griffiths to refer to Peter O'Toole, who appears in a joke cameo in *Casino Royale* (although he admits that it could equally have referred to propsman Mickey O'Toole). It might be that the suggestion that 'The Girl Who Was Death' be made as a 90-minute telemovie (vetoed by Lew Grade) came as an attempt to cash in on the publicity for *Casino Royale*. Unlike *Casino Royale*, however, 'The Girl Who Was Death' is a conscious and deliberate parody, rather than something that happened to evolve in that direction.

'The Girl Who Was Death' sends up elements of a number of James Bond films and books. Just to give a few examples, the Turkish bath sequence parodies a near-identical one in *Thunderball* (which featured Guy Doleman, Number Two in 'Arrival', as the hapless victim); the novel *Moonraker* has a mad Nazi German scientist who attempts to blow up London with a rocket and is killed by his own invention; and beautiful ice-goddesses with ambiguous, sexual/fatal, relationships to the hero feature in most Bond stories. The primary target of the episode, however, is closer to home: the spy series produced by independent television (although the BBC's *Adam Adamant Lives!*, featuring a gentleman hero with a penchant for Edwardian dress and a with-it Swinging '60s blonde girl sidekick, could also be referenced here) . Many of these series, such as *The Saint*, *The Baron* and *Man in a Suitcase*, feature globe-trotting, Bond-lite heroes saving the world from foreign villains, usually done on the cheap through sets and back-projection; and they were known at the time for their increasing silliness and/or strangeness. *The Avengers* in particular appears to be singled out; while the show had started out reasonably seriously, by 1967 it was full of ludicrous villains along the lines of Schnipps, strange gadgets and incongruous disguises, and also portrayed a kind of unrealistic fantasy England, with no multiculturalism and with working class characters being either criminals or genial idiots.

In 'The Girl Who Was Death', in keeping with the worst excesses of the genre, then, we have a Napoleon-obsessed villain, whose plans are either thoroughly inconsistent (in that he plots to destroy

London and yet still intends to give bits of it to his henchmen and daughter) or, arguably, use a fantasy weapon of a type that it is impossible to invent (a rocket that will have London 'in ruins', but leave Chelsea Barracks, Bond Street and various monuments intact), and are rather pointless anyway (as the rest of the UK would promptly start fighting back). The original script also contains even more surreal touches in keeping with this genre, for instance Mr X finding a plastic rose that broadcasts a message from Sonia (which in the final version becomes, slightly altered, Sonia's dialogue in the car chase sequence), and a long scene in which Mr X visits a replica of the Hampton Court Maze at the funfair, only for it to transform into a jungle with hostile natives and talking parrots, and then, when he emerges, has to fight off an assassin disguised as a gardener and a gunman on stilts. While it is obvious why this latter sequence was cut (even if filmed on as tight a budget as possible, it still would not have contributed enough to the story to justify the expense of mounting it), it may have partly inspired the novel *The Prisoner's Dilemma*'s reality-TV sequence. 'The Girl Who Was Death', by characterising such programmes as children's stories, is skewering the writers and audiences of popular spy drama.

One of the main targets of the story appears to be *Danger Man*, with an actor named John Drake briefly appearing and McGoohan dressing in Drake's customary light coat and cap when going to meet his contact, Potter – who happens to be played by Christopher Benjamin, who also played an agent named Potter in *Danger Man* (in 'Koroshi'/'Shinda Shima', a story in which Kenneth Griffith also appears). The sequence where Mr X receives his instructions via record also recalls, as well as *Mission: Impossible* (which used records instead of a self-destructing tape player in its first season; as *Mission: Impossible* had not been transmitted in the UK at this point, it is unclear whether this is just a coincidence or whether somebody on the production team was aware of the American series' conventions), a scene in the *Danger Man* episode 'Koroshi' in which Drake receives a photograph slipped into a record sleeve. On an inadvertently surreal note, after 'Living in Harmony' was transmitted on the ATV Midlands network, 'Koroshi' and its sequel 'Shinda Shima' were shown for the first time, as fill-ins for the *The Prisoner* time slot, which is not only ironic, but must have been very confusing to the audience.

This send-up may not be totally justified, as *Danger Man* is far less guilty than most '60s spy dramas of the sort of ludicrous excesses sent up here; and, indeed, the second series contains a number of episodes that challenge and question the same spy genre clichés (with the hero ditching his first-series Aston Martin in favour of a Mini, and with the British establishment frequently being depicted as corrupt and uncaring). However, it does contain its share of back-projection, gadgetry and glamourisation of the secret agent lifestyle, and, in a few stories, a certain amount of xenophobia. The final two episodes, featuring, respectively, secret orders of assassins with political ambitions and bad guys with technology-filled bases on Japanese islands, show disturbing signs of going down the James Bond route. Even more specifically, 'The Girl Who Was Death' comes across as an attack on Markstein, who story-edited the final two episodes of *Danger Man*, and who continually argued that *The Prisoner* should be a spy series with a novel twist rather than a psychedelic exploration of genre. Looked at in a certain way, then, 'The Girl Who Was Death' could be seen as McGoohan explicitly divorcing himself from his dramatic roots and his connection with Markstein, making it plain that he now considers spy stories a less than worthwhile intellectual endeavour.

FIRING THE CANON: THE PLACE OF 'THE GIRL WHO WAS DEATH' WITHIN *THE PRISONER*

Despite, or perhaps because of, its satirical aspects, 'The Girl Who Was Death' is explicitly located within *The Prisoner*, rather than divorced from it. Although the story was filmed without the use of Portmeirion (except for the helicopter sequence, in which sharp-eyed viewers may discern part of the Welsh coastline briefly in the footage seen when Mr X looks down), the Village is never far away: the story begins with a painted village, actually a reworked illustration from the children's encyclopaedia that was standing in as the storybook, the *Odhams' Encyclopaedia for Children* (with new pages pasted over its original ones). The original illustration is entitled 'The Village', and the title is still discernible on close inspection of the reworked picture in question; however, in keeping with *The Prisoner*'s stance on religion (as well as bringing it symbolically closer to the Village itself), the spire of the village church in the original picture has been overpainted with Portmeirion's bell tower. As well as the real Village and the idealised village of the start of the story, we encounter another village, which is a film set and a ghost town (referencing the way the Village seems to be an unreal fiction) and, like the real Village, contains a helicopter. A note on the bottom of a beer glass is in the familiar modified Albertus font, and we meet yet another colonel (Colonel Hawke-Englishe, killed at the start of the episode). Although the Prisoner appears to go out of the Village, conceptually at least, in this story, he has in fact never escaped it.

Other aspects of the story reference earlier episodes of *The Prisoner*. Schnipps dresses as Napoleon, as the Doctor did in 'Dance of the Dead' (and, like the Professor in 'The General', is a history expert); the lighthouse sequences were filmed at Beachy Head, where the landing sequence in 'Many Happy Returns' was set (a brief glimpse of the same lighthouse is visible in the background in 'Many Happy Returns'), and which is briefly referenced in 'Do Not Forsake Me Oh My Darling'. The sequence in 'Hammer into Anvil' in which the Prisoner convinces Number Two that he is receiving mysterious messages through listening to a recording of 'L'Arlesienne' is also referenced in Mr X's getting his instructions from a record (meaning that the sequence in 'The Girl Who Was Death' provides a further condemnation of the paranoid beliefs of Number Two in 'Hammer into Anvil'). The fact that the story crosses genres is not particularly a deviation for the series, as we have already had a genre-crossing episode in 'Living in Harmony' (which also features a fiction in which Number Two, his beautiful female assistant, and the Prisoner are all characters). Additionally, 'A, B and C', with its psychedelic take on the spy story, can be seen as a precursor to 'The Girl Who Was Death'. Aspects of the episode also seem to be explicit criticisms of 'Do Not Forsake Me Oh My Darling', for instance the presence of a scientist with a fantastical invention, and a visual joke about bad back-projection. In a cut scene from the original script, Sonia explicitly identifies Mr X with Number Six when he is on a boating lake at the funfair (calling 'Come in, Number Six, your time is up'). Although the music is mostly different from the usual *The Prisoner* themes, we do get a souped-up version of 'Boys and Girls, Come Out To Play' during the second cricket match.

The story also picks up on several of the continuing themes of the series. The infantilising aspects of the Village are to the fore, with the whole plot turning out to be a children's story. For the second time only in the series, we see actual children – who, unlike the children in 'Living in Harmony', are explicitly genuine inhabitants of the Village. The practical reason for the previous lack of children within the Village is the expense and difficulty of employing child actors; one might, however, argue that it contributes to the surrealism of the Village, and aesthetically opens the door for the displays of childish behaviour that we see from Village adults. Here, however, the Village set-up changes again in that the presence of children is taken for granted; in the original script, the children call the Prisoner 'Uncle Six,' indicating that they have some kind of previously-established social relationship with him. We also get references to nursery rhymes – 'the butcher, the baker, the candlestick maker' – as well as games and funfair activities. Finally, the Prisoner infantilises both Number Two and his assistant, and the series' viewers, with his fourth-wall-breaking greeting 'Goodnight children – everywhere' (which is a reference to the popular radio slot *Children's Hour*). By it being pointed out to them that they have just enjoyed a children's story, viewers are included in the Villagers' infantile behaviour.

We also see the presence of doubles and doppelgängers, as elsewhere in the series. Alexis Kanner once again appears, uncredited, both as the photographer and as the voice on the record (in an interview with Arabella McIntyre Brown on The Unmutual website, he says that he was asked to play the role of photographer only at the last minute, having come along on the location shoot as company for David Tomblin, and that he made up his dialogue based on the mode of speech of an East End driver of his acquaintance), and Mr X mistakes two different women for Sonia at the funfair. We have fictional doubles of real Village people, as in 'Living in Harmony', and the surreal doubling when a department-store mannequin transforms, apparently by magic, into Sonia between shots. Christopher Benjamin appears in his third role in the series, one that has apparently crossed over from *Danger Man*. We also see themes of death; the titular Girl appears as an old crone with a shawl over her head and dresses entirely in white throughout, associating her with the Angel of Death and with the colour of mourning in East Asia. Her romantic banter with Mr X, of a kind normally taboo within the series, is seemingly allowed because of its association with death rather than sex; love and death are implicitly equated. The hint of incest between Schnipps and Sonia (she dresses up as Josephine, implying that she is his wife and puts herself in the place of his dead wife, also called Josephine; Schnipps describes his daughter as 'a girl after my own heart'), associates sexuality with corruption and taintedness. Her penultimate confrontation with Mr X takes place in a ghost town, appropriately enough considering the themes of death within the Village.

The Village is also, once again, global. 'The Girl Who Was Death' is yet another story that sees the Village become the world and vice versa, and the first pages of the storybook (which are actually the genuine end-papers of the *Odham's Encyclopaedia for Children*) show a crowd of diverse children from around the world in national dress. The henchmen of Sonia and her father have a multinational array of weapons – a British Bren gun and Vickers heavy machine gun, Russian SKS semi-automatic rifles and a German *Panzerschreck* bazooka and stick grenades – possibly as a nod to the universal nature of the Village. The presence of weaponry is also in keeping with the fact that, within *The Prisoner*, weapons (particularly guns) feature prominently in the world outside the Village, but, aside from fantasy weapons like the gas gun in 'The Schizoid Man', are not a presence in the Village itself – until 'Fall Out'. This suggests an association of the world outside the Village with violent death. Although the original script has Mr X wielding a gun of his own, this was excised before the final version, in keeping with the character already set up for the Prisoner. 'The Girl Who Was Death' thus continues the themes of the series and expands upon them.

AN ARMY OF NAPOLEONS: NATIONALITY AND PREJUDICE

One other explicit target of 'The Girl who Was Death' would seem to be the 'Little England' mentality: that is to say, the sort of British conservatism that idealises a nonexistent England of warm beer, cricket pitches and spinsters cycling to Evensong across the village green, frequently associated with Royalism, mild to severe xenophobia and right-wing attitudes. These sorts of images are ridiculed in 'The Girl Who Was Death': the sites of Mr X's confrontations with Sonia include a cricket game (referred to in the script, which is a wealth of humourous description, as 'the kind of which maudlin exiles dream'), a local pub, a twee little English village, a funfair, and a lighthouse off Beachy Head; Mr X wears a Sherlock Holmes outfit with long Edwardian sideburns; and the Colonel is said to have died 'one short of his century' (ridiculing the alleged upper-class English preoccupation with fair play, not interrupting cricket games, and silly minutiae of performance that are of interest only to insiders). The presence of an enemy who is obsessed with a French general, and whose allies include a Yorkshireman, a Welshman, a Scotsman and an Irishman, also reflects the abovementioned xenophobia (particularly in relation to Europe) and fear of the regions outside the South East of England, and the possibility that they might demand independence. This sort of mentality can also be found to some extent in the James Bond films mentioned above, taking place as they do in a kind of fantasy England that is still a major player on the world stage, with a posh British hero fighting against sinister foreigners. By implication, then, since all of these feature in a children's adventure, they are part of a storybook view of the world, suitable only for children.

It is also interesting to consider the original set-up with regard to the villain. Schnipps was first supposed to have been obsessed with Hitler rather than Napoleon, hence his German name (Sonia's *pickelhelm* may also be a survival from this, although it may equally have to do with the fact that the weaponry she uses is antique and, in two cases, German, or might reflect the general Europhobia of the abovementioned Little England mentality, which is as much anti-German as anti-French). Although he does not dress as Hitler, he wears instead a white lab coat with an Iron Cross. The scale model of London on a dais in the middle of Schnipps's room, which featured in the original script, recalls Hitler's model of 'Germania', the new Berlin he envisioned building, as well as the model of Fort Knox in *Goldfinger*. The henchmen, called *Gauleiters*, were all to have been wearing Hitler wigs and false moustaches (possibly explaining why, although they are wearing Marshal's uniforms, the credits refer to them as 'Napoleons') and all to have had the same rank and uniform: the SS rank of *Obersturmbannfuehrer*.

The most obvious reason for changing the Nazi references to Napoleonic ones (which Kenneth Griffiths, in an interview on The Unmutual website, has claimed was down to Patrick McGoohan) is that the wounds from the Second World War were still too raw in 1967 for them to be addressed in British telefantasy (while the same is not true of American series, the Americans were on the whole not as directly and personally affected by the war as the British). The original plan might also have been seen as somewhat offensive: while the final version does equate Irish, Scots and Welsh devolutionists to little Napoleons, that is slightly less contentious than comparing them to Hitler (one line cut from the original explicitly identifies Welsh nationalism with Nazism, when the Welsh *Gauleiter* says 'Jow, it's a great day for the Nationalists'), particularly for a series with an Irish lead actor and filmed largely in Wales. While having a children's story that reflects prejudice against the regions cleverly implies that even the most innocent tale may have an unpleasant agenda, the original version was rather too ethnically offensive to bring this across subtly. It might also have been changed because sending up the British obsession with the Second World War and Nazism might have hit a bit too close to home. In any case, though, the Napoleon theme works better in that it ties into the association of Napoleon with madness and the kind of fantasy-megalomania of spy series villains.

GOODBYE LOVER:
POSTMODERNISM IN 'THE GIRL WHO WAS DEATH'

More than any other episode of *The Prisoner* so far, 'The Girl Who Was Death' plays with the conventions of television. The storybook pictures that open and close each act explicitly fictionalise the story, situating it in a non-real context; the whole episode ultimately acknowledges that the series the viewer is watching is simply that: a fiction, perhaps with no message, perhaps with many messages. Originally, these were to have been freeze-frames of the action in the story, rendered as drawings, so as to further fictionalise the events of the narrative. Sonia plays with the back projection, causing it to twirl round with her finger, and making Mr X genuinely dizzy in doing so. As well as acknowledging the ubiquity, and occasional artificiality, of back projection in ITC series, this not only indicates that this is a television programme, but also suggests that the narrative is genuinely real to its characters – that television narratives, like the Village, have their own rules. The Prisoner also breaks the fourth wall when he gives his final line direct to the camera, addressing the unseen viewers whom he has been entertaining with stories for the past 15 weeks.

'The Girl Who Was Death' is also particularly rife with in-jokes. Kenneth Griffiths had not only played Napoleon in a 1963 ITV adaptation of *War and Peace* (which won an Emmy for the production) but had also played Hitler in the 1958 film *The Two-Headed Spy*. The shop signs in Witchwood incorporate the first names of production team members: David Dough (David Tomblin), Leonard Snuffit (Len Harris, a camera operator on the series) and Brendan Bull (Brendan J Stafford, the director of photography). The casting of Justine Lord also had a hint of humour: as well as appearing in such spy series as *The Saint*, she had also appeared in the film *Deadlier than the Male*, another spy-satire that explicitly targeted the stereotypical femme-fatale of the genre. The telephone in Number Two's office is once again the large Expressionist red telephone, symbolising the failure of his plan and also, possibly, foreshadowing the traumas the next Number Two is to undergo in the following episodes (as 'The Girl Who Was Death' was always intended to come late in the series).

Other aspects, while not so postmodern, are worth watching out for. McGoohan's absence for part of the story (as he was in Hollywood filming reshoots on *Ice Station Zebra*, which extended the production time on 'The Girl Who Was Death' to four weeks), makes for a fun game of spot-the-stand-in during the funfair sequence for those who know what to look for: although it is so well done that it is likely not to be noticed on first viewing, the footage alternates wildly between shots of the funfair, shots of the funfair with Justine Lord, shots of the funfair with Frank Maher standing in for McGoohan, and inserts of McGoohan with the funfair shown in back projection. Mr X's frilly shirt and string tie not only recall the garb of '60s pop stars such as Jimi Hendrix and Cat Stevens, and the outfit worn by the Judge in 'Living in Harmony', they also presciently foreshadow that of such future telefantasy characters as

Department S's Jason King and Jon Pertwee's take on Doctor Who as a kind of James Bond-figure.

In particular, however, 'The Girl Who Was Death' plays with the series itself, especially with regard to the nature of its central figure. We have a rare case of sevens appearing: Mr X drinks seven shots of liquor, and Schnipps has seven henchmen, indicating that even *The Prisoner*'s own conventions are not sacred, or possibly highlighting the fiction-within-a-fiction aspect of the story. The final image in the Prisoner's storybook shows a man at sea trying to harpoon a white whale, perhaps equating the Prisoner's quest for Number One with Ahab's pursuit of Moby-Dick; however, it also raises the possibility that the Prisoner is not in fact reading out of the Village Storybook, but making up a story based on what the pictures in it suggest to him (explaining why the helicopter incident is associated with a picture not of a helicopter but of an aeroplane), meaning that the whole episode may be an exercise in free-association on the part of the Prisoner. At the end of the story, the screen in Number Two's office activates at the Prisoner's will, suggesting that the Prisoner is slowly gaining control of the Village through his own self-discovery; he puts a clown in front of the monitor, indicating that he has made fools of Sonia and Number Two.

'The Girl Who Was Death' firmly establishes the post-Markstein era of *The Prisoner* as one of surreal genre-bending and exploration of social and individual psychology. This sets the scene nicely for the final two stories, which will develop the series to its logical, if bizarre, conclusion.

Episode 16:
Once Upon a Time

First UK Transmission Date: Thursday 25 January 1968: Scottish,
7.30 pm – 8.30 pm
Written and Directed by: Patrick McGoohan
Credited Cast: Patrick McGoohan (The Prisoner); Leo McKern
(Number Two) Angelo Muscat (The Butler); Peter Swanwick
(Supervisor); John Cazabon (Umbrella Man); John Maxim (Number
Eighty Six)*
* Not in finished episode

SYNOPSIS: All other attempts to find out why the Prisoner
resigned having failed, Number Two obtains permission to try
'Degree Absolute', a form of interrogation based on psychoanalytic
techniques in which the Prisoner will be regressed to childhood,
and he, Number Two and the Butler will be locked in a self-
contained underground bunker, the Embryo Room, for seven days,
during which time the Prisoner will be taken, symbolically, through
the stages of his life to date. Together, they go through the
Prisoner's childhood, graduation, first job (in a bank) and
recruitment to the secret service; however, at this point Number
Two becomes sufficiently involved in the process that events from
his own life (notably his detention by the Germans in the Second
World War) begin to blend in to those from the Prisoner's. The
Prisoner finally regains control of himself and his own psyche, and
he and Number Two swap places, with Number Two collapsing
dead at the command 'Die, Six, die!' The Prisoner is released and is

taken, at his request, to meet Number One.

ANALYSIS: This episode is one of the strangest and most controversial of the series: Markstein (whose name still appears on the credits, and who still appears in the title sequence, since the episode was filmed sixth) loathed it, describing it as 'absolute gibberish', and McGoohan has asserted that he was so concerned about the possibility of ridicule from the production crew that the shooting script was released under a pseudonym, 'Archibald Schwartz', rather than his own name. However, it is here that the greatest mystery of the series – what the Prisoner is doing in the Village, and how he can escape – is finally revealed, in a way, to the viewer.

SCHOOL DAYS:
THE EMBRYO ROOM, CHILDHOOD AND GROWING UP

This episode represents the culmination of the themes of childhood and infantilisation throughout the series. Here we actually see the Prisoner regress to childhood and 'grow' to adulthood over seven days, while Number Two enters his senility/second childhood. The Prisoner is locked in the 'Embryo Room' (= the womb), with a single adult giving him all his attention and playing a parental or quasi-parental role; again, the Prisoner is the sole focus of all attention in the role-playing scenarios, with a kind of infantile self-absorption. At the end of the story, however, the Prisoner leaves the Embryo Room as an adult, able to take on adult roles and to discard the forced infantilisation of the Village.

As ever, the nursery rhymes in this story take on a particular significance. Again we get songs relating to childhood or youth featuring in the music ('Twinkle, Twinkle Little Star', 'Pop Goes the Weasel' and 'The Eton Boating Song'). The choice of nursery rhymes reflects the events that occur throughout the episode: 'Jack and Jill', for instance, refers to climbing a hill and then falling down it (the Prisoner has an uphill emotional climb, which ends in the toppling of Number Two); 'The Grand Old Duke of York' describes a similar climb up and down a hill (having climbed his 'hill', the Prisoner then returns to society), and also to a failed attempt to take the throne away from the King, as the rhyme refers to the Battle of St Albans during the Wars of the Roses (and thus perhaps to Number Two's failed attempt to gain mastery over the Prisoner); and 'Humpty Dumpty' tells of a person in power (such as Number Two) collapsing and not being repairable. Although this Number Two memorably claimed 'I don't want a man of fragments' in 'The Chimes of Big Ben' (echoed here in his phone conversation with his unseen superior), in the end he becomes a man of fragments, to be reborn next episode, his persona as Number Two destroyed.

The 'Margery Daw' see-saw sequence, following on from this, thus becomes a full-blown battle for identity through the form of a nursery rhyme. After Number Two's line 'Jacky shall have a new Master,' he and the Prisoner then focus on who shall assume which role, with Number Two apparently attempting to define the Prisoner as 'Jacky' (note that he rises on the see-saw as he says the word) and the Prisoner apparently resisting, insisting on redefining himself as 'Master,' or possibly redefining Jacky as the Master (the Prisoner is, however, always in the descending position as he says this, indicating that Number Two still has the upper hand; this might mean that he is acknowledging Number Two as the Master, but, given the Prisoner's usual rebellious streak, it seems more likely that it is an act of defiance rather than capitulation. The original script makes it seem, much more clearly, as if he is asserting that Jacky is the new Master). Number Two suddenly throws in 'Mother', to which the Prisoner responds 'Master' (perhaps suggesting that he sees himself as the master of his mother; see the section on Oedipality, below). Then Number Two tries 'Father', a role he himself has formerly assumed, at which the Prisoner becomes violent – by the logic above, rejecting the role of Father, or else reacting with Oedipal hostility to his father's authority. The Prisoner offers a new, more egalitarian role, that of 'Brother', to which Number Two suggests 'Friends', upon which they apparently agree. In the original script, 'Father' is followed by 'Lonely', suggesting an anti-social role for the Prisoner as well as the social ones that remain. It is uncertain here whether the Prisoner did actually have a brother or not, as what seems to be going on is a struggle for identity, with the Prisoner rejecting authoritarian / parental relationships in favour of egalitarian ones. The see-saw on which the pair sit recalls the revolving see-saw in the Village's

Control Room: however, the two observers in the Village are not in control of the motion of the device, indicating that their identity is dictated by outside forces, where here Number Two and the Prisoner are able to negotiate between themselves. The 'Margery Daw' sequence sees not a battle between individual and society, but a battle for identity, in which the initially infantile, voiceless Prisoner gradually assumes both voice and role.

The other nursery rhyme to feature with this prominence is 'Pop Goes the Weasel', which gives rise to a frenzied sequence of minimalist dialogue on the theme of 'pop', referring back to the recurrence of both the nursery rhyme and the word 'pop' throughout the series, as well as to balloons, fathers and the title sequence seen at the end of the alternate version of 'The Chimes of Big Ben'. It could equally be taken to be an allusion to pop art, or pop culture, both of which the Prisoner self-consciously references. The phrase is also here referred to as an acronym for 'protect other people'; however, this idea comes from Number Two rather than from the Prisoner, suggesting that it is a reference not to the Prisoner's own altruism, but Number Two's insistence that he put his society's, or his superior's, needs first.

The Prisoner's time in the Embryo Room is explicitly focused around the 'Seven Ages of Man' speech from Shakespeare's *As You Like It*. The ages are: the infant, the schoolboy, the lover, the soldier, the justice, the older man, the second childhood. These have to follow in sequence, it seems: the Prisoner is puzzled when he is asked why he resigned while still in 'schoolboy' mode. He can discuss it allegorically, through the conversation about his refusal to reveal which pupil spoke in class (the upshot of which is that it is his own business what he knows, and he would rather submit to punishment than explain further), but not directly, because it is not something that would be within a schoolboy's experience. At the same time, a continuity is maintained throughout regarding the conflict between authority and the individual: note that the Butler (who is referred to in the original script as 'Angelo', a designation that appears in only one other script, 'Face Unknown') replaces his cane with a truncheon as the Prisoner passes from schoolboy into adult, indicating that the mode of punishment may change, but the fact of punishment remains the same.

However, one key aspect of the Seven Ages of Man theme is that it is *not only* the Prisoner who is under scrutiny. We get through only the first three or four ages with the Prisoner (although 'the lover' must be taken to refer to youthful passions in general rather than, as Shakespeare had it, sexual passions), and the other ages are covered by Number Two; he appears as a justice (literally) and an older man (as teacher, parent and employer) and finally reverts to second childhood (which has previously been seen in the repeated visual theme in *The Prisoner* of elderly people playing children's games) before dying. The two overlap on the age of the soldier.

A key aspect of this story is that the Prisoner and Number Two swap roles over its course, with the Prisoner, as he gains mastery over the situation, becoming the psychoanalyst and Two becoming the patient. This is explicitly flagged up in a conversation that takes place after the Second World War bombing-run sequence: Number Two and the Prisoner discuss how Degree Absolute is based on techniques used in psychoanalysis, in which the patient must learn to trust his doctor to such a degree that sometimes they swap places. The significance of the conversation being placed here is that the bombing-run sequence is not, as the viewer may assume upon first seeing the episode, an anachronism (as the Prisoner, who is the same age as Patrick McGoohan, would not have turned 19, the age the bomber is said to be, until 1947, two years after the War ended), but a case of the Prisoner reliving an incident that was actually experienced by Number Two (although the story does not parallel Leo McKern's life as it does McGoohan's, the fact that the actor was born in 1920 means that the character he played could easily have been around the right age to take part in such bombing missions – McKern did indeed serve in the military in the Second World War, albeit the Australian army rather than the British Royal Air Force. In the original script, the Prisoner is said by Number Two in the boxing sequence to be 'Junior Boxing Champ, 1944', which would have indicated even more firmly that the bomber cannot be the Prisoner). One may note that in the German interrogation sequence is the only time, until the end of the story, that the Prisoner can utter the number 'six' (aside, that is, from when he queries Number Two's use of the numeral in the schoolboy sequence); this is because he is not himself, but is impersonating Number Two. The role-swap appears to take place, in fact, shortly before the bombing-run sequence begins, when the Prisoner asks Number Two to kill him

EPISODE 16: ONCE UPON A TIME

(as Number Two had earlier asked him), and Number Two says 'In the war you killed,' identifying the Prisoner with himself. It may even be that the two characters are aspects of the same person, or that Number Two is a figment of the Prisoner's imagination: Number Two lives the second half of the Seven Ages for the Prisoner, and, as Number Two dies, he is called Six, suggesting that, on the seventh day/Seventh Age of Man, he dies for Six. Depending on how one looks at it, the Prisoner must either destroy Number Two, or integrate him into himself, to succeed.

It must also be said that there are actually some areas of overlap between the characters to begin with. Both are likely to have experienced public school and a career in intelligence, and one might question which of the characters, if not both, worked for a bank, and which was arrested for dangerous driving. In fact, the dangerous-driving sequence also shows signs that the experiences of the two men are bleeding into each other: as Number Two/the Judge accuses the Prisoner of driving too fast in a restricted zone, he also, randomly, interjects phrases like 'How many dead?' and 'Unrestricted murder on the public highways!', which do not appear to relate to the Prisoner's actual crime. The paradox can be explained as Number Two's wartime experiences, in the air force, becoming confused with the Prisoner's own experiences as a fast driver (note also that the Prisoner's resignation becomes conflated with the crime, when he explains that he was driving too fast because he was 'on a mission' and this mission was 'confidential,' so he will not tell Number Two what it was and would rather accept incarceration than explain). Earlier in the story, Number Two echoes his attempts to find common ground with the Prisoner in 'The Chimes of Big Ben' by saying 'I'm not an inmate' and rejecting the normal order of the Village and his role as Number Two, ordering the Butler to remove the traditional breakfast and insisting on doing things his own way. The scene also appears to present a witty reversal of Pavlov's experiments (which are referenced elsewhere in the series), in that, when the Butler rings the bell, Number Two rejects the offered food. When Number Two wakes in the Prisoner's house, he rises and walks to the window in echo of the Prisoner's actions in the title sequence; the view he sees, of a waitress in the café, is similar to the one that the Prisoner saw from the bell tower in 'Arrival'. The presence of Rover in Number Two's chair also suggests that Number Two is under surveillance in the same way that the Prisoner is. The stage for the role-swapping between the characters is thus set early on, and is an important part of the Prisoner's defeat of Number Two and reintegration into society.

Furthermore, there is some overlap here not only between the characters, but between characters and performers. McGoohan drew on details of his own life experience: he attended public school, had boxing as a hobby and worked in a bank (and, as Fairclough wittily points out, he ultimately went on to play a spy on television in the same way that the fictional Prisoner is recruited from the bank into the secret service). There is a hamper in the background marked MP (suggesting, among other things, 'McGoohan, Patrick'). Leo McKern reportedly had, depending on which source one reads, either a breakdown or a heart attack during the filming of the story (propsman Mickey O'Toole says in an interview on The Unmutual website that the actor was laid up in Shenley Mental Hospital for a week) and had to take time off (filming continued with a stand-in; Anton Rogers has recalled that he was under the impression that they were still filming parts of the episode following the shooting of 'The Schizoid Man'), which is not surprising when one considers what an assault on the personal identity of the performers this story must have been.

A TECHNIQUE USED IN PSYCHOANALYSIS: THE EMBRYO ROOM, IDENTITY AND AUTHORITY

The fact that the death of Number Two, who has been identified with father-figures throughout the story, features so prominently in the Prisoner's rehabilitation has led many to suggest that 'Once Upon a Time' has Oedipal themes. Certainly, these appear to be here on a symbolic level. Number Two, played by a corpulent, bearded man who is older than the Prisoner, explicitly takes on the father role at the outset (asking the regressed Prisoner if he has always spoken well of his mother, reinforcing the Oedipal aspects of the scene), then becomes a series of paternal authority figures (teacher/headmaster, coach, judge, managing director, German officer and so on). The Prisoner also expresses an antagonistic reaction to all these roles, and, ultimately, the death of Number Two is what allows him to walk free from the Embryo Room. It thus seems that there is, on the symbolic level, an Oedipal relationship between the two.

It is harder to claim that there is a genuine wish to kill the father/the male authority figure involved in this scenario. The Prisoner's sudden violence at the mention of the word 'father' seems to have more to do with role definition, and his rejection of Number Two as father, than with any Oedipal tendencies. In fact, it is worth noting that, despite the Prisoner's apparent rejection of authority in the Village, he has, throughout the series, continually gone back to the establishment (in 'The Chimes of Big Ben', 'Many Happy Returns' and 'Do Not Forsake Me Oh My Darling'), even when there is ample evidence that it is his superiors who had him put in the Village. He has been firmly characterised as a member of the British establishment throughout; seen in that light, his refusal to tell the Village authorities why he resigned seems to have less to do with Oedipal feelings towards them, and more to do with the fact that he's not certain whose side they are on. Furthermore, there are marital themes in the story as well as Oedipal; Number Two defines their relationship in the Embryo Room as being 'till death us do part,' and the phrase 'degree absolute' puns on 'decree absolute,' the final settlement in a divorce. However, one thing 'Once Upon a Time' does do is expose the inherent contradiction of the relationship between authority and society, and it is this that seems to be at the heart of the Prisoner's inner conflict.

The key sequences here are the ones relating to the Prisoner's school career. Number Two's speech in the role of teacher/headmaster exposes the inherent contradictions of authority: he urges his pupil to be a member of society, which he defines as people working together, and yet he expects the pupil's respect for authority to override his respect for society, and cause him to betray a fellow pupil. When the pupil will not, he is punished. Murder is shown as acceptable if it is sanctioned by authority (the bombing of civilians in the Second World War) but not if it is through the actions of an individual (dangerous driving, stabbing someone while at fencing practice, etc). The Prisoner's actions are thus not anti-society, just anti-authority; the message is that authority can override society. In the graduation sequence,

Number Two as headmaster announces that he is 'proud' that the pupil has 'learned to manage his rebellious spirit' – thus implying that the Prisoner did, in the end, conform to authority. The Prisoner then continues on in the establishment, joining first a bank and then the secret service, before suddenly resigning.

The crucial nature of this change of attitude is emphasised when Number Two actually rings up the Prisoner, at the opening of the story, to ask 'Why do you care?' This, it would seem, is the true question: not why he resigned (since we know he gave his reasons to his employers from Number Two's dialogue in 'Arrival'), but why he continues to resist authority – and, in particular, why he resists authority from both sides, rather than taking the conventional action expected of a dissatisfied spy and defecting. The fact that Number Two asks the question, however, also suggests that Number Two himself is beginning to question his own complacency towards the corruption and evils of authority, and to think that the Prisoner's response might actually be the correct one. The line 'The door is open ... You're free,' (the first section of which was cut in the final version) recalls the Prisoner's own 'The gates are open. You're free to go,' from 'Free for All', an episode dealing in part with submission, and resistance, to authority, emphasising that this is the central focus of the Prisoner's conflict.

This is reinforced in the discourse about death and fear in the story. In a cut line in the fencing sequence, Number Two says 'Kill me and you're mine,' which suggests that, if the Prisoner did give in to Number Two's taunts of cowardice and kill him, he would be buying into Number Two's ideas about honour and shame, thus becoming, mentally, 'his.' In the parallel scene in which the Prisoner urges Number Two to kill him, Number Two will not do so, because he cannot kill him until he is told why he resigned, indicating that the Prisoner has power over him through refusing to comply with his wishes. The Prisoner finally says that he resigned for peace of mind, and because he knows too much about Number Two, calling him the enemy: since Number Two represents authority, he is both saying that he regards authority as the enemy, and because 'too many people know too much – I know too much,' implying that he knows too much about what his superiors are up to, and doesn't want to play the game any more. At the end, Number Two becomes afraid of the Prisoner, and dies behind bars, implying that fear is a prison, and that all authority figures have an aspect of fear in the way they maintain their power; by ceasing to fear authority, the Prisoner emerges victorious.

The real conflict addressed by *The Prisoner* is thus revealed in this episode: the conflict between the demands of authority and the needs of society. What seems to prevent the Prisoner from discovering Number One, and becoming truly at one with himself, is his trust of the establishment conflicting with the repeated evidence that it is evil and/or has betrayed him. The symbolic Oedipality and rejection of parental figures forms a part of his coming to terms with this fact. The Prisoner's rebirth at the end of the episode thus symbolises his acceptance that authority figures are not always right; that he can make a breach with the establishment, and become literally his own man.

ALL THE WORLD'S A STAGE:
THEATRICALITY AND CONNECTION

It has been noted by critics that 'Once Upon a Time' owes much to minimalist theatre, particularly the 'Theatre of the Absurd' that came out of the counter-cultural artistic movements of the late 1940s, 1950s and 1960s. Although some of this was dictated by necessity – 'Once Upon a Time' was apparently written as a cheap episode in an attempt to keep the series' budget under control, and its 30 scenes are the fewest of any episode in the series – the effect recalls Pinter's and Beckett's two/three-hand plays; and, indeed, 'Once Upon a Time' was staged as a play at the Edinburgh Festival in 1990, on a double bill with Beckett's *Endgame*. The scenes where Number Two views images of the Prisoner at the outset (on a viewscreen that is not only covered by a theatre curtain, as it usually is, but sports a proscenium arch; the curtains part in a way reminiscent of the openings of theatrical performances) are clearly edited and carefully positioned, reminding viewers again that they are watching a television programme. The Inuit-style snow-goggles that the Butler and Number Two wear seem almost like a minimalist version of theatrical masks. In fact, although it would not become a form of popular drama for some time, this story sometimes feels like an improv night, with an invisible audience shouting out scenarios ('Student accused of talking in class!' 'Airman captured behind enemy lines!' 'Man up before the judge for speeding!') for the actors to perform. *The Prisoner*'s hinting at a postmodern awareness of itself as text thus culminates in the most openly theatrical episode of the series.

The idea that this episode is the culmination of the series is reinforced in the way that elements of the Village – miniature tractors and pedal-bikes, straw boaters, the tinker-toy device seen in 'Arrival' and the see-saw – feature in the Embryo Room, as if everything we have seen so far is just a play performed with these props. The montage of clips Number Two views at the outset (referencing similar sequences, even featuring some of the same clips, in 'Free for All' and 'Do Not Forsake Me Oh My Darling'), also plays with theatricality and televisuality, in that the clips are identical to those that the viewer has seen (and, since the montage in 'Do Not Forsake Me Oh My Darling' took place in the Prisoner's mind, may suggest that what we have seen so far is all a product of the Prisoner's own imagination). The fencing and boxing recall both 'Hammer into Anvil' and 'The Schizoid Man' (where Curtis suggests Olympic boxing as a potential competition), and we see Napoleonic prints on the walls of the trailer, recalling 'The Girl Who Was Death' (which also contains a boxing sequence; Number Two's urging the Prisoner not to be a 'lone wolf' recalls the fact that *Lone Wolf* was the original title for *Danger Man*). The chair on the dais (described in the original script as a 'throne') looks back to the chair in the Council Chamber, and forward to the throne that the Prisoner will ascend in the next episode. We again see the recording/playback (computer?) device from 'A Change of Mind' (which also appeared briefly in 'Dance of the Dead'); it plays a similarly ambiguous role here, it being uncertain whether it is recording the events (and if so, why), playing recordings (as the sound of children playing ceases when the Butler presses a button on it) or doing something else entirely (as the tape keeps rolling when the Butler presses the button, suggesting that it isn't actually a playback). The music in the school sequences is the same as in the cricketing sequence of 'The Girl Who Was Death' (and these are also connected by their joint referencing of the British establishment). The self-contained trailer is a visual metaphor for the Prisoner's cottage (being a cottage interior behind prison bars) and also for the

Village itself (self-contained, with all modern conveniences, and able to move around, but still a prison). Props and scenery thus actively emphasise that the Embryo Room represents the Village.

Thematically, we also see the Faustian and Cocteau-inspired surrealism of 'Dance of the Dead' in 'Once Upon a Time', as well as the storytelling and childhood-regression themes of 'The Girl Who Was Death' (which itself might reasonably have been called 'Once Upon a Time'), the reality-bending nature of 'Free for All', and the role-playing of 'Living in Harmony'. However, the ironic fact that this story was filmed early in the production order, in December 1966 (right after 'The Chimes of Big Ben', with McKern's contract being extended for a further two weeks after completion of work on the latter story), means that, with the arguable exception of 'Dance of the Dead', this is as much a case of 'Once Upon a Time' extending its influence over the rest of the series as looking back on what has already come to pass. 'Once Upon a Time' thus appears to reflect, but actually shapes, the nature of the Village that we see in *The Prisoner*.

The Embryo Room also picks up on the running themes of the Village. We have already discussed infantilisation, psychoanalysis, postmodernism and the use of aspects of McGoohan's own life in the story. A scene cut at a very late stage (as Number Eighty Six, who does not otherwise feature, is still listed in the credits) involved a discourse between Number Eighty Six and the Prisoner that both reflects, and explains, the playing with time of other episodes such as 'The Schizoid Man': 'Beautiful day.' 'Yes. What day is it?' 'Today. Every day.' 'What about tomorrow?' The boundaries are blurred between the Village and outside society, when Number Two, as the judge, sentences the Prisoner to pay a fine of 20 units, then, later, tells him that he is a member of the Village. He also talks about the Prisoner as a 'unit' of society ('Units are not for me,' the Prisoner responds), connecting people's value to society with money, and redefining them as numbers. The number-play that underlines key episodes such as 'Free for All' continues here, with jokes about the Prisoner being good at maths and 'rebelling … against the figures'; initially, he buttonholes a Villager and demands to know what his number is, but the man seems frightened of the question, and, when the Prisoner reaches the number seven, says 'Quiet!' The Prisoner refuses to say the number six, except, as noted above, when role-playing as another man; significantly, this also marks the point at which he begins to come back to himself as a rational adult, perhaps indicating that he now recognises himself as more than the number six, breaking the power that the Village had over him by defining him as such.

We also, however, see the running suggestion that the central character is a dead man. Number Two says to the Prisoner, 'You're dead,' and, at the end, Number Two (whose identity has become confused with the Prisoner's), dies at the words 'Die, Six, die.' Number Two earlier says 'I am a good man ... I *was* a good man,' again associating the Village with death; the whole story involves the Prisoner going down into a cave (echoing the running theme of caves and caverns), locked away from the world, representing either death or, possibly, the womb, as discussed above. Number Two's death is itself surreal and symbolic; it's unlikely that the drink was poisoned, as the Prisoner drinks from the same bottle (albeit less than Number Two does), but people have been known to have heart attacks when under stress (as witness McKern's own, coincidental, health problems). In either case, at this point in the series, realism and cause and effect have largely taken a back seat, and one should look to the meaning, rather than the logic, of the sequence.

Given this episode's influence over the rest of the series, the question arises as to how much of an idea McGoohan had about how *The Prisoner* would end at the point when 'Once Upon a Time' was written. The original script states that the trailer/cage 'will have to travel,' as it ultimately does in 'Fall Out', and the last stage direction describes a noise 'as of a rocket launching,' again as featured in 'Fall Out'. However, it may well be that the rocket launching noise in 'Once Upon a Time' suggested its later use rather than vice versa, or that the idea was subconsciously within McGoohan's mind throughout (recall also the line in 'The Chimes of Big Ben' about wanting to be the first man on the moon). As Fairclough points out, however, although it has been suggested that this story was to have been the first season cliffhanger, it is difficult to see how the show could have progressed beyond it: it takes the series as far as it can go outside of the realms of the totally surreal, which it will now finally enter.

The story can be summed up, in some ways, with the Prisoner's assertion that 'Number One is the boss,' at the point when he assumes mastery of the situation. In taking control of himself, Number Six has become Number One, and, whether the Village is real, a dream, a dying vision or a metaphor for psychoanalysis, he has taken charge of it.

Episode 17:
Fall Out

First UK Transmission Date: Thursday 1 February 1968: Scottish,
7.30 pm – 8.30 pm
Written and Directed by: Patrick McGoohan
Credited Cast: Patrick McGoohan (Prisoner); Leo McKern (Number
Two [character credit does not appear on screen]); Kenneth Griffith
(The President); Alexis Kanner (Number 48 [character credit does
not appear on screen]); Angelo Muscat (The Butler); Peter
Swanwick (Supervisor); Michael Miller (The Delegate)
Known Uncredited Cast: Frank Maher (Double for Patrick
McGoohan); Patrick McGoohan (Number One); Roy Beck (Machine
Gunner/Double for Number One)

SYNOPSIS: Following on from the events of the previous episode,
the Prisoner is taken to a room where his old suit is returned to him.
To the tune of 'All You Need is Love', he proceeds, with the Butler
and the Supervisor, along a corridor lined with jukeboxes to a large
underground cavern. The cavern is governed by the President, a
man in full judicial regalia, and contains a strange, massive,
mechanical cylinder with an electronic eye and an assembly of
figures, dressed in robes and Greek theatrical masks, which the
Supervisor joins. The Prisoner is invited to ascend a throne and
observe the proceedings as a young man, Number Forty Eight, and
the late Number Two (apparently resurrected) are tried for
engaging in rebellion. The Prisoner is then offered the return of his
old house and car, money and passport, and told that he is free to

271

go, but asked to lead them. When he takes the stand, however, the assembly drowns him out with cries of 'Aye, aye, aye.' The Prisoner then goes to meet Number One, descending in a lift and finding the two rebels imprisoned in capsules marked 'Orbit 48' and 'Orbit 2'. He climbs a staircase into the body of the mechanical cylinder, which turns out to be a rocket, and finds a robed and masked figure, designated as '1', holding a crystal ball. Taking the crystal ball, he sees his own face rising out of the Village and being locked behind bars. Smashing the crystal ball and unmasking the figure, he finds a rubber ape-mask, and, unmasking it further, his own features beneath. The figure laughs dementedly, as does the Prisoner. The Prisoner then locks the figure up inside a higher chamber in the rocket and frees Numbers Forty Eight and Two. Together with the Butler, they go on a rampage with Tommy-guns to the tune of 'All You Need is Love'. The rocket is fired and the Village evacuated; the Prisoner and his cohorts flee in the trailer from the Embryo Room, which is mounted on the back of a lorry. Returning to London, Number Forty Eight goes off to hitch-hike, Number Two enters the Houses of Parliament, the Butler goes into 1 Buckingham Place, and the Prisoner himself is last seen driving his car along a runway.

ANALYSIS: *The Prisoner*'s final episode is, not surprisingly, the most multilayered, complicated, and controversial of all. Much as the title 'Fall Out' has a number of different meanings (a command to break ranks, the consequences of an action, the residue of a nuclear attack, the act of two people ceasing communication), the Prisoner's final journey, and ultimate encounter with Number One, is rich in symbolism and suggests many possible interpretations, some deeply disturbing.

By his own account, McGoohan wrote the script for this episode in 36 hours before production began, although it is likely that he had been turning over ideas for it in his head since the writing of 'Once Upon a Time', which would explain how he could come up with such a good story on such short order. All the clips from 'Once Upon a Time' that were originally chosen by McGoohan to introduce the story are ones in which he does not speak (although this was not the case in the finished version), indicating that he was initially setting the stage for his minimalist dialogue in 'Fall Out'. Because so much time had elapsed between the filming of 'Once Upon a Time' and 'Fall Out', the story also provides a way of dealing with the issues that the former story raised, and that have developed in the series in the interim.

OEDIPUS IN THE UNDERWORLD: THE UNDERGROUND ROOM, THE VILLAGE AND THE PRISONER

Fittingly, given the role that caverns and caves have played throughout the series, the Prisoner's departure from the Embryo Room takes him even deeper underground, suggesting a journey into the subconscious, or the passage of a soul into the underworld (the robes that the assembled, and Number One, wear are referred to as 'shrouds' in the script), or the revelation of what lies beneath the Village society. As the Prisoner, the Butler and the Supervisor do so, they pass by jukeboxes displaying records of songs that have been fashionable over the years, representing popular culture (and possibly, particularly since 'All You Need is Love,' which plays over this sequence, was a number-one hit, punning on 'Number One'). The underground chamber the Prisoner enters appears, like the Embryo Room, to be a mirror of the Village itself – or, as in the Celtic myths in which fairies enchant their victims to believe that their humble surroundings are beautiful and expensive, the Village with the glamour thrown off. Troops, in military-police-style uniforms, march around in echo of the Villagers' constant parading; two doctors in a makeshift medical area represent the hospital; a blue-lit empty throne echoes the one in the Council Chamber; and the two men on the see-saw are now holding machine guns instead of cameras, suggesting a parallel between surveillance and more violent forms of control. The see-saw also ceases to go up and down once the Prisoner enters the chamber, but circles in perfect equilibrium, suggesting a temporary balance between the 'sides,' occasionally tilting (and even stopping) in response to the emergences and disappearances of Number Forty Eight and Number Two, and, later, the Prisoner himself. The President, like Number Two in 'Once upon a Time', is dressed as a judge (indicating that he is a 'president' in the sense of a chairman rather than a leader).

Once the Prisoner and his escorts have arrived, the Supervisor dons a robe and mask and, in doing so, sacrifices his individuality, becoming a faceless part of the mob. The masked observers are all named for various movements or aspects of society, some in opposition to each other (they include, among others, 'Anarchists', 'Education', 'Intelligence', 'Therapy' and 'Reactionists'), indicating that all movements, however opposed, are part of society, and/or that all political movements are ultimately the same thing. The original script refers to the assembly as looking like the United Nations in session. Further to this, at one point the person known as 'Anarchists' accuses Number Forty Eight of breaking social rules and going against the community, indicating how social movements can come to resemble, or incorporate, their opposite: anarchists' movements become focused on rules, right-wing governments adopt left-wing policies when politically expedient, and so forth (note also the reversal of court procedure, when the President shouts 'Guilty! Read the charge!'). Later, the Tommy-guns used by the Prisoner and his allies were the type of weapon used by law enforcers and gangsters alike during the Prohibition era in the US. The masked figures thus appear to represent society as a whole, and the new scenario to incorporate society's contradictions within itself.

The masked figures and the President, however, also appear to be a kind of blank slate and to adopt aspects of others' characters. Their masks recall Greek dramatic masks, with black and white, tragedy and comedy, integrated on them. When Number Forty Eight is on trial, the Prescident speaks in 'hipster' language with him, and the masked figures dance and jive like hippies (or possibly are flung into an incoherent frenzy by his music, in an echo of conservative myths about the debilitating effects of rock and roll). When Number Two is announced, by contrast, the President starts to laugh uncontrollably – as Number Two himself will later – and, when the newcomer is brought before them, the President and masked figures laugh and applaud like upper-class men enjoying a speech. More significantly, however, when the Prisoner is not present, the masked figures wander around aimlessly, and the President sits idly in the Prisoner's chair, like performers when a show is over. When both the Prisoner and Number One leave the Village, so do the Villagers. The figures we see thus appear to become extensions of others' personalities, most notably the Prisoner's; ironically, since the Village has been continually trying to get the Prisoner on its side, the series ends with it joining him – or, possibly, through their battle, they have absorbed aspects of each other and become (literally) one.

For the most part, the Prisoner is an observer of the proceedings, both as the Prisoner, on his throne, and as Number One, using the green artificial eye (which is the same object that appears in the Control Room in the title sequence and elsewhere). The President draws a parallel between the two when he says to the Prisoner 'You see all,' making him a kind of human All-Seeing Eye. The eye communicates through electronic noises, recalling the use of bells and noises elsewhere in the series, and its themes of Pavlovian conditioning (Number Forty Eight also rings a small bell at his neck, either as a funeral knell or a Pavlovian summons); according to the original script, the bells and buzzers also consciously recall the accept/reject noises on the popular music programme *Juke Box Jury*, tying in with themes of popular culture and music. The Prisoner then goes on to observe himself directly in Number One's chamber; when he locks the hatch on Number One, the electronic eye closes below. The eye closing does not end surveillance, since images of events continue to play on the rocket's video screens, but symbolises Number One becoming lost to the people of the Village, and the end of their contact with their controller; anarchy can thus ensue.

There are also numerous references to the past of the series, linking the proceedings of 'Fall Out' deliberately with what has gone before. All of the main cast had appeared in earlier episodes of the series (Michael Miller had appeared twice, playing a Villager in 'The General' and the repentant Number Ninety Three in 'A Change of Mind'). The fact that the estate agent is named after set-dresser John Lageu was an inside joke on the part of the production staff, and McGoohan was reportedly not pleased to discover it. The extended theme tune that begins the episode originally accompanied the driving-around-London sequence in 'Do Not Forsake Me Oh My Darling'; and 'For He's a Jolly Good Fellow', as heard here, was a dominant musical theme of 'Free for All'. Rover, finally, does not appear at the end of the end credits, having perished during the launch of the rocket in the episode.

Moreover, this is the story in which the Village finally goes out into the world, or possibly vice versa. The defining theme, 'All You Need is Love', was first played during the 1967 One World broadcast,[16] and also reflects the globalist aims of the peace movement. The presence of a rocket also seems like a parallel of real-world political events, with much debate and protest centring around the Cold War race for nuclear dominance (the rocket seen launching at the end is in fact footage of a real Blue Streak ballistic missile), leading to such half-facetious, half-horrified phrases as the subtitle to *Doctor Strangelove*: 'How I learned to stop worrying and love the Bomb.'

The Village physically influences the world in this story (as in 'Many Happy Returns'). At the President's order, the 'For Sale' sign is taken off 1 Buckingham Place (the estate agents' phone number is given on the sign as '546 0001 or 2'), and the Prisoner's car is returned (although this model, like that in 'Do Not Forsake Me Oh My Darling', is another replacement for the original, this one hired directly from Lotus) and given a polish. Number One's chamber is dominated by globes, and, at the end of the story, the Butler, Number Forty Eight, Number Two and the Prisoner all pile into the trailer (already defined as a Village in miniature) and drive out into the world; as the geography of the Village has always been ambiguous, they emerge suddenly onto the A20 to London (in the same episode in which the location of filming for the Village is finally revealed on screen). Meanwhile, the Villagers evacuate *en masse*, causing the Village to spill out into the world.

Upon returning to London, the Prisoner performs the 'Dem Bones' dance for a policeman, then returns to 1 Buckingham Place, where the door opens like those in the Village, revealing an interior characterised by Village-style rounded arches; the hearse drives by as he and the Butler arrive. In the ending as originally scripted, the Prisoner says 'Be seeing you' as Number Two leaves to enter the House of Lords (although the door of 1 Buckingham Place does not hum open as the Village doors do). In a sense, as Bob Fitter notes in Issue 22 of *In the Village* (Spring 1999), the Prisoner starts the series by awaking in what seems to be the same place, but with a different view, and ends it in the same place, but with a different perspective. Here, then, the Village and the world become fully and explicitly integrated, and identified, with each other.

---

16 This was the world's first television programme done by satellite link-up, in which various nations around the world all contributed short segments in a kind of global variety show.

THE BONES IS YOURS, DAD:
NUMBER FORTY EIGHT AND NUMBER TWO

Over the course of the story, we encounter two characters who are explicitly said to represent different forms of rebellion, Number Forty Eight and Number Two. However, the symbolism associated with their rebellion is complex, and suggests in both characters a strong connection with the Prisoner himself.

Number Forty Eight, for instance, has aspects of the Prisoner about him: his refusal to wear his number, his childish fits, the formlessness of his rebellion. He is referred to as 'the prisoner' by the spokesperson of the assembly, 'Anarchists,' who accuses him of 'total defiance of the elementary laws which sustain our community, questioning the decisions of those we voted to govern us, unhealthy aspects of speech and dress not in accordance with general practice, and the refusal to observe, wear, or respond to his number.' At the same time, he clearly focuses on the rebellion of the young against the old; his conversation with the President, using slang terms like 'dad' and 'baby,' is rife with double-entendres suggesting a parent/child relationship between the two: he says 'I'm yours, Dad,' indicating both a concession (I submit to you, I will conform) and an accusation (I am your child, thus, you made me this way, and my behaviour can also be blamed on you). He cries out 'Take, take!' referring either to the idea that the old are jealous of what the young have, or the belief of the old that the young live off them parasitically, or both. After saying this, he kneels cruciform, suggesting that he is being falsely accused. In a culmination of the themes of infantilisation, then, Number Forty Eight represents rebellion in its youthful state.

Beyond this, however, Number Forty Eight is also associated with death and birth simultaneously. His cruciform pose could equally suggest the death and resurrection of Christ; he dresses in an old-fashioned coat and top hat, which as well as being in line with the youth fashions of the day, recalls Mr X's costume in 'The Girl Who was Death' and the Judge's in 'Living in Harmony' (as well as that of the Kid, also played by Alexis Kanner), the Village council, the undertakers, and Baron Samedi, the *vodoun* divinity who wears a black coat and top hat. When he says the scripted line 'I'm born all over,' he pronounces the second word like 'bone'; the pun thus implies at once death and resurrection and sexuality ('bone' as a slang word for phallus, and one result of sexuality being birth). He rises up out of the ground in clouds of steam, suggesting rising out of hell (in a cut line, Number Two addresses the 1 cylinder/rocket as 'you evil-smelling demon,' and in the script the steam from the rocket is described as 'fumes'), the water-cannons used in the 1960s to douse civil unrest, and, again, birth (particularly as it is accompanied by a piston-like device going up and down, suggesting sexual congress). Ambiguous symbolism thus accompanies Number Forty Eight's arrival and behaviour.

This incorporation of contradictory elements culminates in his singing of the Negro spiritual 'Dem Bones', the second religious reference to appear in the series (the other being to church doors in 'The Chimes of Big Ben'). In keeping with the youth's acts of rebellion, the spiritual is a genre of music noted for concealing a subtext of rebellion under a text of religious imagery, with slaves coding references to their escape attempts in language referring explicitly to going to Heaven, crossing the river Jordan, Moses' deliverance of the captive Israelites, and so forth. This genre was being rediscovered in the 1960s through the folk-music revival and the rise of Black ethnic consciousness in North America and Europe. At the same time, however, the song refers to death and resurrection, fitting in with the religious imagery of the episode as well as its psychoanalytic themes (as the damaged psyche reconnects itself and is reborn), and the connectedness of society; as the hipbone connects to the thighbone, so all people in society are both connected and yet distinct as individuals (the text on which the song is based, Ezekiel 37: 1-14, refers allegorically to the uniting of the scattered tribes of Israel as one society). In the original version of the ending, both the Prisoner and the Butler enter 1 Buckingham Place as 'Dem Bones' plays, fading out on the line 'Hear the word of the Lord,' bringing in ideas of death and, also, Christianity and divinity. 'Dem Bones' thus encapsulates not only Number Forty Eight's rebellion, but the themes of the episode and the series.

The resurrected Number Two from the previous episode also represents not only rebellion, but other, more complex concepts. Number Two's resurrection is deliberately not explained as such – although it is in keeping with the death and birth/resurrection themes seen in the Number Forty Eight sequence – and there are a number of possibilities in keeping with what we have seen before in the series (Number Two actually asks the President how he was killed and brought back, and is told that some things won't be explained to him; effectively, this is the writer saying to the audience that he will not answer all their questions). If the story is all happening in the Prisoner's head, then he can easily imagine the revival of a dead character; if the Prisoner is dead, then it is no surprise that he encounters dead people on his journey to the afterlife (and Number Two is referred to as a 'late' Number Two). While McKern's shave and haircut was really prompted by the fact that the actor, who had changed his hairstyle and lost the beard since the filming of 'Once Upon a Time', did not want to wear a wig and false beard throughout, the physical transformation of the actor fits with the mental transformation of the character. The description of the revival as 'a revolution' by the President puns on the meaning of the word in its sense of coming full circle and Number Two's own 'revolution' against the Village.

The resurrection also includes a playing with televisual conventions as in the back-projection sequence in 'The Girl Who Was Death', as the President winds back the film of Number Two's death before the medics revive him, implying the television show having a symbolic impact on the real character (and recalling the way in which the dead are resurrected in Cocteau's *Orphée*, the film of their collapse winding back and the bodies rising up again). The President's laughter also references the way in which Number Two always laughs in the title sequence, as the image of Number Two on the screen appears to laugh at himself on the ground; when Number Two laughs, his audience ceases laughing. Later, Number Two will breach the fourth wall as he addresses his parting 'Be seeing you' directly to the camera. Number Two's apparent resurrection thus incorporates postmodern and self-knowing aspects.

Like Number Forty Eight, Number Two is likened to the Prisoner. Although he explicitly represents the rebellion of the older, establishment man (and his speech, beginning with 'A most extraordinary thing happened to me on my way … here,' recalls both after-dinner speakers and theatre comedians), the parallels between the two made in 'Once Upon a Time' continue. He speaks of being a valuable man, and so not surprised to wake up and find himself here (like the Prisoner, whose symbolic death in the outside world prior to his arrival in the Village is paralleled by Number Two's physical death in the Village prior to his arrival in the cavern); his narrative of being abducted and awaking to find himself in the Village parallels the Prisoner's own. The box in which the Prisoner is given the key to his house, money, passport and so forth is described in the original script as looking like a 'miniature coffin' (the final version has a somewhat more generic casket), indicating that he also is associated with death. Number Two speaks to the Prisoner as though to a younger colleague who has 'made it.' Later, Number One is seen wearing a grey turtleneck under its robe, as favoured by many Number Twos. More than this, however, we see the Speedlearn process on the screen as he revives (this is explicitly noted in the script, meaning that it is not a directorial whim); in 'The General', the Prisoner was about to use the Speedlearn process to disseminate ideas of freedom and rebellion among the populace. Here, Number Two appears to have absorbed the Prisoner's ideas about freedom and rebellion (although the fact that he has evidently fully absorbed the ideas, and is not just parroting them, suggests that he was receptive to them already). Number Two, like the Prisoner later, confronts Number One and survives, coming to terms with his own individuality; he, like Number Forty Eight (and like the Prisoner in the usual title credits) stands cruciform when he is led away by the troops.

After their expressions of rebellion, Numbers Forty Eight and Two are seen in the Sentence Room repeating their rebellious acts (singing and laughing respectively) in tubes, cryptically marked 'Orbit 48' and 'Orbit 2'. The third tube, simply marked 'Orbit', opens for the Prisoner, although the Butler then appears and directs him to the spiral staircase instead. Two more tubes marked 'Orbit' are also in Number One's chamber, suggesting two more individuals yet to come (or, simply, that they are intended to house Numbers Two and Forty Eight when the rocket is launched). The 'Orbit' designation, as well as perhaps suggesting egocentricity (the world revolves/orbits around Number One/the Prisoner?; the Prisoner's rebellion revolves around his own ego?), or that the pair are stagnating in their rebellion, going around in circles (orbiting) until the Prisoner arrives to act as a catalyst for their escape, also suggests that the two are about to be shot off into space, in line with the large number of science fiction stories referencing the idea that space may become a kind of latter-day Australia, a dumping-ground for domestic undesirables. However, it also implies that the rocket, when it fires off, will be populated, and controlled, by three types of rebellion: those of youth, age and the fully integrated personality. Although the trio are not in fact on the rocket when it launches, they symbolically launch their rebellion on society when they join the Prisoner in gunning down the troopers, then flee out into the wider world.

SHAVE AND A HAIRCUT, SIX BITS: THE PRISONER AND SOCIETY

The Prisoner's character is explored through the events of 'Fall Out'. When he emerges from the Embryo Room, he is offered his own suit on a mannequin with his face, as the Supervisor says 'We thought you would feel happier as yourself,' suggesting a reintegration of the Prisoner after his psychoanalysis in the previous episode. As his shadow falls across the doors and on the wall behind the mannequin, he reaches out for the throat of the mannequin/doppelgänger as if to strangle it, suggesting a confrontation of his shadow-self. The moment he touches the suit, however, we hear the Marseillaise, suggesting that his reintegration into himself is an act of rebellion, even, as the song that follows – 'All You Need is Love' – suggests, of love.

The song's lyrics, also, suggest aspects of the Prisoner's rebellion. Principally, the line 'There's nothing you can say, but you can learn how to play the game,' recalls how the Prisoner learns how to play the game by the Village's rules, and, in doing so, sometimes becomes one of them (as in 'Hammer into Anvil') and sometimes rejects and subverts the Village (as in 'The Girl Who Was Death'). In 'Once upon a Time', the Prisoner's ability to emerge victorious depends on his being able to figure out the 'game' and take the upper hand away from Number Two. When 'All You Need is Love' returns later in the story, it is to accompany visually the physical revolt of the Prisoner and his other selves, Number Forty Eight, Number Two and the Butler, symbolising the revolutionary aspects of the song and the Prisoner's own journey. The lyrics to 'All You Need Is Love' also emphasise simultaneously the contrasts of absolute freedom and absolute tyranny. Phrases like 'There's nothing you can do that can't be done,' 'Nothing you can sing that can't be sung,' 'Nothing you can know that isn't known,' 'Nowhere you can see that can't be shown,' and so forth, all suggest both that one is completely free to do what one likes, but that, like everyone else, one is also in danger of inadvertent mass conformity; the horror of individual freedom is that everyone else too is as free.

The psychoanalytic aspects of the Prisoner's victory have also been brought out in post-hoc commentary relating to the episode. While these will be dealt with in more detail in 'Essay 5' below, an ATV press release issued after the event to help baffled viewers says that the Village 'symbolised the prison that is man's own mind,' and thus, perhaps, that the Prisoner's escape is from his own psychological demons. David Tomblin, quoted in *The Prisoner: The Original Scripts vol. 2*, says that the story represents 'a man destroying himself through ego,' a cryptic remark that could refer either to the Prisoner's confrontation with Number One or to McGoohan himself; certainly, the parallels with McGoohan's passage from doing other people's shows, to running his own, recall the Prisoner's discovery that he himself, in the end, is the one in charge of the Village. McGoohan's own mysterious comments on the episode include 'Man's biggest enemy is himself' and 'Get rid of Number One, and we are free'; however, it is unexplained how one is to get rid of Number One, when Number One is oneself. It may mean death, or reconciling oneself to one's own nature, or the rejection of negative impulses; the episode could be interpreted in a number of ways on a psychological front.

A key theme of the Prisoner's encounter with the President and the masked chorus is the integration of the individual and society. The President, upon acclaiming the Prisoner, calls him a true individual, says that only his rebellion is right, and asks him to show them the way. There is a crucial double meaning, however, when he calls the Prisoner a 'man of steel,' a phrase associated both with the comic book superhero Superman and with Stalin. What the President offers is thus a poisoned chalice, because, in the first place, how can the Prisoner's rebellion be any better than Number Forty Eight's or Number Two's (indeed, as noted above, the latter rebellions may be aspects of the Prisoner's own), and, in the second place, how can one be an individual if one has to be shown by others how to be an individual? This is underlined when the crowd, who have previously taken on key attributes of Number Forty Eight and Number Two as they spoke, drowns out the Prisoner's own words with cries of 'Aye, aye, aye' (which could equally be interpreted as 'I, I, I,' or indeed 'Eye, Eye, Eye,' like the Eye on the rocket, ever watchful, keying into the series' perceptions of surveillance). This could be taken as suggesting that the Prisoner's own key attribute is overwhelming individualism or egotism, but more likely the horrible irony of how the individual, imprinting himself onto society, becomes a dictator; without opposition, everything the Prisoner says becomes meaningless. This could explain the look of horror on the Prisoner's face at the crowd's responses. The President also says that the Prisoner should not be referred to as a number of any kind, and yet, in the end, he finds he is still a number, even if that number is One. Finally, the Prisoner can meet Number One only by walking away from this dictatorship of the individual, descending once again to confront what turns out to be himself – or does it?

LOOKING OUT FOR YOU: NUMBER ONE EXPLORED

While the topic of Number One is sufficiently large to warrant its own essay, the symbolism of the Prisoner's confrontation with it must be briefly dealt with here. The story seems to imply not that the Prisoner is Number One, but that he *becomes* Number One, beginning after he defeats Number Two in 'Once Upon a Time'. Throughout the early scenes of 'Fall Out', the Prisoner appears to develop a connection with the cylinder with the electronic eye: when the President vetoes the Prisoner's decision to use hipster-talk, the cylinder intervenes, but the President thanks the Prisoner for the idea. When Number One and the Prisoner face the surveillance screen, the image of One is the apparent 'mirror-image' of the Prisoner, and vice versa. The red telephone in One's chamber suggests that perhaps Number One *was*, surreally, on the other end of Number Two's telephone, and thus that Number Two's ultimate belief, in 'Hammer into Anvil', that the Prisoner in fact represented the authority controlling the Village may ironically have been proved correct. As the Prisoner confronts Number One, the voice-over stammers 'I, I, I'; the Prisoner symbolically accepts Number One by grinning and laughing in imitation of it, and then shuts it into the top of the rocket (which also looks like a '1', as rockets do) and fires it into space, perhaps to become the first man on the moon (see 'The Chimes of Big Ben'). On the one hand, then, the confrontation with Number One appears to be about a journey of self-discovery, and the Prisoner's coming to learn that he has control over himself and his (mental) environment.

On the other hand, there is also the implication that Number One represents the negative side of the Prisoner's personality: his confrontation with Number One is presaged by his encounter with the mannequin, and the cavern with the President and masked figures appears to be a kind of negative image of the Village. The telephone in Number One's chamber is the red Expressionist 'anxiety telephone' seen in 'A, B and C', 'Hammer into Anvil' and 'The Girl Who Was Death', suggesting that Number One is in the place of formless anxieties. Max Hora's take on the story is: 'He is not a prisoner of the Village, but a prisoner of himself. His enemy is within himself. The "goody" is also the "baddy". The hero and the villain are one and the same. He ceases to be *the* Prisoner of *the* Village … but, as he returns to his London home, the front door opens automatically – just like the doors in the Village … Until he overcomes his own problems and his own weaknesses, he will certainly remain *a* prisoner in *a* village. His Village travels around with him – in his own mind.' Number One thus may be the mad(wo)man in the attic, the bestial ape in all human nature; the confrontation between Number One and the Prisoner thus involves the Prisoner coming to terms with his negative impulses, learning how to lock them away when necessary, and then re-emerging as an integrated person. The psychoanalytic patient, having resolved his inner struggle and confronted his dark side, thus leaves the therapeutic environment (destroying it as he does so) and goes out into society.

I AIM FOR THE STARS, BUT SOMETIMES I HIT LONDON: THE RETURN TO SOCIETY

The story ends with the Prisoner and his three associates apparently returning to society and reintegrating into it, throwing the Village's guns and robes out of the trailer (for the sharp-eyed, a camera crew can be briefly seen on the verge as they do so), with Number Forty

Eight going hitchhiking, Number Two entering Parliament and the Prisoner being last seen driving down an airstrip, as in the title sequence (of which more later). However, does this make them necessarily complicit with society? In the original script, there is some cursory dialogue as Number Forty Eight and Number Two leave, although the sequence is much better without it, becoming more generally symbolic. The young man continues to rebel, aimlessly wandering from one side of the motorway to the other as he hitchhikes in defiance of the law (this also echoes a cut sequence earlier in the original script, in which the Prisoner, the Supervisor and the Butler emerge into a large corridor with traffic going down both sides, regulated by signals, and the Prisoner disrupts the traffic by refusing to obey the signals; when the Supervisor exclaims 'You mustn't,' the Prisoner replies 'I must'). Many commentators mention at this point that the road in question is the A1 doubling for the A20, though how any viewer is expected to tell the difference is beyond us. The older man may well be re-entering Parliament, but as an independent MP or subversive civil servant. On the road, all three of them frighten the Establishment, in the persona of a bowler-hatted gentleman who finds the sight of them dancing and drinking coffee in a trailer shocking (according to Alexis Kanner, interviewed on The Unmutual website, the Bentley the man drives was McGoohan's own).

Mention should also be made here of the Butler. The Butler has no number, doesn't speak, and is never referred to by name, number or title (being called the Butler only in the series' usual closing credits). He is also constant; while other Villagers come and go, he is always there, and always as himself, never a doppelgänger or double. Consequently, some of the crew had speculated that the Butler was Number One (and the Butler walking towards the Prisoner as he is taken to meet Number One is thus an in-joke). In the original script, when the Supervisor dons the mask and robe, the Butler is offered the same, but looks at the Prisoner and shakes his head; the Prisoner is then offered the outfit, but simply looks at it. This both marks the Butler's distinct status and links him with the Prisoner. We never find out who the Butler is in terms of the Village hierarchy; what we do know, however, is that he follows the person who is in control. Hence, as noted in the dialogue, the reason why he stops following Number Two and starts following the Prisoner in 'Once Upon a

Time'. He seems in 'Fall Out' to exist as an extension of the Prisoner's personality, acting without needing to be prompted. The fact that he returns to 1 Buckingham Place thus suggests that the Prisoner is now in control, having aspects of Number Two as well as Number One; he is a man in charge of his own destiny.

The question remains, however, of what it is that the Prisoner is doing at the end of the story. He appears to be repeating his initial act of resignation in driving down the road as in the title sequence, which many have interpreted as indicating that the programme is cyclical, and that the Prisoner will ultimately return to the Village (this sequence is missing from the original script). However, this interpretation can be questioned: the animated sequence that appears at the end of the episode in some prints, featuring gates clanging shut over the Prisoner's face (three times in the 1984 Channel 4 repeat and once in the 1992 repeat), was not there in the originally transmitted version, and although the credit 'Prisoner' is superimposed on the image of the Prisoner driving through London, he then reappears on the runway with no such superimposed designation. Without the gates and designation, he could be seen as driving out into the world, a free man, with no need to resign, just to drive as far and fast as he wants. One might note that, when he looks into Number One's crystal ball, he sees the gates slamming on his face three times, but then breaks that ball, rejecting that future for himself. He does not appear to have achieved Nirvana, or any sort of rejection of the world, since he is still very much in the world and, evidently, enjoying its pleasures. Some might facetiously suggest that, since the Lotus he drives at the end is not the car he drives in the title sequence, but a look-alike, he is on his way to report the theft of his car and its replacement with an identical model, now that he has the opportunity to do so. More seriously, the parallel with the beginning of his initial act of rebellion suggests that he is integrating his rebellion into society, or that society needs rebels, and thus that, like Number Forty-Eight and Number Two, he is repeating his old patterns, regardless whether he is in the world or not.

However, there is also a more sinister interpretation. The chamber in which the Prisoner finds Number One is the reused rocket interior set from 'The Girl Who Was Death', with Schnipps' map of London visible under the globes (as this story was the previous one in production order, a lot of the sets, to say nothing of certain of the cast, were reused from it). This establishes the obvious parallel with a story made up from the Prisoner's own mind (and thus, being his mental images becoming reality), in which the central figure is a madman determined to fire a rocket to destroy London. Here, the Prisoner launches a rocket, which effectively contains himself, and then goes back to London, having succeeded in his rebellion in the Village. McGoohan, in the Goodman interview, observes that the level of violence the Prisoner achieves in 'Fall Out' is unlike any previously seen in the series ('shooting everyone in sight,' as he notes), and alludes to this representing the idea that violence, and particularly war, is occasionally needed as an agent of social catharsis: 'Sometimes in the course of history … you find that the build-up of these frustrations within people, that it comes to a conflict area, where a war can clear the air.' With this in mind, it is easy to see the Prisoner as taking his rebellion to the outside world, not to conform with it, but to start a chaotic, violent revolution, as he did in the Village, unleashing his individualism on an unsuspecting world. The cyclical nature of the story, and the importance of the rocket, is, therefore, that the Prisoner himself is now a metaphorical rocket aimed at London, to destroy, or transform, society through rebellion.

The ending of *The Prisoner* has multiple layers, meanings and aspects to it, but all of them seem to focus on the destructive, yet ultimately positive, power of rebellion, particularly when it is not isolated into the formless acts of individual youths and older men, but integrated into both the self and society.

Essay 5:
Who Is Number One?

The final story, 'Fall Out', centres around a powerful symbolic sequence: the long-signposted discovery of the identity of Number One. On the assumption that this sequence does not simply constitute symbolism for symbolism's sake, we will here unpack some of the potential interpretations, bearing in mind that this is one area in which the idea that no one interpretation works universally for *The Prisoner* is particularly true.

The identity of Number One remained a mystery to the cast and crew until the final episode. Some have indeed suggested that it was not even decided upon by McGoohan himself until shortly beforehand. Elements of 'Free for All' and 'Once Upon a Time' , however, indicate the possibility that he had already had a few thoughts along those lines. It is also worth noting that the Prisoner has, since the first episode, been seen to live at 1 Buckingham Place; and that in the title sequence, when the Prisoner asks 'Who is Number One?', Number Two effectively replies 'You are, Number Six'. It might be assumed, as seems to be the case in the title sequence, that Number One would be the person in charge of the Village, since Number Two appears to be his deputy; however, the Village numbering system indicates that low numbers do not inherently involve high status, and the meaning of the numbering, where there is one, is contingent upon the episode. The revelation of Number One as an apparently mad duplicate of the Prisoner himself, rather than a Bond supervillain or some previously-seen character (for example the Butler) has subsequently had any number of commentators and casual viewers scratching their heads. ATV's press release on the subject dodged the question, saying 'As with an abstract painting, several people could look at the final episode and draw their own different conclusions.' We shall here consider a few possibilities: One as the individual, One as society, One as the shadow-self or the id, and One as metaphor for God.

NUMBER ONE AS THE INDIVIDUAL

Number One can, first, be interpreted as being the individual, isolated from society and in opposition to it. Certainly the possibility exists that *The Prisoner* is all about a search for personal identity (and thus, one-self/the I). In the *Danger Man* episode 'The Professionals', a diplomat remarks that secret agents have so many different identities that he wonders if even they really know who they are (and Drake himself is also something of a mystery in terms of his personal identity), and in 'Do Not Forsake Me Oh My Darling', we learn that the Prisoner has had a variety of different identities, suggesting that over the previous 16 episodes, he has been searching for an identity lost in the psychological rigours of being a secret agent. In discovering Number One, he then rediscovers his own individualism, and his identity as an individual.

This is supported by certain aspects of the character. The physical appearance of Number One, for instance: when we first see him, he is distinguished from the other robed figures in that his robe bears a number '1' (which looks like an 'I') inside a circle. When the Prisoner takes the hood and masks off Number One, he reveals himself – and, when the Prisoner looks into his face, the screen and the crystal ball, he sees himself reflecting into infinity – and, when he does so, the figure leaps up and acts, doing what, apparently, it wants to do. Earlier, when the hidden Number One expresses its will, it is always the Prisoner's will also (as in the sequence where Number Forty Eight is granted permission to speak in slang). A number of the earlier stories have focused on themes of the individual rebelling against a society that wishes him to conform; in this, the series picks up on the focus on individual freedom common to the popular culture of the 1960s.

More than this, however, the final episode focuses on the tyranny of the individual as well. When the Prisoner expresses his individuality, the community blindly follows it, and he realises that what he has done is not to give them individual freedom, but to impose the will of a single individual on society. He then sets them free by destroying society (in the form of the Village), and sending the Villagers out in the world (symbolised by the departures of Number Forty Eight, the Butler and Number Two). He fires the rocket into space with Number One on it, reflecting his remark in 'The Chimes of Big Ben' about his desire to be the first man on the moon, and, if this is his aim, he has made Number One a true individual in divorcing him fully from all human society. Having unleashed his individuality, the Prisoner now returns to society, not to become an integrated member, but to keep on rebelling.

While some aspects of this reading are convincing, the question remains of whether or not it is possible to have an individual without society, and, furthermore, whether granting everyone their individualism would not cause more problems than it solved (as it would ultimately lead to total social breakdown). Furthermore, there are many aspects of Number One that recall society as much as, if not more than, they do the individual, and it is to this contradictory set of aspects that we now turn.

NUMBER ONE AS SOCIETY

According to another reading, Number One represents society: it may be capricious and irrational, but it is in all of us, and we are part of it. The dichotomy between individual and society is a false one, since society is made up of individuals, and individuals define society. This reading is borne out by the fact that the series has, up until now, had a strong theme of the individual becoming integrated *into* society as much as rejecting it: in 'Once Upon a Time', 'Hammer into Anvil', 'It's Your Funeral' and others, Six acts for the benefit of the, or a, community. In 'A Change of Mind', he appears deeply affected by the isolation he experiences, and on close examination it can be seen that the Prisoner is never fully able to survive without other people. In 'Once Upon a Time', we see the Prisoner starting off as antisocial/childlike, and then gradually coming to master the rules of the miniature 'society' that he has been placed in, and his reward is to meet Number One at the end. Writer Daniel O'Mahony has argued that the Village represents one of sociologist Erving Goffman's total institutions, absorbing and subsuming its members into it. Even as a rebel, the Prisoner needs people – perhaps especially as a rebel, since there is little point in rejecting society if there is nothing there to reject.

In terms of symbolism, Number One is seen garbed in the same costume worn by the people who made up the symbolic 'society' seen earlier in 'Fall Out', and holds a crystal ball, representing possibly the future, and possibly the world as a whole. When the Prisoner unmasks it, he finds a duplicate of himself, indicating that he is a part of it, but, since they are in fact two beings, it is not him in the literal sense. Number One imposes his will on the community in the story through the green surveillance eye, suggesting social sanctions or the imposition of the collective will. It may thus be that Number One does not only run the Village, but, in fact, *is* the Village, representing its collective will as a society.

Despite this, the metaphor does not fit seamlessly. Number One is still a single unit, and has the face of the character identified as the classic nonconformist or rebel. It also, as noted above, has a number of traits that seem to represent individualism (although it can be argued that this simply represents the tension between individual and society, since society is made up of individuals and individuals must to some degree conform to a society). Its actions upon unmasking are not terribly social, as it gibbers, runs around and then gets itself sealed into a rocket and shot out into space.

NUMBER ONE AS THE DESTRUCTIVE SHADOW

Returning to the psychoanalytic themes of earlier stories, it may be that Number One represents the negative side of oneself, the dark side of the personality. It has some similarities to Jung's concept of the Shadow: the opposite of the ego; the hidden aspects of oneself, some creative and some destructive. The Shadow may be rejected, but more healthily should be accepted and integrated into oneself, as one cannot function without it (note that, in the title sequence, the shadow of the Prisoner dominates as he walks down the corridor). Certainly, McGoohan himself appears to see aspects of the destructive Shadow in the character: he told the *Women's Journal* that Number One was responsible for 'death, torture and war' and 'the worst enemy is Man himself'; in a letter to an unknown newspaper quoted in *Free for All* (Issue 14, spring 2005), he says: 'Number One is the worst part of oneself. Number One made Hitler. Get rid of Number One and we are free.' This, again, suggests that Number One is some hidden, perhaps negative, part of the personality: that everybody has their own Number One. Contemporary critic James Thomas also thought that the programme represented some form of self-discovery for McGoohan: 'For 17 weeks, McGoohan has been trying to escape from a constricted society ... a tireless rebel who would not conform to the Big Brother mentality and who at last found himself face to face with the truth. And the truth seemed to be a kind of self-humiliation, in which McGoohan discovered that his personal ego was the beginning and end of his troubles.'

Number One seems to represent aspects of the Prisoner's negative side – anarchic, irrational, incomprehensible, lashing out at everyone and everything – suggesting that the flip-side of freedom and individuality is anarchy and incomprehensibility. It is not, however, released until he removes the masks (one of them an ape, acknowledging the animal/primitive society symbolism inherent in Jungian interpretation), peeling away the layers of personality and, Jung-like, going deep within to expose the unacknowledged aspects of his mind. Rather than destroying or killing Number One, the Prisoner smiles and imitates it, accepting it as part of himself. The Prisoner and Number One are thus distorted mirror images of each other: the firing off of the rocket thus represents how one can try and deny or repress one's Shadow side, but it eventually comes back, in this case, presumably, to explode on London.

Again, however, there are challenges that can be raised to this interpretation. Principally, we have in the past seen the Prisoner exposing aspects of himself, particularly negative ones, of which he does not seem totally aware, and they are different to that seen here: in 'Checkmate', he appears as a domineering bully, and in 'Hammer into Anvil' as vengeful, slightly sadistic, and incapable of realising that to use the Village's tools is to become like the very people he despises. Number One, however, does not appear to act out any negative impulses along these lines, but simply to act irrationally. Also, when the Prisoner exposes Number One's face, he too laughs manically and runs around, suggesting that he is aware of, not repressing or hiding, the aspects of his personality that Number One represents. It, therefore, may be that there are other psychological readings of Number One.

NUMBER ONE AS ID

Following the rival, Freudian theory of psychoanalysis, Number One thus might be seen as the id, which can be roughly defined as encompassing the unconscious, primitive, instinctual drives of the personality (for example sexuality, aggression, pleasure, survival), as opposed to the superego (internalised social regulations) and the ego (the aspect of the personality that achieves a balance between the two). Number One could, therefore, be seen to represent the primitive drives over which civilisation and self-consciousness form a veneer.

The Number One we see in 'Fall Out' certainly does recall infantile and primitive desires: the ape mask can be argued to represent the primeval, or animal instinct. Number One itself acts like an infant, gibbering and lashing out. Like the Id Monster of the film *Forbidden Planet*, which represented Doctor Morbius's repressed feelings of jealousy, anger and sexual desire, here Number One represents the Prisoner's desire to destroy society, smashing the crystal ball with the Village reflected in it (and, in doing so, also rejecting his own imprisonment), and celebrating anarchy. The Prisoner, after acknowledging the id, goes on to act upon the repressed desires that Number One represents, but in a rational way that acknowledges the role of society and social custom, destroying the Village and going out to bring his message of rebellion to the world. The two masks could represent the superego (the Greek tragedy mask, worn by the members of the mock-society earlier) and the ego (the ape, representing the individual person).

In some ways, also, the whole programme could be seen as being about coming to terms with the id and, perhaps, acting upon its impulses at times. The conflict between the Prisoner and his captors is at least partly focused on the fact that his reasons for resignation do not make sense to them, being led by desire and emotion rather than by rational sociopolitical planning. 'It's Your Funeral' suggests as a reason for the Prisoner's daily visit to the bell tower, 'Perhaps he enjoys the view.' The childhood/infantilism symbolism throughout the series, and particularly in 'Once Upon a Time', might suggest that this is all about the developing individual coming to terms with his desires and the pressures of society, and learning to balance them as an integrated ego.

However, the main problem with this reading is that the Prisoner does not seem to need much help in coming to terms with his inner desires, as he has expressed his anarchic tendencies over and over, and even given them free rein before the climax of 'Fall Out'. He also does not necessarily come to terms with society in this story, as there are a number of readings suggesting that the Prisoner in fact rejects, or sets out to destroy, society. While psychoanalysis is one of the key themes of the series, then, the Freudian interpretation may not cover all aspects of the identity of Number One.

NUMBER ONE AS GOD

The large amount of Christian religious symbolism in the series, and in particular in 'Fall Out' (with characters standing cruciform, spirituals being sung, and people being raised, literally and symbolically, from the dead) might suggest another reading: that Number One represents God, at least as he appears from a Judaeo-Christian perspective (since this is the one from which the writers, directors and production crew were, for the most part, coming): a mysterious being that we are all seeking, that created us and watches over us, and whose existence, or continued presence, is sometimes in doubt.

As well as the religious symbolism noted above, Number One is portrayed throughout most of 'Fall Out' as unseen but omnipotent and omnipresent: observing everything that happens and making its cryptic wishes known not through direct speech but through physical events. McGoohan, asked about the religious symbolism in the Goodman interview, and in particular the idea that the Village is a kind of purgatory and 'Fall Out' represents Judgement Day, observed: 'That was again always at the back of my mind from as long as I can remember, as a child, we're going through purgatory here to a certain extent, so I suppose there was a certain symbolism in that. Not very deliberately so; unconsciously so, but as a part of my philosophy and thinking, a certain amount of it did emerge … using the song "The hipbone's connected to the thighbone, and hear the word of the Lord."' One can thus interpret Number One as a kind of vengeful deity presiding over a symbolic Judgement Day.

It is also possible to see Trinitarian symbolism in the set-up with Number One: the Father (Number One, omniscient but absent during the trials of Numbers Forty Eight and Two), the Son (the Prisoner, who stands cruciform in the title sequence and also in a familiar publicity still from 'Fall Out', has shown himself as a man willing to stand against authority, and, although he is not precisely self-sacrificial, is frequently shown to have a strong compassionate side and willingness to help the vulnerable) and the Holy Spirit (the rocket, which carries Number One out into the universe): these are both one and the same and separate, in a paradox that imitates the doctrine of the Trinity. The exodus of the Prisoner, Number Two and Number Forty Eight could be seen as an imitation of the apostles' quest to bring the Word of God to the rest of the world. As mentioned above, in the original script, the series' last scene was to have had the Prisoner and the Butler going into the house at 1 Buckingham Place to the tune of 'Dem Bones', and to have faded out on the line 'Hear the word of the Lord.' The Prisoner's quest, thus, might be seen as a journey to find God and come to understand His will, and then bring that understanding to others.

In a further twist, aspects of 'Fall Out' also seem to represent another facet of divinity: the way Man tries to usurp God. As noted in the analysis of 'Fall Out', the Prisoner takes charge in a way explicitly flagged up as recalling Stalin's role as the dominant personality influencing the Soviet Union. In this reading, God (Number One) is replaced by Man (the Prisoner) in the eyes of the people; however, the Prisoner realises the danger of having a single individual dictating the views of the populace. God's will may be contradictory, in that it is mediated through a variety of different doctrines and may equally be rejected by individuals, but Stalin's will is capricious and dependent on specific whims and circumstances, and, since Stalin is not omniscient, becomes dangerous and destructive. The story, therefore, may reflect the legend of Adam's Fall, as Man thinks that he can become like God (although, here, the Prisoner apparently rejects the temptation rather than succumbs to it), or, possibly, the atheist argument that God is simply a projection of human desires and fears. 'Fall Out' thus explores the relationship of God to humanity.

While this is certainly a significant reading, and one that acknowledges the fact that McGoohan's own Catholicism was no small influence on the series, it has to be said that the story is nonetheless more than a religious allegory, and to read it solely in religious terms would be to miss the other potential readings. It may be that, rather than focusing on a single aspect of Number One, we should embrace the multifaceted nature of the character.

In the end, then, no single reading – psychoanalytic, religious, or sociological – fully explains the Number One sequence at the end of 'Fall Out'. Viewers are, therefore, invited, through the multivalent nature of the character, to interpret the story according to which aspects of it resonate the deepest with them. As Gregory notes, 'The revelation may also suggest that any individual constructs his or her own psychological reality, and that the Village is a mental prison of his own making' – for the viewer, as much for the protagonist (and, indeed, the creator), of *The Prisoner*.

Deemed Unmutual: Eric Mival's Unmade Stories

When analysing television series, one can sometimes gain as much insight from considering the story ideas and scripts that did *not* make it into production as those that did.

As full details , and accounts of who pitched a story for the series, can be found in Robert Fairclough's *The Prisoner: The Original Scripts vol. 1*, there is little point in reiterating them here, except to note that those who made unsuccessful pitches included two former *Doctor Who* story editors, Donald Tosh and David Whitaker, and that John Kruse, scriptwriter of the 1957 film *Hell Drivers*, a savage drama about truckers that had featured Patrick McGoohan as the villain, was asked to contribute but turned the offer down, saying that he found the concept of the series too dark. George Markstein commissioned two stories, 'Don't Get Yourself Killed' and 'The Outsider', that made it into script form but were ultimately not pursued, as relations between him and McGoohan broke down; after Markstein left, replacement scripts were sought from, among others, the production staff, including film editor Ian Rakoff (whose submission eventually became 'Living in Harmony'), film librarian Tony Sloman and music editor Eric Mival (who came up with two ideas that made it to the detailed outline stage but no further). After the series finished, Alexis Kanner claimed that there were discussions about him and Angelo Muscat starring in a spin-off/sequel series, based around 'Fall Out', but this sounds like wishful thinking (although it is worth noting that the character Johnny Quill in the proposed Everyman series *The Outsider* does bear some resemblance to Number Forty Eight in 'Fall Out', particularly in that we first encounter him hitch-hiking, and walking up one side of the road and down the other as he does so).

Before considering 'The Outsider' and 'Don't Get Yourself Killed' in detail, it is worth looking briefly at the two Eric Mival ideas.

TICKET TO ETERNITY

The first Mival storyline, 'Ticket to Eternity', was to have focused around the idea of a church in the Village, a kind of cult with distinctly Russian Orthodox stylings, which purports to promise literal eternal life. The Prisoner is offered this in exchange for revealing his secrets, and to allay his suspicions, he is given a 'demonstration' that appears to involve his travelling through time in a capsule to a decayed and abandoned Village and there finding his own diary, which says that the offer was genuine, and that he told all and met Number One. He becomes suspicious, and discovers the whole thing to have been a hoax, set up by the Village.

The most obvious reason why this script was abandoned is the overt references to religion. As with sex, McGoohan explicitly avoided open references to religion and faith within the series; while this isn't to say that it does not play a role, it is on a symbolic rather than an explicit level. Within the televised series, the Village has no churches or temples (although places of worship do feature in the original novels), and the team even filmed around the statue of the Buddha that sits at the foot of the Green Dome Portmeirion, to avoid showing it.

'Ticket to Eternity', however, openly references religion, and in a way that would be impossible to write out (as it is central to the premise). In addition, it could be easily read as implying that religion, particularly Christianity, offers only a bogus eternal life, and is under the control of the state, which, while an interesting subject to explore, would probably have been too controversial for the 1960s, when the social climate regarding religion was much more rigid than it is today (and even now, dramas on controversial religious themes like *The Second Coming* and *Jerry Springer: The Opera* tend to attract a large amount of criticism from viewers, albeit mostly from organised pressure groups with specific political ends rather than individuals). Although writers such as Dennis Potter were engaging in criticisms of Christianity at the time, notably in his 1969 teleplay *Son of Man*, this was generally not considered appropriate for early-evening commercial fare.

Leaving aside the controversial subject matter, the idea that an entire duplicate Village in decay could be created to such a degree of accuracy that it would fool one of its inhabitants, while not actually impossible within the fantasy guidelines of the series, does seem considerably more extreme than just partially replicating the contents of a single London house. While the series did tend towards the bizarre in terms of the Village's plans, they always stayed ever-so-slightly believable, whereas this scenario is far too dreamlike and strange to be designated as such. Also, the bogus final entry in the Prisoner's diary sounds nothing like him (' ... finally let them know all. It was really worth it. Met No. 1 – not such a bad bloke – goodbye to all my readers'), suggesting that the Village authorities were also slipshod over the significant details.

Mival has said that the reason why he made the priests of the church resemble Russian Orthodox ones was that he had been recently working on a documentary on Russia, *Red Reflections*, which at one point featured a monastery, and that he had found the monks there 'formidable-looking.' However, this depiction also fits in with the implication that the Village may be Soviet-run (although the Soviets were anti-religious, they did tolerate the Church to some degree, as without it they would have lost control of the peasantry, which reflects the state-control theme of 'Ticket to Eternity'). It would have seemed strange, exotic and vaguely Eastern European to contemporary audiences in a Britain, which did not yet see itself as globalised or multicultural. The themes of caves, of bizarre and expensive scenarios developed seemingly for the sole benefit of the Prisoner, and of things that the Prisoner considers personal, like his diary, turning out to be public, all pick up on earlier successful aspects of the series. However, in the end, these aspects are not enough to balance out the more controversial ones.

FRIEND OR FOE

Mival's second story sits even more uneasily with modern audiences, in that it deals openly with racial politics. It involves the Prisoner striking up a friendship with a Black activist and orator, Mike X, who has recently come to the Village; the pair plan to escape together, but before they can do so, Mike is apparently killed by Rover. However, he then returns, claiming that he faked his own death; he and the Prisoner fake the latter's death as well and return to London, where Mike introduces the Prisoner to his friends. The Prisoner initially trusts them, but becomes suspicious when he sees a white streak on Mike's skin. He pulls off a brown rubber mask, to reveal one of the Villagers who had previously been seen as a heckler at Mike's speeches.

It is this last detail, in fact, that is ironically the main redeeming point of the narrative. If the story had been written such that it was unclear whether or not Mike had been a White man in disguise all along, then it would have suggested that only White people can be popular, smart or charismatic; but it is made clear that Mike himself is the author of all his own work, and the fake Mike is one of his key hecklers. However, it is still difficult for a modern audience to take; although the practice of White actors putting on make-up to play Black or Asian characters was taken for granted in the 1960s, this is definitely not the case now, and even without this, the story still comes across as a bit too right-on and patronising. In this, it is rather like another unmade story, 'The Outsider', which attempts to tackle feminism and the oppression of women similarly directly; since the Village is generally gender-egalitarian and multicultural without particularly calling attention to this as unusual, to explicitly flag up political issues in this way seems odd and out of place. Finally, there really was a Black activist in London at the time called Michael X (born Michael de Freitas), which might have raised issues of representation, or even brought about lawsuits.

As with Mival's other story, there are nonetheless a few thought-provoking aspects to the outline. The idea of the Village having a 'Speaker's Corner,' where orators are encouraged to speak, and thus to inadvertently reveal their secrets through the goading of trained hecklers, is quite a clever one (and reminiscent of 'The Outsider''s sequence in which Number Two attempts to get the Prisoner to reveal his secrets through overconfidence), and it is perhaps a shame that this element was not pursued further in the televised series. Mival apparently wrote the story at least partly in an attempt to get a good role for a West Indian actor friend of his, and one of the areas in which the series is lacking is in strong central roles for non-White characters. The ending, with the two friends tramping back to London along the motorway and then finding it to be really all part of the Village, weirdly foreshadows 'Fall Out' (McGoohan reportedly never saw Mival's outlines, which were considered and vetoed by Tomblin only). The theme of death, and of dead characters returning, also picks up on things seen throughout the series.

While neither made it very far into development, then, it is interesting to consider the two story outlines above in indicating how far *The Prisoner* would go in tackling controversial subjects, and where the series' unspoken artistic boundaries were.

Unmade Stories 1: The Outsider By Moris Farhi

SYNOPSIS: While out making a geological map of the cliffs near the Village, the Prisoner observes a plane crash. He finds the Pilot, who claims to be a meteorologist and not to know about the Village; the Prisoner is suspicious of him, tying him up in a cave outside the Village, but is willing to give him the benefit of the doubt to some extent, and fakes the Pilot's death to put the Village authorities off the scent. He suggests to the Pilot that they escape together. Number Two engages the Prisoner in a rigged game of poker to try and find out how he thinks, but the Prisoner becomes suspicious of Number Two's motives, and, when presented with a winning hand, throws it away. The next day, the Pilot is discovered by Rover; he escapes with the Prisoner's help, but the Prisoner is concerned and says they must try to escape that night, using the Pilot's homing beacon and a large bonfire as decoys while they contact the air-sea rescue helicopter (which has been seen searching for the Pilot) on the beach, using a light. Number Two summons the Prisoner to the Village's thermal baths, interrogates him about the Pilot, then, when the Prisoner fails to cooperate, tortures him in the Village hospital, with similar results. The Prisoner attempts to shake off Number Eighty Three, a seemingly brainwashed woman claiming she wants to serve him, as he goes to the cave, but the Pilot captures her and she continues to follow them while claiming she does not want to leave the Village. The Pilot and the Prisoner are rescued by the helicopter, but when the Prisoner awakes he finds himself back in Number Two's residence, with the Pilot very much at home. The Pilot explains that the whole experience was simply an exercise in psychological warfare intended to break down the Prisoner.

ANALYSIS: Turkish-born Moris Farhi was quite excited about writing for *The Prisoner*, considering it to be the best series in production at the time. Unfortunately, this points to the story's main weakness: the script is visibly full of enthusiasm, and of knowledge of what sort of elements had appeared in earlier stories, but low in terms of consideration of what the series is actually about on a deeper level.

THE INSIDER: THE STORY AND ITS PROBLEMS

One reason why the story was not carried forward may have been that it is more in the conventional action-adventure vein than is usual for the series, even when compared to fairly prosaic episodes like 'Hammer into Anvil' and 'The Chimes of Big Ben'. While it might have made a reasonably good entry in a more conventional ITC spy series, the plot is fairly thin for an episode of *The Prisoner*, being reminiscent of many a Second World War drama (soldier crashing behind enemy lines and being uncertain whether his rescuer is a Resistance member or a Nazi sympathiser who is stringing him along until s/he can contact the authorities). Beyond that, the story is not particularly deep or clever, and there are some elements that, while nominally within the remit of *The Prisoner*, are at odds with the rest of the series in terms of their treatment. The dialogue, one or two good lines aside, is not really inspiring, even when one takes into consideration that scripted lines never seem as exciting as those spoken on screen (an unfortunately typical example from the Pilot: 'I suppose you'll get a medal for this. But then sometimes tin glitters more than gold'), suggesting that 'The Outsider' needed to go through a few more drafts before it would really work. There are a couple of mistakes (the constellation of the Great Bear, for instance, being referred to as 'The Big Bear'), and the idea that the Prisoner smuggles the Pilot's gear out with his helmet under his shirt and his boots tied to his shins and concealed under his trousers conjures up a ridiculous mental image of a baggy-legged, pot-bellied McGoohan attempting to remain inconspicuous.

'The Outsider' also has very similar elements to other early *The Prisoner* stories, in a somewhat distorted format. Number Eighty Three, for instance, is superficially close to the Queen in 'Checkmate', who was also a woman mentally conditioned to desire the Prisoner; and the Prisoner falling asleep in the helicopter and waking up in the Village resembles the ending of 'Arrival' (in that both involve a supposed escape by helicopter that proves to be bogus). The idea of the Prisoner trying to escape and being betrayed by a seemingly friendly figure recurs in many early episodes. A number of elements, however, appear to have been grafted on more for effect than because they add anything to the story. These include as a politician making a platitudinous televised speech (as in 'Free for All'); the Pilot's use of a made-up language described as a mix of Latin and 'Nordic', recalling the use of random foreign and made-up languages throughout the series; and the brief implication that, as in 'The Chimes of Big Ben', the Village is in the Balkans. The re-use of elements in and of itself isn't a problem (consider the large number of later stories that more or less blatantly reference 'The Chimes of Big Ben', and the fact that all the original novels have borrowed from the series to a greater or lesser degree of success), but, taken as a whole, and in consideration of the fact that few of these elements actually contribute much to the story, it makes the script seem oddly like *The Prisoner* fan-fiction, as written by someone who enjoys the series, and who remembers a number of evocative elements from it, but who thinks he understands it better than he actually does.

One of the most problematic aspects is the inconsistent portrayal of the story's central guest character, the Pilot. While surrealism and unexpected twists are part of *The Prisoner's* stock-in-trade, characters are generally consistently portrayed throughout. Furthermore, other stories in which a seemingly sympathetic figure turns out to be Number Two, or even simply a Village agent, have the character acting ambiguously, so that one can, for instance, watch 'Many Happy Returns' over and over knowing that Mrs Butterworth is Number Two and not have the story ruined, or her actions called into question – indeed, one can gain more from the story by knowing something of what is going on in Mrs

Butterworth's mind as she carries out her various activities. In 'The Outsider', however, the Pilot's actions are written so as to indicate, unambiguously, that he is *not* Number Two (a script direction, for instance, reads 'His first impulse is to go for his gun holster, but he restrains himself when he sees P [i.e. the Prisoner] is unarmed' – not the actions of a man who knows what the situation really is), which means that the story could only really have been viewed through once without raising problems of characterisation and motivation. If the Pilot is Number Two, why does he desperately try to untie the cords restraining his hands when he hears a helicopter go overhead, despite the fact that the Prisoner is not there to see him do so? And why does he try to bite a genuine cyanide capsule? As he himself says later, he had no guarantee that the Prisoner would stop him from killing himself in time. Why does he put himself at risk from Rover, and why does he look terrified of it when it confronts him, since again the Prisoner is not there to observe his terror? While these actions may make the final twist more of a surprise, they also mean that we lose the subtle psychology and subtext of cat-and-mouse game-playing that is one of the greatest strengths of the series as a whole.

The rigged poker game sequence is also one that is not bad as a concept, but raises problematic questions in the execution. It is in keeping with the theme of game-playing, particularly chess and cards, in the series, even if poker is perhaps a slightly more adult-oriented one than normally seen (as children as well as adults may play chess and certain card games, but are usually discouraged from gambling games; significantly, gambling games appear in the televised series only in dream sequences, in 'A, B and C' and 'Living in Harmony'). The idea of allowing the Prisoner to win in order to determine what he knows about the Pilot from what he asks for as a prize is clever, and in keeping with themes of psychology elsewhere in the series: the Doctor's remark, 'Even the most harmless desire has thousands of connotations – each a virtual trap' also echoes the action elsewhere in the story, as the Prisoner's reaction to the Pilot is another psychological test to understand his motivations. However, since the Village already has an extensive psychological file on the Prisoner (indeed, various Number Twos within the televised series have referred to this fact), it is debatable what new aspect of his personality this testing is going to reveal. It has been firmly established from the first episode that the Prisoner is altruistic, resourceful and anti-authoritarian. There is also no reason in the story why the Butler should, as he does, give the game away to the Prisoner by smiling at inopportune moments. Once again, the sequence is superficially in keeping with successful themes and ideas in the series, but falls down when one interrogates the characters' motivations and actions.

A VINDICATION OF THE RIGHTS OF WOMEN: SEXISM AND WOMEN'S ROLE IN 'THE OUTSIDER'

Considerably more problematic is the treatment of women in this story, beginning when the Prisoner is accosted by a 'plain' woman who tells him that she has been 'wasting [her] time' as a career woman and wants instead to be 'a good wife to a nice man' (implying, one hopes inadvertently, through this description that women seek out careers simply because they are not attractive enough to lure a man into marrying them). While Farhi is plainly not sympathetic to this sort of idea, using it to emphasise the repressive nature of the Village and the casual use of mental conditioning (since the woman has in fact been conditioned to believe that she has been wasting her life, and may well have been perfectly happy in her career), and while anti-sexist messages are one of the staples of *The Prisoner*, the execution of the idea is very out of keeping with the *style* of the series' anti-sexism, which tends to present women casually in positions of power and skill rather than openly polemicise against their oppression, and frequently to celebrate the beauty of women who are not conventionally attractive. Indeed, it is difficult to square the idea that women are being blatantly conditioned into '50s-style housewifery with the Village's image as globalist and Utopian, without the national and cultural prejudices prevailing in the rest of the world.

Even more difficult to take are the story's revelations about the Palace of Fun (a Village building originally supposed to be included in the series but quietly dropped early on, although it still appears on the fold-out map and information board legend seen in 'Arrival'), which seems, among other things, to be running a kind of Stepford Escort Service whereby mentally conditioned young women see to the 'fun' of men. In case the sexual implications of the idea are not clear, we have open references to them in the script, with Number Two remarking that Numbers Fifty Five and Eighty Three are there to 'attend to *our* ... pleasure' (ellipsis and italics in the original), and the Pilot reacting suggestively when he meets Number Eighty Three ('New World Loreleis ... talk about temptation. Are there many like her? ... Maybe this Village is not such a bad place after all'). At the end of the story, the Pilot 'requisitions' Number Eighty Three for his own pleasure. Leaving aside the way all this works against the subtle, even subtextual, treatment of sexuality elsewhere in the series (indeed, seeming rather crass compared with the treatment of the Prisoner's relationships with women in 'The Schizoid Man', 'Checkmate' and 'Do Not Forsake Me Oh My Darling'), this begs the question of what the various female Number Twos thought of the practice. It is difficult to picture 'Mister Peter Pan' from 'Dance of the Dead', the former Number Fifty Eight from 'Free for All' or Mrs Butterworth happily tolerating the presence of a brothel full of brainwashed women for the pleasure of the male Villagers, or to imagine, for that matter, a society in which women are routinely used as sex slaves (and/or conditioned into rejecting the life of a career woman) being so casual about the number of female figures in positions of power. The ideas of gender and sexuality in 'The Outsider' are strongly at odds with the rest of the series.

VILLAGE OF THE DAMNED:
THE VILLAGE AND ITS CHANGES

One of the better aspects of the story is, however, its treatment of the Village. The surrealism of the environment comes into play in the script, for instance through having the man directing the salvage operation dressed, for no apparent reason other than sheer randomness, as a farmer. We have another currency change, this time to 'money units', and the Palace of Fun is described as having a ballroom and a thermal baths. There are also occasional allusions to literature and literary criticism, as when the Pilot asks the Prisoner if he is 'a gamekeeper', referring to the famous analogy of 'gamekeepers and poachers' in cultural studies, to wit, that gamekeepers guard cultural resources, while poachers make illegitimate, but frequently creative, use of these, and the same figure can alternate between being one or the other, or even both. Caves again feature, picking up on the cave-related visual metaphors elsewhere in the series. 'The Outsider' is also one of the more commonly used translations for the title of Albert Camus's famous existentialist novel L'Etranger (as well as being the title to a proposed Everyman Productions series), although there are no other obvious references to existentialism in Farhi's story. At one point, also, the Pilot remarks 'death is peace, my friend,' to which the Prisoner replies that that they are fighting to eliminate death being the only means to peace, which, if the Village is in fact a kind of afterlife, is an interesting comment on the tension between the Village's attempts to get the Prisoner to conform peacefully and the Prisoner's often violent resistance to this.

The story is also interesting in terms of what it can tell us about the changes to the Village's set-up and geography as the series was developed, due to the differences between the situation as described in 'The Outsider' and that in the transmitted episodes. In 'The Outsider', for instance, not only is Number Two's residence the Georgian House rather than the Green Dome, but Number Two is described at one point as watching the outside world through binoculars from the Control Room, which would be windowless (but equipped with a large television screen for surveillance purposes) in the series as filmed. Nonetheless, from the portrayal of the character and allusions to his stature, Angelo Muscat has clearly been cast as the Butler by this point. The beginning of the end titles sequence as described in the script features the prison bars clanging shut and then the Prisoner's face zooming up out of the village to stop behind them, which is an unusual variation on the animation sequence that ultimately wound up in the end credits (but featured in the scripts for a number of early episodes). Rover – which is still the mechanical Rover at this point, judging by a mention of its 'flashing light' – is portrayed slightly differently from in the final version. Real Scotch is apparently drunk, rather than the alcohol-free version used in the series. When addressed as 'Number Six' by the 'plain' woman, the Prisoner does not dispute the identification, but responds with 'Yes?' There is a reference to there being a clock on the Castle, which is not present on Castell Deudraeth in real life, but this is an excusable mistake if one is not terribly familiar with Portmeirion. Had the story been filmed, these points would no doubt have been changed during script editing.

While McGoohan's facetiously stated reasons for rejecting the story were that 'heroes don't birdwatch' and 'heroes don't sweat',[17] the probable real reasons can be discerned from the extant script itself, which is unfortunately superficial and difficult to reconcile thematically and practically with the rest of the series. Farhi did, however, make one key contribution – in encouraging his friend Roger Parkes to submit the script that later became 'A Change of Mind'.

---

17 While the latter is clearly a reference to a scene in which the Prisoner sweats under a sun lamp, the former does not have an obvious referent in the script, and so is probably a reference to the Prisoner's mapping of the cliffs early in the story, as he would need an excuse to be wandering around the cliffs making notes.

Unmade Stories 2: Don't Get Yourself Killed By Gerald Kelsey

SYNOPSIS: The Villagers are all taking 're-educational lectures' through audiophones – except the Prisoner, who is refusing to participate, to the irritation of the Head of the Faculty of Educational Adjustment (or HOF), whose job it is to re-educate Villagers on whom other methods have failed, and who appears to be frustrated with his duties and locked in rivalry with Number Two. The Prisoner encounters members of the Escape Committee, who are trying various schemes to flee the Village and who urge him to join. He attends one of their meetings and is proposed for membership, but is sceptical of their activities; he learns from Number Two that in fact all their plans are easily thwarted by the Village authorities without their knowing. Learning that one of the Committee, the Miner, has apparently found a seam of gold, and kept this discovery secret, the Prisoner approaches Number Two and offers to work for the organisation that runs the Village. While taking a loyalty test as a prerequisite for his new job, the Prisoner approaches the HOF and intimates that he has a way to make him rich; the HOF promptly helps him to pass his tests, and suggests that he might be able to assist the Prisoner in stealing a helicopter that they can use to flee the Village. When the Prisoner reveals to the HOF that he will be paid in gold ore, the HOF makes the connection with the Miner and attempts to approach the Miner on his own terms, to cut the Prisoner out of the deal, but the Miner inadvertently kills the HOF while protecting his gold. The Prisoner and the Miner attempt an escape in the helicopter, but the Miner's insistence on keeping his gold with him means that they are both caught, and the Prisoner reveals to all concerned that his hoard was only iron pyrites – fool's gold.

ANALYSIS: 'Don't Get Yourself Killed' starts fairly strongly, but is nowhere near as interesting or well-coordinated as 'Checkmate' (also by Gerald Kelsey). There are, however, a few intriguing ideas raised and connections made that deserve consideration in terms of the series as a whole.

WORKING DRAFT: PRACTICALITIES AND PROBLEMS

'Don't Get Yourself Killed' appears to have been an early story in the commissioning process, as it refers to the Georgian House and a Rover with a blue flashing light (the taxis are also said to have similar lights in the script). A remark regarding the taxi-driver girls always getting their man appears, suggesting that the script did not get very far into the editing process before being rejected (as McGoohan would have excised such a comment). Whether it or 'Checkmate' was commissioned first is unknown, although we do know that Markstein was responsible for approving both stories. The author's own explanation as to why McGoohan rejected the script was that 'the action was shared amongst too many other characters'; however, large-cast *The Prisoner* stories are not unknown, so it is likely that this wasn't the only reason. Fairclough (in *The Original Scripts, vol. 2*), suggests instead that a lack of connection between the re-education and Escape Committee plotlines may have been the reason. Our own main criticism is that the plot of the story fails to gel into a coherent whole: while there are a number of interesting ideas, and although it makes a few good points about human nature, it lacks the psychological insight of 'Checkmate', or the overall connection of other, finished *The Prisoner* stories.

The story bears a number of similarities to 'Checkmate'. Both involve brainwashing and the Prisoner's escape plans being scuppered by associates who are secretly working to their own agendas. The Number Two portrayed here is similar to the one seen in 'Checkmate', particularly regarding his interest in Eastern culture. As 'Checkmate' referred to characters by names rather than numbers ('Rook,' 'Queen,' 'Man with the Stick' etc), so the script for 'Don't Get Yourself Killed' similarly refers to characters as 'HOF,' 'Icarus,' 'Bottleman' and so forth.

Other aspects of the script recall certain transmitted episodes of *The Prisoner*. The re-education plot is similar to a key aspect of 'The General', with a computer seen to be leading a class at one point (Fairclough, in *The Original Scripts vol. 2*, suggests that Greifer got his idea from Kelsey's story, but, since education and the use of computers for paedagogic purposes seem to have been concerns of 1960s telefantasy stories in general, the two writers might simply have been thinking along similar lines). The computer itself, interrogating Villagers in a lecture room, also is reminiscent of the talking mechanical device seen in 'A Change of Mind'. The use of birds to carry secret messages recurs in 'Hammer into Anvil', and in both stories the activity is used in tacit acknowledgement that this is a cliché of spy stories. The scene where the Head of Faculty drinks in a café recalls that in which Number Two is discovered patronising an illegal still in 'Free for All' (although the presence of Scotch and vodka in the café suggests that the writer was still working only from a draft script of 'Arrival', as it was later scripts that introduced the idea that drinks in the Village were non-alcoholic). Number Two at one point references 'Arrival' in saying 'We try to avoid square pegs in round holes.'

Although narrative problems and inconsistencies appear in many transmitted episodes, the script for 'Don't Get Yourself Killed' has a number of fundamental flaws in its logic, to such an extent that these might partly explain why the script was finally rejected. The Prisoner appears not to have thought his plan through, since he did not consider the possibility that the HOF might try to cut a private deal with the Miner and get himself killed by the notoriously unhinged individual in the process; for that matter, it is unexplained how the Miner manages to have suffered no comeback from having killed a man earlier in his stay in the Village. The idea that the Prisoner realises early on that the 'gold' is iron pyrites, and uses this to play the HOF and the Miner off against each other, is a clever one,but iron pyrites being mistaken for gold is a cliché, and it also raises the question of why, if the Miner is supposed to be a brilliant mining engineer, he can't tell the difference between the two quite different metals (while there is the implication in the script that he is insane, this does not seem to have affected his professional abilities to a great degree in other areas). Equally, if the Faculty's re-education courses are aimed at prisoners for whom all other methods of getting them to cooperate have failed, the question arises of why all the Villagers are taking them – are they all backsliding? While it is a minor point, the German that the Shopkeeper and a Village woman speak in the opening sequence is spelled in the script as it sounds phonetically to an English-speaker, rather than in actual German words: 'Bitterschen' instead of '*Bitte schön*', for instance.

THE GREAT ESCAPE: THE ESCAPE COMMITTEE STORYLINE

The concept of the Village 'Escape Committee' is arguably the story's strongest attribute. It is an obvious riff on, or possibly send-up, of the genre of books and films (largely British, but with some notable American examples) about escapes from prison camps in the Second World War. Some of the plans mentioned in the story recall well-known real-life escape attempts, such as tunnelling out of camp, or, in the case of Icarus's flying machine, the attempt by British POWs at Colditz to build a glider (which still exists and has been displayed at the Imperial War Museum). The initial sequence of a woman and the Shopkeeper speaking German also recalls Second World War films, as does the Prisoner's suggestion that the HOF's academic qualifications are 'Honours, Auschwitz.'

In particular, there seem to be strong connections between the Escape Committee plotline and the film *The Colditz Story* (1955). This film, based on the memoirs of an escapee from the camp, depicts Colditz as divided by rivalries between prisoners of different nationalities, all jealously guarding their escape plans, and shows the attempted resolution of these differences through the appointment of 'escape officers' to liaise about escapes and ensure that there is no duplication of effort/ideas. It also illustrates how individuals and small groups could, by keeping their plans secret, accidentally impede similar attempts through accidentally crossing wires with other escaping groups. The film additionally gives the impression that escape was as much an intellectual outlet and/or form of entertainment for bored officers as a practical activity, as echoed in 'Don't Get Yourself Killed' in Number Two's comments about the Escape Committee being a 'form of therapy' for inmates. A sequence in the film in which the Polish prisoners discover, and plan to execute, an informer in their ranks, but the man is saved when the British Commander brings their plans to the attention of the Camp Commandant, also foreshadows how, in Kelsey's script, the Escape Committee ultimately collaborate with the authorities against the Prisoner to protect their own interests. Ironically, though, the message of *The Colditz Story* is that escape is possible only through selflessness – being willing to assist in all escape plans, in the understanding that other people rather than oneself might be the ultimate beneficiaries – which makes for an interesting contrast to the individualistic message of *The Prisoner* and its protagonist's own isolated situation.

There is also an element of social satire to the Escape Committee's portrayal, with the Committee being so obsessed with their own rules and procedures, and with ensuring no duplication of plans or efforts, that they are hindering their own escapes and helping the authorities, indicating how organisations are often led astray from their main purpose through increased bureaucratisation. This also recalls some *Danger Man* episodes in which the British civil/diplomatic services' obsession with procedure and custom gets in the way of actual intelligence work and/or humanitarian concerns. One example is 'The Affair at Castelvara', in which a British ambassador's refusal, on the grounds of propriety, to use an incriminating film that Drake has uncovered against a political official means that an attempt to save a condemned political prisoner is undone.

Most interesting, however, is how the Escape Committee exists as a comment on the relationship of rebellion to authority in the Village. The Committee are not interested in escape in and of itself, but in their own metatextual idea of what a 'correct' escape is, which eventually causes them to see no contradiction between their own stated mandate and their decision to report the Prisoner's escape attempt to Number Two. They are also, whatever their activities, not escaping in spirit, since they have absorbed, and mindlessly repeat, the messages disseminated by the Village authorities against individuality and in favour of cooperation, suggesting that their lack of physical escapes serves as a metaphor for this conformist spirit; Number Two takes the news that the Prisoner has joined the Escape Committee as 'a sign that he's settling down' rather than an indication of further rebellion. This idea might have worked nicely as a satire on the way all revolutionary movements are ultimately coopted and compromised (an idea taken further in the books *A Day in the Life* and *The Prisoner's Dilemma*), but as it stands, it fails to go very far.

SENTIMENTAL EDUCATION:
THE LECTURES, PSYCHOLOGY AND TECHNOLOGY

Another of the more noteworthy aspects of the script is the periodic introduction of the Lecturer, transmitting propaganda under an educational mandate as part of his/her (the script leaves the character's gender ambiguous) formal lessons, and reinforcing them through repetition. There is a distinct echo of Chairman Mao's *Little Red Book* in some of these aphorisms, such as 'Wisdom demands acceptance; acceptance reaps happiness' and 'Memories are delusions; reality is destiny.' Others include 'Individuality is the expression of revolt against the community,' which serves as an articulation of one of the key issues at the heart of *The Prisoner*, and 'In society, no individual has the right to elevate his desires above those of his fellow citizens. No individual has the right to assume his thoughts and ideas are more valid than those of the rest of the community …' – an all-too-familiar attitude in recent years on certain internet forums, where debate is stifled by people asserting that all opinions, however ridiculous, are valid. The fact that the Ornithologist begins repeating the Lecturer's phrases is an early indication to the Prisoner that the Escape Committee has compromised itself. While the use of propaganda is a common theme of the Prisoner, it might have been worth exploring the way in which it is here absorbed unconsciously through the process of education.

The story does flag up the global nature of the Village, but only in ways relating to the spy, or prisoner-of-war, genre of fiction. As well as the German spoken at the start, the Faculty's lectures are said to be transmitted in 'English, French, German, Russian and Chinese,' the languages of the major players in the Cold War at the time. The HOF drinks neat vodka, which in spy series is usually code that the character is Eastern European in origin, or at least a Russian sympathiser. At one point, Number Two refers to Villagers as 'guests,' picking up on the holiday-camp theme. We also see, once again, group therapy cropping up as a remedy for the Prisoner's constant individualism, and education being linked with brainwashing and mind control: more pointedly, Number Two's observation that the Escape Committee's activities constitute 'a form of therapy' brings in the idea that counter-cultural activities may, in fact, achieve nothing but a form of catharsis, which thus prevents anti-establishment forces from actually achieving any form of meaningful social change.

The story also flags up an idea that would become the central conceit of the novel *The Prisoner's Dilemma*, not to mention one of the great issues of the computer age, when the HOF says to the Prisoner, 'I shall have a duplicate of your mind on a set of punched cards … Set a problem; the computer will think your thoughts, give us the answer. We shall know what you plan before you do' (and the Prisoner, cleverly, points out that such a computer program is useless unless one knows the right questions to ask it). However, the idea is effectively thrown away in one line in this story; and, in any case, it has been convincingly argued that the notion of a human mind being analogous to a computer program is largely a fallacy. Like many other ideas put forward in 'Don't Get Yourself Killed', the idea of replicating the Prisoner's mind on computer is not developed in the way that it might be.

'Don't Get Yourself Killed' is closer to the type of story that we actually saw in the series than the other unmade script, 'The Outsider', and contains a number of good ideas that might well have made worthwhile contributions to it. As it stands, however, none of these ideas really gets the development it needs, and the story is less a challenging view of the role of escape in society than a curious riff on prisoner-of-war films and spy series.

Out Of The Village: The Influence Of *The Prisoner* On Later Popular Culture

The Prisoner is unusual among television series in terms of the degree to which it has influenced subsequent popular culture, particularly regarding television and film, to the point where many designers or filmmakers may not even be aware that they are drawing on it. While all television series borrow from their predecessors to a certain extent, even more ubiquitous ones, such as *Star Trek*, have not had such a powerful influence on style and subtext in popular culture in general; it is not insignificant that *The Prisoner* has contributed an adjective, 'Prisoneresque', to popular usage, a situation normally reserved for particular directors and writers (Lynchian, Hitchcockian, Heinleinesque, etc).

This, consequently, makes it impossible to track down and indicate all the films, programmes and so forth that have been identified as inspired, consciously or unconsciously, by *The Prisoner*. Almost every surreal comedy or drama, from *The League of Gentlemen* to certain *Doctor Who* serials, can be (and usually has been) described as 'Prisoneresque', and yet it is unlikely that every single writing/production team set out with a conscious intention to develop McGoohan's ideas; it is just that, like that of *Metropolis* before it, the ethos of *The Prisoner* has penetrated far enough into the public consciousness that it is easy to reference it without realising one is doing so. Numerous programmes also include direct references to the series in passing (the character of 'Number Six' in the revived *Battlestar Galactica* was, according to series creator Ronald D Moore, deliberately named after the Village's most famous inhabitant, for instance; and there are numerous *The Prisoner* inside jokes scattered throughout *Babylon 5*). Producers and directors have also been known to evoke associations through casting people linked with the series (as David Cronenberg does in his 1981 film *Scanners*, in which Patrick McGoohan features as a sinister psychologist engaged in the physical and mental manipulation of the minds of unwitting subjects). It is impossible to see, let alone list, all the various pieces of film and television that have been inspired by *The Prisoner* in some way.

Furthermore, the show's popularity and easily-recognisable iconography, plus its positive focus on freedom and individuality, means that it is easy for, say, an advertiser, music video director or filmmaker to evoke particular sensations in his or her audience through employing a few of the more familiar images from the series (a man driving down an airstrip in a sports car as a sign of liberation, for instance, or a white balloon rolling along a beach as a sign of oppression and menace). Music videos in particular frequently incorporate imagery recalling *The Prisoner* to evoke a variety of moods, including oppression, psychedelic madness or just a superficial aura of 1960s cool. In some cases, this referencing seems to be direct and purposeful, but in others, it seems to be part of a more general, scattershot attempt at building a mood or setting a scene. Consequently, it might be inaccurate, even counterproductive, to claim a deliberate influence from *The Prisoner* on all such productions.

Bearing this in mind, we shall now consider a few of the more notable ways in which *The Prisoner* has manifested itself in later films and television series, with the caveat that this is a highly idiosyncratic overview, heavily influenced by the authors' own viewing tastes, that of necessity barely even scrapes the surface of ways in which the series has influenced later popular culture.

FILMS

Numerous films, particularly of the postmodern style favoured in the 1980s and 1990s, include *The Prisoner* references to a greater or

lesser degree. *Killing Zoe* (1994), written and directed by Roger
Avary, for example, takes the ethos of *The Prisoner* out of the realms
of telefantasy by applying it to a 'straight' hostage drama. It has a
hip, retro visual style utilising bright primary colours, and features,
amongst other things: a scene in which a character describes the plot
of 'A, B and C' while stoned (also mentioning the events of 'Once
Upon a Time' and 'Fall Out' in passing); druggy nightclub scenes
later on that recall those in 'Free for All'; criminals wearing carnival
masks (recalling both 'The General'and 'Dance of the Dead'); an
anti-hero, Eric (played by Jean-Hughes Anglade), who dresses in a
black polo-neck shirt and charcoal suit and perishes in a machine
gun confrontation with armed guards, adopting a stance
reminiscent of Alexis Kanner's in 'Fall Out' as he does so.
Prisoneresque imagery thus lends a hint of unreality to the
proceedings, and also highlights the idea of Eric acting as a kind of
rebel against society through his drug-fuelled criminal activities.

Another film often said to have been influenced by *The Prisoner* is
Terry Gilliam's *Brazil* (1985), although it is possible that the
similarities derive merely from the fact that Gilliam, as a member of
the *Monty Python's Flying Circus* team, was a pioneering figure in
the development of the kind of surreal, knowing comedy found in
Britain in the 1960s that was a heavy influence on *The Prisoner*. Like
The Prisoner, the film has a largely-British (but significantly
international) cast and focuses on totalitarianism, bureaucracy and
terrorism. While it is rather Prisoneresque in terms of its use of
surrealism and genre-mixing to condemn social surveillance and
bureaucracy, and its focus on an 'everyman' protagonist who comes
to realise the true, horrifying extent of state-sanctioned violence and
torture in his society, there are also strong visual parallels, first
between the machines-filing-an-identity-card scene in *The Prisoner*
title sequence and a number of similar sequences in *Brazil* (one
unfilmed sequence was to have involved vast walls full of filing-
cabinet drawers), and secondly between 'Fall Out' and the final
scenes of the film, which involve the hero escaping through an,
apparently imaginary or illusory, act of ultraviolence; a pitched,
chaotic battle; and the protagonists fleeing their corrupt society in a
truck with a house on a trailer bed.

The film *Dark City* features a protagonist who wakes up in an
unfamiliar location that is a self-contained, surreal place with a

distinctive, retro style (although, in this case, a city rather than a village), in that, while the inhabitants seem happy, they are in fact being manipulated by a group behind the scenes who are conducting experiments involving the wiping of memories and the implanting of new ones, although here they are searching for the secret of individuality rather than trying to eliminate it. It is the protagonist's ability to retain his individuality that piques their interest, and, like the Village authorities in 'Fall Out', they seek to acquire that ability for themselves. The climax involves, essentially, the shattering and rebuilding of the entire environment by the protagonist, who then escapes out of the city to Shell Beach.

The Matrix, as well as containing open homages to the series (including an image of Guy Doleman from 'Arrival' on a television set in the first film, and a black cat being used to indicate glitches in the Matrix throughout), has been cited as a *fin de siecle* take on *The Prisoner*. This is certainly apparent in the film's themes, which involve an 'everyman' protagonist of great integrity and moral sense who learns, through the use of drugs, that the world he knows is just an illusion, concealing a reality of cruel oppression – but that the bulk of the people would rather embrace the comforting illusion than face the painful reality. He (Neo, often called 'The One') and his colleagues adopt new names as symbols of their rebellion (relating to the Prisoner's rejection of his Village designation, and the adoption of chesspiece-related names in 'Checkmate'), and use the authorities' own techniques to bend reality for their own ends. In the second film, it is revealed that Neo is being used as a kind of fault-tester by the creator of the Matrix, the Architect, which the original novel *Who is No. 2?* suggests may be the Prisoner's role in the Village; and the novel *The Prisoner's Dilemma* has the Prisoner explicitly being used to fault-test the Juliet computer system.

Finally, while its creators may not have come right out and cited *The Prisoner* as a direct inspiration, the film *The Truman Show* has such close parallels with the series that it is difficult not to see it as such. The idea of an artificial village whose inhabitants are all really actors, performing in order to get particular responses out of a single man who is unaware of the contrived nature of his situation, albeit for entertainment rather than intelligence purposes, reads like a corporate-media-focused updating of the scenario of *The Prisoner*;

FALL OUT

the film was made using the real-life American resort community of Seaside, Florida as its setting, and the visual character of the town pervades the film much as that of Portmeirion pervades *The Prisoner*. The village's defences against escape – artificial weather and spontaneous fires – are as surreal as any faced by the Prisoner, and Truman is under 24-hour surveillance from a group of figures in a technology-filled control room, whom he finally confronts and forces to allow him into reality. While the idea that the Village was a metaphor for television remained subtextual for most of the actual series, *The Truman Show* develops it into a new concept.

TELEVISION SERIES

The Prisoner has also had a great deal of influence on subsequent television productions. One early example is the 1970 ITC series *UFO*, which included a number of *The Prisoner* personnel both behind the camera (Rose Tobias-Shaw, Brendan J Stafford) and in front of it (Derren Nesbitt, Wanda Ventham, Alexis Kanner). It had begun life as a fairly trashy and superficial humans-versus-aliens show from Gerry and Sylvia Anderson (previously responsible for, among others, *Stingray*, *Thunderbirds* and *Captain Scarlet*), but, in its second production block, underwent a radical rethink whereby David Tomblin was brought in to reverse its flagging fortunes at Lew Grade's insistence. As a writer, staff director and informal advisor, Tomblin encouraged *UFO* towards greater flights of Prisoneresque psychedelia, introducing the idea that the alien menace might not, in fact, be as straightforward as had been thought, but something much more sinister and psychological, and bringing in stories like 'The Cat with Ten Lives', featuring Alexis Kanner as a man apparently under the psychic control of a Siamese cat, 'Mindbender', which involves breaches of the series' fourth wall as its protagonist sees his life as a film, and 'The Long Sleep', which includes controversial scenes of recreational drug use.

Peter Falk was a self-confessed fan of *The Prisoner*, and so it is not surprising that there should be several episodes of *Columbo*, the long-running detective series, directed by or guest starring Patrick McGoohan, who also sometimes acted as co-writer and co-executive producer, and occasionally all of the above on the same episode. It

325

adds an extra layer of knowing self-parody to it, however, that one of the episodes he directed and guest-starred in, 'Identity Crisis', was itself an out-and-out homage to *The Prisoner*. Among the various nods to the series are the fact that McGoohan's character, Nelson Brenner, is a spy who is somewhat like the Prisoner, wears a white-piped black jacket at one point, makes free use of the catchphrase 'Be seeing you' and spars verbally with Columbo in a way that recalls the confrontations between the Prisoner and Number Two. According to Falk, McGoohan also rewrote much of his own dialogue for this story. Another such episode, 'Ashes to Ashes', while not an actual homage or parody, ends with Columbo telling McGoohan's character, 'It's your funeral.' The episodes thus not only testify to Falk's fondness for the series, but also McGoohan's own ability to make fun of himself.

This can also be seen in the *The Simpsons* episode 'The Computer Wore Menace Shoes'. While *The Simpsons* has regularly used *The Prisoner* references as part of its general arsenal of humourous pop-culture imagery, this particular episode revolves around Homer Simpson being kidnapped to an island of people who have invented things that the authorities do not want to come into general use; not only does he don a white-piped black blazer and engage in a chase scene with Rover, but Patrick McGoohan also guest stars as the voice of Number Six. The twist is that Homer, when his escape attempts prove futile, comes to like the island and decides to stay.

This particular twist was also employed in an earlier homage to *The Prisoner*, known as *The Laughing Prisoner*, screened in 1987 in an episode of the Channel 4 music programme *The Tube* (1983-89). Jools Holland, presenter of *The Tube*, was an unashamed fan of the series, and had already sent up 'The General' in an earlier episode (to the question 'WHY?' the computer calmly responds 'WHY NOT?'), and Channel 4 had re-screened *The Prisoner* in 1983-84. *The Laughing Prisoner* features Holland driving a familiar-looking Lotus 7 from the Tube studio to resign from his job (at the real-life headquarters of Channel 4), and being kidnapped to the Village, revealed to be a secure facility for housing certain showbusiness personalities who have inexplicably resigned from their jobs (of Number Six, we learn: '20 years ago, he resigned from a highly successful television series, *Danger Man*. Since then, he's been here. A Prisoner of this village, and no-one can understand *why*'), under the aegis of Number Two, played by Stephen Fry (also a fan of the show). The episode, filmed on location in Portmeirion in January 1987, featured song numbers by XTC (who wore Village-style blazers), Siouxie and the Banshees (with Siouxie Sioux in a striped top) and Magnum.

The late-1970s British series *Blake's 7*, which shares with *The Prisoner* a concern about government surveillance and social control through physical and psychological conditioning (and provides a direct homage to 'Fall Out' in its final scene, in which a black-and-white clad Paul Darrow stands surrounded by masked and armed troopers), tends for the most part to explore those themes through straight sci-fi drama. A couple of episodes, however, become more Prisoneresque, most notably 'Terminal', the third-series finale. Unusually postmodern for *Blake's 7*, the story focuses on the psychology of the protagonist, Avon, and his mounting egomania and obsession with his group's former leader, Blake; an establishment figure is able to use this aspect of his personality to condition his behaviour, encouraging him to come to an artificial planet where he undergoes a drug-induced hallucination. In an inversion of the way that the Prisoner, in the series, overcomes his hallucinations and finally triumphs through sheer ego-focus, Avon's own egotism means that he fails to recognise that he is being led, and allows his selfish impulses to triumph over his better nature, putting himself and others in danger. *Blake's 7* thus both uses, and inverts, imagery and ideas from *The Prisoner*.

Gangsters, Philip Martin's surrealist comedy-drama about multiracial gangs in 1970s Birmingham, was frequently compared to *The Prisoner* by contemporary reviewers. There are certainly a number of parallels between the two, not least in that *Gangsters* was promoted as a gritty, realistic tale of organised crime, and, when it proved to be a postmodern fantasia involving references to Bollywood film and Warner Brothers crime drama, deliberately cartoony cliffhangers and ironic pop-music interludes, viewers reacted with incomprehension and hostility, much as with *The Prisoner*. Although none of its creators has, as far as we are aware, directly acknowledged an influence, *Gangsters* employs many of the same techniques and ideas as *The Prisoner*, using surrealism and popular culture to explore social issues; in this case, multiculturalism, alienation and the relationship of writers to their creations, rather than faith, psychology and Cold War politics.

While it is not often cited as having a connection with *The Prisoner*, Dennis Potter's equally surreal drama *The Singing Detective* (which came out in 1986, only a few years after the Channel 4 repeat of *The Prisoner*) has a number of clear links with the earlier series, most notably in the sequence in which the occupants of an entire hospital ward mime and dance to 'Dem Bones', and in the numerous doubles, even triples, that appear throughout, but also in being a metatextual series that takes inspiration from its creator's own life, and that uses conventions of popular media, such as pulp detective novels, to encourage the audience to explore and question the very programme they are watching. The ending features characters from a detective novel that the protagonist had written apparently breaking through into real life and confronting their creator, and the protagonist coming face-to-face with his own fictional alter ego.

Mention should also be made of 'Number Seven', an episode of the Canadian computer-animated series *ReBoot*, which is a fantasy involving characters who inhabit a computer (that appears, metaphorically, as a small town) and whose function it is to play computer games (glowing cubes that descend upon the town, transforming it into the game landscape, and then withdraw once completed, occasionally carrying characters off with them) with the unseen, godlike User. This story is a full-on spoof of *The Prisoner* (while also containing an oblique reference to the *Danger Man* episode 'The Ubiquitous Mr Lovegrove', in that the whole story is revealed to be an hallucination suffered when a character is struck on the head by a golf ball), complete with visual references to the title sequence (including a character being picked up and filed away in a giant filing cabinet as he repeats the 'I will not be pushed ...' monologue), characters who are literal numbers (one of the series' conceits from the beginning, taken to its logical extreme), a black-and-white-masked jury and a chorus of 'Dem Bones'. This is not simply gratuitous spoofery, however, but actually provides the basis for an exploration of the series' characters, in particular Matrix, who was been accidentally separated from his home computer as a child and has grown up inside computer games. In the 'Number Seven' scenario, Matrix hallucinates the computer/town he grew up in into a kind of Village, in which he himself is forced into the persona of the series' villain, Megabyte;

seemingly friendly figures from his past try to force him to conform; and, when he finally confronts Number One, this turns out to be the child he was before his adventures in the computer games began, and whom he had rejected. 'Number Seven' is thus part spoof and part psychological exploration of one of *ReBoot*'s central characters.

Most recently, at the time of writing, the American TV series *Lost* has employed some of *The Prisoner*'s premises, involving a small cast trapped on a mysterious island, which may be a hallucination, a kind of afterlife, a social experiment, a microcosm of society, or all of the above. The final episode of the second series, in true *The Prisoner* fashion, raises as many questions as it answers. The story also acknowledges its origins in that one cache of food the castaways discover is labelled with the modified Albertus font seen in *The Prisoner*.

In the UK, *Life on Mars* has been hailed by fans and critics as an intellectual successor to *The Prisoner*. The story follows the adventures of Sam Tyler, a policeman who, following a car accident, wakes up in what appears to be 1973, but various hints, coincidences, surreal occurrences and strange dream sequences suggest that the explanation may be more psychological. *Life on Mars* shares with *The Prisoner* a fondness for surrealism, a tendency to play with genre conventions and expectations, strong psychoanalytic subtexts and a structure involving a strongly-defined, well-drawn protagonist surrounded by a cipherlike supporting cast.

Appendix:
Original *The Prisoner* Fiction

The Prisoner: I Am Not a Number!

(*also known as* The Prisoner: Book 1)

Publisher: Ace Books (1969)/Hayakawa -Science Fiction Series 3228 (1969)/Presses de la Renaissance (1977)/Hayakawa Bunko (1979)/Dobson (1979)/NEL (1979)/Boxtree (1992)/Presses Pocket (1992)/Carlton Books [omnibus edition] (2002)/iBooks (2003)/downloadable ebook (2003)
Author: Thomas M Disch

SYNOPSIS: A nameless man has dinner with a woman called Liora, during the course of which he reveals that he has resigned from his (evidently secret-service) job and is going to retire to Wales. He takes the sleeper train to the Pembroke coast but, once he is asleep, he is drugged and the train diverted. He awakes in a train station in an unknown Italianate village. Taking a 'local' taxi he finds a converted gatehouse identical to the one he has purchased for his retirement, evidently waiting for his arrival. He attempts to ring Liora, only to find that the number she gave him appears no longer to exist and that he has instead accidentally contacted a shop in Covent Garden named Better Books. He attempts to flee the Village, and is attacked by two men and a strange white balloon device/creature called a Guardian. Returning to 'his' residence, he is contacted, over a 'false window' televisual device, by a poetry-quoting man calling himself Number Two, who addresses him as Number Six. Resolving to escape, the Prisoner becomes fascinated with the Village church, beneath which he discovers a corridor and a sequence of rooms, in one of which he discovers 17 reels of film, apparently involving himself. He then piles up a random selection of other films he finds (apparently involving other Villagers), places one of his own films on top, sets fire to the stack and flees, taking with him two of his films concealed in canisters belonging to two other, unrelated films. The Prisoner escapes the Village using a portable aluminium cage to protect himself from the Guardians, returns to London, contacts Thorpe and the Colonel, views one of the reels of film (showing the events of 'Many Happy Returns') and is recaptured.

Number Two and the female doctor Number Fourteen attempt to find out what the Prisoner is up to by influencing and observing his dreams, but he resists them. The Prisoner is persuaded to accept the post of Village Mayor, and as such is given the task of showing around a new arrival, who turns out to be Liora; she does not know him and claims her name is Lorna. He discovers that it was she he spoke to at Better Books. Both, along with Number Fourteen and her brother Number Seven, take part in a Village production of *Measure for Measure*, which conceals another escape attempt involving a balloon; however, Number Seven and Liora/Lorna are the only ones to flee, leaving a note revealing that one of them was Number Two all along. Through mental conditioning, Number Fourteen apparently convinces the Prisoner that he is Number Two, and that Number Six no longer exists. As Number Two, he acts as a model Village chairman, and is rewarded with the opportunity to meet Number One. Number One is revealed to be 'Granny Bug', an old woman who, when the Prisoner attacks her, turns out to be at least partly mechanical. Number Fourteen takes charge and orders the Prisoner to leave the Village, revealing that an unspecified amount of what has gone before has been a dream or guided hallucination.

ANALYSIS: The initial three *The Prisoner* novels, *I Am Not a Number!* [18], *Who is No. 2?* and *A Day in the Life*, were originally published in the USA by Ace Books, the first two in 1969 and the

---

18 There is some confusion as to the actual title of this particular novel: the US edition and the first British paperback edition appear to be entitled simply *The Prisoner*, with 'I am not a number! I am a man! A free man!' as a teaser blurb on the British edition, and the omnibus edition also calls the first book simply *The Prisoner*; however, the title *I Am Not a Number!* has subsequently made it onto at least some publishers' lists and into some reference works, so we shall continue to use it in this volume, for clarity's sake.

third in 1970. They were subsequently reprinted numerous times, including in France (in hardback in 1977 and paperback in 1979, with the text translated into French) and in the UK (where, for some reason, the hardback editions of the first and third titles appeared in September 1979 but that of the second was delayed until 1981, and the paperback editions were published in that same order from 1980 to 1982). They have been most recently reissued by Boxtree, who put out the first two titles in 1992 and followed this up with an omnibus of all three in 2002. These novels are certainly interesting additions to the series' mythos, if not its actual canon, and are worth considering in some detail.[19]

I Am Not a Number! has an interesting premise and comes from the pen of a writer well-versed in the sort of mind-bending images for which the series is known, and who is also able to get away with concepts which that the series avoided, although the writing style might prove off-putting to some readers.

Thomas M Disch was in many ways a good choice to write the first *The Prisoner* novel, even though he allegedly took the commission less out of interest in the series than because he needed the money. He had been one of the first American writers to take part in the New Wave, a principally British literary sci-fi movement whose emphasis on the surreal and the psychological was a key influence on *The Prisoner*'s form and themes: he had written, among other things, 'The Squirrel Cage' (1965), a short story about a man who finds himself imprisoned in a room with only the barest amenities and a typewriter, with no memory of how he got there or why. Perhaps surprisingly, in view of this background, he apparently had never seen *The Prisoner* when he took the commission. Although he reportedly watched only three episodes by way of research and was otherwise largely uninformed about the series, the scene where the Prisoner views a sequence from 'The Schizoid Man' cleverly amalgamates aspects of both script and finished episode (reinstating a cut line from the script for instance), and includes some lines that exist in neither version, suggesting that Disch was actually rather conscientious in his research (there is in fact some evidence from the book that he had seen the original

---

19 For space reasons, we have limited ourselves to covering only the officially-licensed books based on *The Prisoner*; there have also been numerous unofficial publications made available, for instance Roger Langley's trilogy of novels, *Think Tank* (1984), *When in Rome* (1986) and *Charmed Life* (1990).

scripts of at least two episodes).

However much research he did beforehand, Disch's approach to the commission was, ultimately, to reinvent *The Prisoner*. If applied to just about any other series, this approach could be expected to make the novel incompatible with the original version: the first *Doctor Who* novelisation, *Doctor Who in an Exciting Adventure with the Daleks* (1964), also deviates strongly from the events of the TV series, and is consequently impossible to reconcile with it. *I Am Not a Number!*, however, can be reconciled with the original despite the differences between them, because *The Prisoner* is a series in which the characters, concepts and details can change radically from episode to episode; therefore, to have a story in which the past and present circumstances of the central character are quite different from how they are described in the television series simply adds to the layers of meaning surrounding it. Is the book a retelling of the same story from a different perspective? A fantasy or hallucination on the part of the Prisoner, based on what he has seen and heard in the Village? Another attempt to break him through distorting his perception of reality? In the final analysis, also, the reader does not even know if the story takes place after the end of the series, if it is set in a parallel universe in which the events of the series were different, or if the events of the series have simply been repeating themselves over and over with variations for an unknown period of time (see below), particularly given the fact that, at the end of the story, we do not know how much of it is real, if indeed any of it is.

he Prisoner's initial encounter with the Village in *I Am Not a Number!* has several parallels to that in 'Arrival', if in altered form: he attempts to take a taxi out of town, only to learn that it is a local service; he visits a café to gain more information; he attempts to make a non-local phone call; he is contacted by Number Two; he resolves to escape. At the same time, however, there are some powerful deviations from the initial set-up of the TV series: the ITC notes on the production explicitly state that there is no railway station in the Village (whereas one features prominently in *I Am Not a Number!*), for instance, and there is also a police station (when the Waitress in 'Arrival' says that there is none). The Prisoner is also able to make a non-local call with minimal fuss, although it is to what turns out to be a wrong number. The diminutive butler appears, but is the Prisoner's manservant in London, and does not seem to be a part of the Village set-up at all (although whether this means that the story takes place after 'Fall Out', when both had gone to London, or the Butler's change of location is a deliberately surreal inversion of the normal order of events, is uncertain). All of this serves to make the novel seem like the TV series, and yet strongly different from it in execution.

Despite his reported unfamiliarity with the bulk of the series, Disch appears to reference aspects of it at a number of points. Certain of the events in the book seem like deliberate echoes of the premises of key episodes of the television series: the Prisoner being made Mayor of the Village (and, ultimately, Number Two), akin to the events of 'Free for All'; the Prisoner being encouraged to participate in a Village theatrical production that is simply a cover for an escape attempt, as with the art contest in 'The Chimes of Big Ben'; the Prisoner having his dreams influenced by a Number Fourteen and resisting, as in 'A, B and C'; the Prisoner encountering people from his past in the Village, as in 'Arrival' and 'Dance of the Dead'; and the Prisoner helping a new arrival to settle in, as in 'The Chimes of Big Ben'. A long description of the events of 'The Schizoid Man' (albeit with variations) also features prominently. The fact that the book opens with a sequence of the Prisoner having dinner with a woman is also interesting in that the original shooting script of 'Arrival' mentions, in the sequence where Number Two shows the Prisoner a folio of pictures of the latter at various points in his life, an image of the Prisoner dining with a woman, which was excised from the final version. The original Mrs Butterworth, a frightened and hostile old woman who later is revealed to be Number Two, is also recalled in the figure of Granny Bug in the novel.

The connections between the Village and the rest of the world, a prominent theme of the TV series, also come to the fore in *I Am Not a Number!*, but, once again, in a slightly different way. Unlike in the TV series, there are a number of references to real-world publications, such as *National Geographic*, *Analog* and *Car and Driver*, although the Village newsagent's, unsurprisingly, carries no newspapers, nor does it carry political and current-affairs magazines like *The Spectator* or the *New Statesman*. There are more references to American characters, publications and so forth than there are in the series (where Al Mancini in 'The General' and the

Western setting of 'Living in Harmony' are the only US presence), no doubt a purposeful inclusion on Disch's part. Although the Village has a train station, this is no more a way out than any other escape route that the Prisoner has tried; while the Prisoner does escape to London, it once again proves to be strongly connected to the Village. At the end of the story, also, the similarities between the Village and London (and thus the wider world in general) are highlighted. While Disch goes out of his way to reference the real Portmeirion in the sequence in which the Prisoner discusses his 'retirement' destination with Liora (although the location is never named, there are a number of hints from the geographic references that the Prisoner is in fact retiring to Portmeirion), it is left open whether the Village is in the location of the real Portmeirion, as the train that the Prisoner takes West from Paddington is diverted from its route at Cheltenham, and we do not know where he goes from there.

In addition, Disch references the idea that the Village is a symbolic concept. On page 20, the taxi driver and the Prisoner have the following exchange: 'I think it *represents* something ... People come here from other places. Like you. And they see our village, and they get the feeling that something has always been *missing* from their lives.' 'And the Village represents that, the thing that is missing from their lives?' 'It was only my idea.' The Village that the Prisoner is in may thus not be an actual place, but a concept, or a state of being that people seek out unconsciously.

The references to television, and the televisual nature of the series, become the subject of metatextual themes within *I Am Not a Number!* The 17 reels of film the Prisoner discovers beneath the church apparently relate to the 17 episodes of the series itself. This not only leads to surreal sequences in which the Prisoner apparently watches his own television programme, but also, since there are differences between the films and the televised versions, causes one to wonder which, if any, are the most accurate record of the events presented. The sequence in which the Prisoner makes contact with Thorpe and the Colonel highlights this: the conversation the Prisoner has with them is similar, but not identical, to the one they have in 'Many Happy Returns' (some lines being the same and others more or less close paraphrases); and later, when the Prisoner is seen viewing the film reel that he has stolen, the conversation that he views is again similar to, but different from, both his just-completed conversation with the two men and the sequence in 'Many Happy Returns' (Disch is also plainly not working from the original script of the episode, as this scene was rewritten heavily from the original version, which bears little resemblance to what was televised). Where the Colonel is dressed for golf in 'Many Happy Returns' and the Prisoner apologises for interrupting his golf game, the filmed sequence the Prisoner views in *I Am Not a Number!* actually takes place on a golf course, with Thorpe explicitly said to be dressed for golf, paralleling the way the Prisoner's actions in the novel suggest, but are different from, the events of such episodes as 'Free for All' and 'A, B and C'. The sequences also recall the way one can view a film over and over, but from different perspectives, or gain different insights from repeated viewings of the same events. The description of scenes from 'The Schizoid Man' in the church sequence also differs from the way they appeared on screen, in ways that suggest both that Disch had a copy of the original script and that he was intentionally taking liberties with both the original and the televised version. This consequently begs the question of what it means if the Prisoner is watching himself on television, but what he is seeing differs from the episode that viewers have seen. In this, Disch's novel not only eerily foreshadows the discovery of the alternate prints of 'Arrival' and 'The Chimes of Big Ben' in the 1980s, but also raises the question of whether the Prisoner has simply been having a number of similar adventures, over and over, fo-r an unknown period of time, leading readers to wonder if the TV series itself might not necessarily document the first time that the Prisoner has come to the Village. By suggesting that the Prisoner has simply been repeating a series of similar actions and events over and over without recollection, like a character in a TV series that is being played over and over (or, given the slight variations between the different versions, like a character in a formulaic TV series unaware of the similarities between the plots of individual episodes), Disch draws attention to the series' origins and nature within the novel; however, the fact that there are slight differences between the iterations opens up all sorts of possibilities for speculation.

There is also again the implication that the events of the novel are taking place in the Prisoner's mind; indeed, Disch openly references this on pages 115-116, in a long passage speculating on the possibility that the events the Prisoner is experiencing are a dream, or indeed, a dream within the mind of a greater, unknown dreamer. The Prisoner is referred to as Number Six only by other people, in an indication of how he self-identifies. One of the most notable things about *I Am Not a Number!* is its distinctive tone: cultured, supercilious and perhaps a touch pretentious, focused on literary and classical allusions. As this is not a tone Disch habitually adopts in his writing, but is in keeping with the tone the Prisoner adopts within the series, it suggests that we are essentially viewing the story from the central character's perspective. It is also in keeping with how Disch depicts the Prisoner in the story, choosing between bound volumes of Dickens and Shakespeare for his train journey and, picking up on the copper pans visible in Six's house in the series, revealing himself to be something of a gourmet chef and not above lecturing Number Two on proper cooking technique when the latter calls him unexpectedly during the preparation of a meal. The tone of the book, while making it difficult for the reader to engage with it, appears to be a faithful rendering of the Prisoner's personality in literary form.

More than this, however, all the other characters in the book, barring Liora/Lorna, adopt similar tones, as if they are being given voice by the same interpreter. One might infer from this that it is possible that that they are all inventions of the Prisoner himself, and that Liora sounds distinctive either because she is actually in the outside world and talking with the Prisoner (as in the scenes within the novel in which Number Fourteen communicates with the dreaming Prisoner to influence his ideas) or because – in an echo of one aspect of Stanislaw Lem's *Solaris* – she is so well-remembered by the Prisoner that he is able to give her a more realistic tone. The variations in the conversations with Thorpe and the Colonel could also indicate that the story is pieced together from the Prisoner's own memories, much as dreams can be pieced together from people's real-life experiences. The fact that the residence he finds in the Village contains furniture that he does not actually own but would have liked to have bought in London adds to this impression, leaving it unclear whether this is the result of an amnesiac Prisoner in London acting on unconscious memories of the Village, or whether his incarceration in the Village is a kind of fantasy, perhaps even a sort of wish-fulfilment activity. The ending of the story leaves it ambiguous as to how much of what has passed is actually real, and how much an influenced dream; in true *The Prisoner* fashion, it invites the reader to make up his or her own mind.

Doubles and doppelgängers also appear, particularly with regard to the character of Liora. We never learn what the relationship is between her and Lorna – whether they are the same person or physical doubles of the same person, or whether one is an hallucinated image of the other (it might also be significant that Liora/Lorna's number in the Village is 41, the inverse of 14, suggesting that Number Fourteen may also share aspects of the former woman's character). The fact that the Prisoner's wrong number when he attempts to reach Liora actually reaches her double further highlights this confusion. The Prisoner's viewing himself back on film also raises the possibility that this may be evidence not of a loss of memory, but of another of the doppelgängers that haunt the series (getting seriously metatextual in that the episode he chooses is 'The Schizoid Man', meaning that he may at times be watching the double of a double). Although later books would take a firm stand on the issue, Disch never speculates on the relationship between the Prisoner and John Drake.

The relationship between the Prisoner, Number Two and Number One is also explored. The plot regarding Number Two produces some biting comments on authority: the revelation that the older, poetry-quoting Number Two is an authoritative fake, and that either the friendly Number Seven or the seductive Lorna is the real Number Two, points up how people can be deceived by the trappings of leadership into not questioning who really rules. That the Prisoner himself becomes Number Two can be seen as an observation on the blurred boundary between prisoners and warders, and on how the former easily become the latter; but the fact that the Prisoner was turned into a leader through mental conditioning (or, perhaps, as his conversation with Number Fourteen indicates, through a skilled and convincing performance on his part), and is rewarded only once he proves that he is thoroughly obedient, also indicates that even the warders themselves are under control: we never learn who controls the leaders, or how far up it goes.

One of the more controversial elements in the story is the revelation at the end that 'Granny Bug', the seemingly insane cyborg or possibly robot, is Number One. As Disch was probably aware of the actual ending to the series, this element is likely to have been a considered inclusion rather than simply an attempt to clear up a continuity point. The character, like Number One in the series itself, thus becomes abstract and symbolic, possibly meaning that we are ruled by the human/technology interface, so inextricable from devices and machines that we might as well be cyborgs, or possibly that, as 'Fall Out' might suggest, we are governed by the madman within (the ID, the shadow-self, the gibbering monkey behind the mask). Or, given the way the book holds reality up to question, perhaps it is simply that the Prisoner believes this to be the case. The final chapter is thus a conclusion worthy of the original series in its symbolism and open-endedness.

The book is also noteworthy in that – since McGoohan appears to have exercised little, if any, control over the content of the novels – it is able to feature elements that were avoided, or remained only subtextual, in the series. Thus, although a Number Seven never appears in the series, one features here as a central character (the implication that the story is a dream leaving it ambiguous as to whether or not there ever really was a Seven in the Village); the unusual number may flag up for the observant reader that the character may not be quite what he seems. The book also contains open religious imagery, whereas the series had shied away from doing so directly; as well as numerous similes and references in the text, there is a key sequence focusing on the village church as concealing a means of controlling the Villagers. Although it is tempting to wonder if Disch was aware of the unfilmed episode 'Ticket to Eternity', the similarities between the two are only superficial, so it is likely that he was either picking up on the more understated religious imagery of the series or else filling an obvious gap in the Village infrastructure. In this story, also, the Prisoner is permitted to have a slightly more erotic charge to his relationships with women (although Disch stays faithful to the original in never letting it get above a suggestion): Disch also slyly tests the boundaries of the concept by briefly revealing that one of the reels of film, which evidently relate to the activities of the Villagers, is entitled 14-LESB, suggesting, given the designation conventions seen on other reels, that Number Fourteen had a recorded lesbian encounter at some point prior to the story's outset.

The first *The Prisoner* novel thus, rather than simply pastiching earlier stories, gives us a new take on the series' concepts and imagery that both fits with and adds to the televised stories.

The Prisoner: Who is No. 2?

(US title: *The Prisoner #2: Number Two*, Original UK title: *The Prisoner: Who is Number Two?*)

Publisher: Ace Books (1969)/NEL (1979)/Boxtree (1992)/Carlton Books [omnibus edition] (2002)
Author: David McDaniel

SYNOPSIS: John Drake awakes in what he thinks is his familiar London flat, only to find himself back in the Village, as Number Six. He is contacted by Number Two, learns that he has been permitted to retain his sports car, and is given a workshop, a shed and a small race-track. The Prisoner appears to become a model citizen on receipt of this gesture, fixing the car up, submitting to Village bureaucracy to obtain petrol and parts, and running the car on the track. He requests fibreglass to build a racing fairing, but in actual fact constructs something that can be modified into the hull of a boat, and, using the car as the propulsion engine, escapes under cover of darkness. However, Number Two has stowed away on the boat, the engine dies once they are out to sea, and the boat is found by the Village Rescue Unit and towed back to shore, although it springs a leak and sinks on the way. Number Two is accused of attempting to escape, demoted to Number One Hundred and replaced by the previous Number Four. The Prisoner petitions the new Number Two to be allowed to salvage the wreck and is permitted to do so; he explores the undersea area around the

Village but otherwise does not attempt escape. Number One Hundred contacts him, apparently reveals many secrets, including that the Village has no leaders above him – there is no Number One – and that this is all just an attempt to seize power on the part of Number Four, and proposes a counter-coup. The Prisoner offers his support in exchange for the wherewithal to fix up the car again. He finishes fixing up the car and takes it to the track to run it, observed by an apparently impromptu celebration committee, during which Number One Hundred asks the Prisoner to deliver a smoke bomb to the Green Dome, which will cause Number Two to vacate the place long enough for the coup to occur; he does so, but is then told that the bomb was inadvertently thrown out by the cleaning staff. The Prisoner tries another escape using the car as the basis for a boat, but finds himself somehow coming back to the Village, where he is met by Number One Hundred (apparently reinstated as Number Two) and the Villagers, assuring him that they want him to be happy among them.

ANALYSIS: *Who is No. 2?* is not as brilliantly mindbending a novel as *I Am Not a Number!*, but is nonetheless enjoyable for the most part, with at least two quite clever contributions to the interpretation of the series. However, it is undermined by a certain fixation on technical detail, in particular in the long, tedious descriptions of fixing up and recovering the Lotus 7, which are guaranteed to put off all but the keenest Lotus enthusiast-cum-underwater-salvage expert.

The author of the second book in the series (published third in the UK), David McDaniel, was a well-known American writer of television spin-off books, particularly from the *Man from UNCLE* range. He died in 1977, apparently while attempting autoerotic asphyxiation, but was known in his lifetime as something of a character with an interest in practical joking (which allegedly once saw him turning up with a group of friends to greet Robert Vaughn at a theatre where he was performing, dressed in dark suits with THRUSH patches on the shoulders and claiming to be the THRUSH Public Relations division), and a fondness for questioning the interface between reality and fiction, suggesting something of a philosophical affinity with *The Prisoner*.

Who is No. 2? is explicitly a sequel to Disch's novel: Number Two mentions the Prisoner's 'brief tenure as Number Two' and there are references to the diminutive butler (who never appears) and Granny Bug (the Prisoner also briefly suspects the Village cat of being a similar robot, and later on it is said that the cat has been mentally conditioned to like him). McDaniel also follows Disch in referring to the Rovers as Guardians, differentiated here into 'herders' and 'killers'. Like Disch, he works in a few literary references, albeit on a less exalted level, with Number Two quoting AA Milne ('Now that I'm Six I am clever as clever, and I think I'll stay Six for ever and ever'), the Village Entertainment Committee putting on productions of Gilbert and Sullivan operettas, and the chapter titles all referencing musical movements. The Prisoner once again displays an enthusiasm for cooking, discoursing extensively on the best way to prepare fish, and has dinner with a woman with whom he flirts mildly. One puzzling aspect, however, is that the Prisoner here speaks casually of remembering the events of 'The Chimes of Big Ben', when it was a plot point of *I Am Not a Number!* that the Prisoner had no recollection of his earlier spell (or possibly spells) in the Village, and he does not view the film reel documenting 'The Chimes of Big Ben' at any point (unless, of course, the events of 'The Chimes of Big Ben' take place, or take place again, after those of *I Am Not a Number!*).

Unlike Disch, McDaniel explicitly identifies the Prisoner, from the first line of page 1, as John Drake (although, since he is no longer called that once he appears in the Village, one wonders rather what the author's point was in doing so; fellow *The Prisoner* novel writer Jean Marie Stine, aka Hank Stine, in a 2001 interview, said that McDaniel had inserted the reference solely to find out if McGoohan was proofreading the manuscripts, as the reference to 'Drake' would have been removed in that case), and he is said to be living, not in 1 Buckingham Place, but Upper Berkeley Mews, London. McDaniel also has the Prisoner taking sugar in his tea, and, unlike Disch, refers to him as Number Six within the text. Curiously, also, McDaniel misrepresents the number plate of the Lotus 7 throughout, referring to it as KAR 1260 rather than KAR 120C.

The book has two strong themes that are in keeping with the ideas explored in the series, and that contribute to our understanding of it. Number Two (whom the Prisoner, half-facetiously, refers to as 'the personification of the Village') is here given to quoting and musing on statistics, referring to 'the median man' to mean the average person – 'The median man is the statistical individual for whom the greatest amount of effort produces maximal results' (page 39) – and giving us two extensive philosophical passages on the relationship between numbers, individuals and collectives: (page 15) 'Your parents named you arbitrarily, Number 6 – we have only renamed you as part of our family ... Don't you see that it is in everyone's best interests that we all agree on who we are in such a way that there is a minimum possibility of confusion? Any symbols could be picked and ordered, but they must be specific. Numbers are the easiest to handle, the most efficient. That's all. I don't want you to start arguing relative morality now – we simply cannot change the entire Village to suit your whim'; (pages 40-41) 'Any quantity of individuals can be effectively handled in statistical form – the same formulae can tell how many people are watching a given television broadcast or how many will die in a given holiday weekend ... The behaviour of individuals is of no statistical consequence – whether five hundred people or five hundred and one are killed by motor accidents ... matters not the slightest except to the personal acquaintances and intimates of the five-hundred-and-first ...' The Prisoner counters the latter with: 'Unless the five-hundred-and-first is a politician or film star,' and Number Two responds: 'That only enlarges the effective circle of acquaintances. There again you have tried to make an exception destroy a generality. Exceptions are to generalities what holes are to a sponge. A few more or less don't matter – statistically.' In these passages, McDaniel explores the relationship of individuals to the collective by using statistics both as a metaphor and a representation, questioning the Prisoner's own rejection of numbers as dehumanising, and exploring the true value of individualism to society.

The other strong theme throughout the book is the idea that happiness is inherently subversive, in that happy individuals are not likely to challenge or attack the extant system. The idea behind allowing the Prisoner to have his sports car is to keep him happy, on the grounds that people rebel only when they are idle or unoccupied: as Number Two explains, 'A certain personality type, with nothing to do, nothing to occupy its mind and hands, will go to amazing lengths to find a direction for his energies. What I have done is to channel this *drive* into paths which are readily observable' (page 60). He also adds that the modifications the Prisoner carries out to the racetrack will give him a personal investment in the Village. Indeed, the Prisoner does conform to society in order to complete his project, submitting to bureaucratic exercises and becoming friendly with a number of Villagers. When the new Number Two refuses to let the Prisoner salvage the car from the ocean, the Prisoner threatens to incite revolution, disrupt order, burst Guardians and smash security cameras unless permitted to do so (as he is said to be genuinely angry at this point, this suggests that there may be more here than simply a calculated ploy on the Prisoner's part). In some ways, too, it might be inferred that the deposition and attempts at getting reinstatement by the original Number Two/Number One Hundred are equally a way of keeping him occupied within recognised social channels (particularly as, at the end of the story, it is implied that Number One Hundred has either regained his old rank or never left it, as he is able to speak through one of the Guardians). Indeed, it might even be inferred that the Prisoner's constant escape attempts are themselves a kind of busywork, keeping him occupied at escaping rather than challenging the system. The final message here thus seems to be that our occupations, interests, and even pleasures are to be viewed with suspicion, as they prevent us from questioning what we see around us.

The book also has a minor theme of circles and repetition. As well as the ultimate point of the story being that the Prisoner himself is perpetually going around in circles, both geographically and intellectually always returning to the point that he has left, there are continued references in the text to circles, circling courses, spherical objects and so forth. Number Two's office in the Green Dome is initially described as being like a planetarium dome, or like a molecule with an atom at its heart. The theme of circles thus reflects the actions and mindset of the protagonist. We also have a moment on pages 86-87 when Number Two explores the idea that, as a former secret agent, the Prisoner is a trained killer who has had to learn to accept his role as such, which casts the actions of – and the viewer's sympathy for – the series' protagonist in a different light.

In a further indication of his tendency to overwhelming technical detail, however, McDaniel goes out of his way to attempt to rationalise various aspects of the Village. References to Number Two 'generating' a porcelain cup 'made of insulating plastic' to hold his tea, and, later, the observation that some of the Prisoner's record collection may have been 'duplicated' from albums in his collection in London, might be taken to imply that the Village's ability to seemingly spontaneously generate whatever artefact is needed derives from some kind of *Star Trek-/Forbidden Planet-/Tintin and the Lake of Sharks*-style replicator machine. Elsewhere, the author attempts to explain the origins and nature of the Guardians, stating that they are neither organic nor mechanical but 'Colloidal Mechanisms,' and presents an underwater sequence in which the Prisoner observes a Guardian emerging from a hole, which seems to exist only to reference the scenes in the TV series in which Rover appears to be generated spontaneously under the sea. The – possibly mendacious – sequence in which Number One Hundred claims that Number One was the founder of the Village, that the number was retired when he left, that the whole point of having the Prisoner in the Village was as a fault-tester, to see if he could find a way of successfully escaping from it and correcting for that, and that the Village is owned and run by the British government, also falls into this category. The problem with these sequences is that they do tend unnecessarily to take some of the mystery out of the series: a 'technobabble' explanation for the weirder aspects of Village life is no better than no explanation at all, and in the end McDaniel's attempted rationalisations simply serve to reduce Rover to a mere device and the Village itself to an intelligence installation, whereas part of the appeal of the TV series was that one never knew quite what was going on, or how certain things had been achieved.

The TV series itself is referenced more extensively in this book than in the first one, with McDaniel, like Disch, appearing to have read a couple of the scripts at least. In particular, the original shooting script of 'Many Happy Returns' seems to have been the root of some of the discontinuities in the story, as it has the Prisoner living in a flat suspiciously similar to that described here (although this must be a deliberate discontinuity, as McDaniel apparently viewed the finished episode, since he refers to a location for the Village near Spain, which tallies with the transmitted version but not the script). A cut scene from 'Dance of the Dead' also has the Prisoner awakening to the faint sounds of London traffic, which die away when he lifts the curtains, recalling the 'hologram' disguising the location of the flat in *Who is No. 2?* The incident in which the Rescue Unit has to cut the Prisoner's boat-cum-car loose actually strongly resembles a real-life incident during the filming of 'Many Happy Returns', in which the Prisoner's raft had to be severed from the boat towing it, because it was so heavy that the vessel was in danger. At one point, a reference is made to the Prisoner birdwatching, which, if McDaniel did not know the story about one of McGoohan's stated reasons for rejecting Moris Farhi's idea being that 'heroes don't birdwatch,' is a bit of a coincidence. The story also has the purported location of the Village as mentioned in 'Many Happy Returns', i.e. the Balearic Islands, near Spain (although, as the Prisoner stays on course throughout his journey yet returns to the Village, this is never actually verified), and has the tedious attention to technical detail of the original script (but not the transmitted version) of that episode, although without the dramatic excuse. The Village cat from 'Dance of the Dead' and 'Many Happy Returns' also appears, and the Prisoner states that he is thinking of calling it 'Number One'; the idea that black cats can be seen as a portent of good luck is referenced. The fact that the acting Number Two is known as 'Two Prime' recalls McGoohan's playing with sub-numbers in 'Free for All'; the pen that the Prisoner is given resembles the one he was given in 'The General'; and the television continues to broadcast images of Number Two despite being unplugged, recalling the way the smashed radio in 'Arrival' and the unplugged telex in 'Dance of the Dead' continue working when they should not. Although Number Two is never outright described as resembling Leo McKern, the personality, 'raucous laugh' and delivery do seem to be inspired by his portrayal of the role. The Prisoner at one point whistles the Irish/Australian folk tune 'Botany Bay' (which refers to the transportation of prisoners to Australia in the 18th Century), in a kind of literary rendition of the numerous children's and popular tunes in the series itself. The Village newspaper is referred to as the *Village Voice* (page 125), although it is unclear whether this is an accidental continuity error or a deliberate link to the famous Greenwich Village publication of the same name.

One final disappointing aspect of the novel is that it all ends rather abruptly, which, coupled with the long, dull passages about fixing up the car/boat, rather gives the impression that the writer was trying to fill up space for most of the book, and then suddenly realised he had to conclude it somehow. Although ostensibly following Disch's continuity, *Who is No. 2?* does not really develop the psychedelic, reality-questioning ideas of the first novel, and remains slightly unsatisfying in not doing much with the positive elements it has.

The Prisoner: A Day in the Life

(US Title *The Prisoner #3: A Day in the Life*, Original UK Title: *The Prisoner 2: A Day in the Life*)

Publisher: Ace Books (1970)/Dobson (1979)/NEL (1979)/Carlton Books [omnibus edition] (2002)/iBooks (2003)/downloadable ebook (2003)
Author: Hank (Jean Marie) Stine

SYNOPSIS: The Prisoner passes a pleasant day in the Village, buying groceries and cigars and playing chess with the Admiral, while some of the younger Villagers try their hands at making a film. The next day, the Village is more hostile, with threatening calls from Number Two and uncooperative attitudes from other Villagers; nonetheless, the young people continue with their film, some quitting their jobs to do so, and the Prisoner again plays chess with the Admiral. The next day, the Prisoner is further ostracised, but continues with his usual routine. He finds a sympathetic companion in a new Villager, Number Seven, with whom he has several conversations about the Village and her life before being brought there. He is then arrested for drug possession; it transpires that the elderly tobacconist, who lived in the Prisoner's house before he arrived, had been growing and selling marijuana and had left a small stash behind, which technically places the Prisoner in possession of it. He is sentenced to death, and is saved only by virtue of contracting influenza, which causes his execution to be postponed in time for the young people to mount a protest. Number Seven contacts him, says that she is working for the Prisoner's former superior, the Colonel, and that he wants the Prisoner to destroy the Village in exchange for his freedom; the Colonel, she claims, is opposed to those who run the Village, a collective of three individuals known as Number One. She helps the Prisoner to escape by helicopter, but once he reaches it, he knocks her out using a gas gun and departs on his own. Apparently returning to London, he contacts the Colonel and learns that the Village is a British installation and that he was sent there because he did not reveal the reason for his resignation. He assassinates the three men: Sir John Wilkinson; the Field Marshal; and, finally, Sir Charles, who appears to be some kind of cyborg. He returns to the Village to find that one of the youths, Number Five Hundred and Sixty Nine, has now become Number Two. After several days the latter announces that everyone is free to go. Back in London, the Prisoner psychedelically experiences London and the Village as being one, and exposes his arrest, detention and return to London as a Village-induced hallucination. Life in the Village returns to normal.

ANALYSIS: *A Day in the Life* is the third and final book in the loose trilogy of *The Prisoner* novels produced in the late 1960s/early 1970s. Arguably the weakest of the three, it deals explicitly with themes of 1960s pop culture and politics while following closely on the thematic structure of episodes of the television series.

Jean Marie Stine (who was writing under the name 'Hank Stine' at the time), author of the 1960s classic sci-fi novel *Season of the Witch* (1968) and, among other things, a number of self-help books, was a long-time fan of *The Prisoner*. Stine was apparently the one who suggested to Ace Books that a series of original *The Prisoner* novels might be a good idea, and, on the strength of this, garnered the contract to do the third book. In a 2001 interview, Stine confessed that while she had watched all of the series, she did not view any of the episodes (or read the scripts) while writing the novel, which goes some way towards explaining the political, impressionistic tone of the story, and the reason why it comes across as a mix of *I Am Not a Number!* and the episodes 'A Change of Mind', 'Many Happy Returns', 'Free for All' and 'Do Not Forsake Me Oh My Darling' (as well as, more peripherally, 'Living in

Harmony' and 'It's Your Funeral').

While the fact that Stine is an American should not necessarily be a problem (both Disch and McDaniel are also Americans, and managed to capture the series' language and feel quite well), in this case, the story occasionally feels like a picture of England written by an outsider. Some of the English accents are rather stereotypical – Number Five Hundred and Sixty Nine, in particular, sounds like a cross between Cliff Richard and Dick van Dyke – and certain sequences – such as the one where the Prisoner, somewhat unusually for a public-school man living around Whitehall, buys fish and chips from a chirpy Cockney at a chip-shop – jar a bit with the UK reader. There are also occasional incongruous Americanisms from some of the ostensibly English characters, for instance 'I'm gonna kick your butt.'

Although not as complicated as, and consequently easier to read than, *I Am Not a Number!* Stine's novel, like McDaniel's, follows its continuity. As in Disch's book, we encounter a cyborg creature, references to Portmeirion itself (the Prisoner's folio of travel pamphlets in the title sequence falls open at an advertisement for Portmeirion, and he himself briefly visits Portmeirion after leaving the Village), and a sequence of the Prisoner cooking a soufflé while being harangued by Number Two over the television – this being heavily indebted to the egg-cooking sequence in *I Am Not a Number!*. Like Disch, Stine implies heavily at the end of the story that some or all of the preceding events have been illusory (also recalling the denouement of 'Living in Harmony'). The diminutive Butler turns up in the Prisoner's house (which seems to be a curious amalgam of the writer's memories of his house in the televised series and McDaniel's description of his residence), working for the Prisoner, who (perhaps facetiously) calls him 'Sancho'. The Colonel and Sir Charles both turn up, with the former being given the surname 'Schjeldahl' as in *I Am Not a Number!*; the ante is here upped slightly when Janet makes a brief cameo appearance. We also have another Number Seven, this one female (and, as before, there is more of a sexual undercurrent in the Prisoner's relationship with her than with women in the TV series). She is also American, following on Disch's trend of referencing American culture.

The story contains direct references to *Who is No. 2?*, particularly in the sequence on page 39 where the former Number Four is now the new Number Two and the circumstances in which the change took place are recalled – in a possible reference to Disch's idea about him being doomed to repeat an endless cycle of adventures without recalling them, the Prisoner can only vaguely remember the events of the previous book. As the implication at the end of *Who is No. 2?* was that Number One Hundred had either regained or never left power, the departure from this here is either an intentional breach of continuity or (more likely) a piece of Prisoneresque ambiguity. As in *Who is No. 2?*, the Prisoner is explicitly identified as John Drake, and the Village as a British installation; Number One is again said to be a thing of actual substance (in this case, a group of three directors), but there is also some ambiguity as to whether or not this is really the case (at the end, after the Prisoner has shot the ostensible committee members, Number Two mentions not having had any contact from Number One in a while, but that could mean anything).

There are also a number of references back to the series itself, albeit more subtextually than in the first two novels. The presence of the Beatles (or a tribute band, or possibly Sergeant Pepper's Lonely Hearts Club Band from the film *Yellow Submarine*, who were the Beatles' identical duplicates) as the Village band, as well as linking in with the novel's title and strong themes of 1960s popular culture, recalls the use of their music at crucial moments of 'Fall Out'. The twist ending in which it is revealed that the tobacconist was Number Two all along recalls similar bait-and-switch plot elements in 'Many Happy Returns' and 'Free for All'. The description of the Prisoner returning to London incorporates the cut sequence from the original shooting script of 'Arrival' of the Prisoner in his car taking a mechanical lift, suggesting that Stine had, at some point, seen that script – but it also includes a description of the sequence that replaced it, of the Prisoner passing a gate using a ticket. It thus comes across as a kind of amalgamation of planned and extant versions. The Admiral seen in 'Arrival' returns, and there is something of the Prisoner's relationship with Nadia in 'The Chimes of Big Ben' reflected in his relationship with Number Seven (and, on page 103, the Prisoner explicitly observes that the proof that he is really in London is 'as solid and real as the chimes of Big Ben'). The sequence in which he returns to London references both 'Many Happy Returns' and 'Do Not Forsake Me Oh

My Darling'. As in 'Many Happy Returns' and *Who is No. 2?*, the Village is given a real-world location (in this case, Aran Island, off the North coast of Ireland) which may or may not be true. Stine thus obliquely references various stories within the series.

Presumably because Stine was unable to review the series before beginning her novel, a few continuity problems do nonetheless emerge. The Lotus 7 is misidentified as an MG (and while it's tempting to suggest that, since the Lotus was given a thorough going-over in *Who is No. 2?*, the Prisoner has acquired a new car, the description of the vehicle's 'jaunty yellow hood' and 'green carriage' suggest otherwise). The Prisoner is here said to have been in the Village because he refused to give a reason for his resignation, whereas in 'Arrival' the viewer learned that the Prisoner did give a reason, but it was not accepted. Like *Who is No. 2?*, also, this book makes the slight error of identifying the Prisoner both as Drake and as a paid killer, when *Danger Man* went out of its way to avoid having the protagonist openly kill anyone, however villainous. McGoohan is also described as having a 'fair Saxon complexion,' surprising in that, being Irish, the actor is a Celt rather than a Saxon; the probable explanation can be found in the fact that *I Am Not a Number!* also uses the adjective 'Saxon' in a brief description of the Prisoner.

The book's main strength is that it captures the protean nature of the Village as it appears in the series: the Village changes character within the book from day to day, and both reflects and is reflected in the outside world. Again, internationalism is brought in, with German and French being spoken in the Village; once more the Prisoner leaves the Village only to discover (in this case, more hallucinogenically than before) that it and the wider world are much the same thing. The themes of technology and humanity also recur, with a Granny Bug-style cyborg being once again in charge of the Village, and the Colonel having a hologram of a city street as a 'window' in his underground office (recalling both 'The Chimes of Big Ben' and *Who is No. 2?*). The idea of reality versus illusion is also addressed, with the Prisoner suspecting London of being an illusion, and, ultimately, being proved right. The book thus develops the nature of the Village, as well as the questions about the uses of technology and the nature of reality, implicit in the series.

Slightly more controversial is the fact that the book focuses on real concerns of the late 1960s to a degree unseen in the original series. While the youth culture of the time is referenced in the characters and events of 'Fall Out' and 'It's Your Funeral', the film-making, protesting youths in *A Day in the Life* come across as a kind of self-conscious representation of the era's young people, making the book read as something of a period piece. Certainly sequences like that in which Number One Hundred and Five's daughter is discovered to be pregnant out of wedlock (a situation echoed deliberately in a conversation between two Cockneys the Prisoner hears later) would never have wound up in the series itself, given the latter's deliberately asexual nature. The idea of Number Five Hundred and Sixty Nine becoming Number Two also seems a bitter comment on the co-opting of the 1960s youth movement, with the rebels of today becoming the cynical politicians of tomorrow. There are references both to an attempt to ban Philip Roth's 1969 novel *Portnoy's Complaint* by what seems like the Village equivalent of the National Viewers and Listeners' Association, and to an apparently conservative women's association sponsoring charity screenings of *Gone With the Wind*. These recall real-life debates on censorship at the time revolving around books such as *Lady Chatterley's Lover* (which was still banned in the USA until 1969) and television programmes with sexual themes, and attempts by conservative organisations to encourage people to consume 'wholesome' (sometimes ironic) alternatives. The Prisoner's arrest for marijuana possession, and references to both the tobacconist and the film-making youths growing the herb in question, recall the drugs debate that pervaded the decade. *A Day in the Life* thus deals openly with political issues current at the time the TV series was made.

Other aspects of the 1960s that feature in the series are given more explicit, arguably heavy-handed, treatment in the book. While non-White characters, and characters who arguably show homosexual tendencies, do appear in the series itself, Number Seven here explicitly identifies two of her acquaintances in the outside world as a 'gay cat' and a 'spade cat' (sic) and describes her peripatetic lifestyle drifting around the drug-fuelled happenings and concerts that are strongly associated with the late 1960s. The IRA are namechecked, and we also get the first open racist in the Village, when a man in the hospital bed next to the Prisoner's reveals himself to be an anti-Semite who wants to blow up the

Village synagogue (in the books, it seems, the Village is as multifaith as it is multiethnic) and speaks casually of the gang-rape of a German girl in which he participated at the end of the Second World War. Numerous concerns of the 1960s, such as youth, censorship and prejudice, which remain implicit in the series, here become explicit.

The popular culture of the day also comes more strongly and self-consciously to the fore in this book than elsewhere. Number Seven is a stereotypically late-'60s figure, leaving her husband to trek around America, attending Dylan concerts and Woodstock, trying soft drugs and sponging off various men as she goes. The Beatles, as noted above, are strongly referenced, with the London sequence being a clear homage to the sort of auditory rush at the end of the titular Beatles song. Stine also opens the book with a description of the Prisoner driving in his sports car along a runway (a clear homage to the series' title sequence) listening to the song 'White Rabbit' from the 1969 Jefferson Airplane album *Surrealistic Pillow* on the car's audiocassette player. Well-known conspiracy and spy series of the time, such as *The Fugitive*, are name-checked. Stine appears to be consciously setting the Prisoner within 1960s popular culture.

The book also comments openly on the philosophy of the era. A sequence on page 121, in which the Prisoner asks Sir John how he can morally justify the existence of the Village, produces the following response: 'Morality has become old-fashioned and without it anything can be justified. You see, when men begin to justify their actions in terms of something besides morality … their country, for instance, or their family, or their race, you can be pretty sure they've done something wicked.' Which, again, seems to be very much a sentiment of the 1960s, in which earlier forms of morality, and the idea that politicians and authority figures are trustworthy, were being strongly called into question. While the series itself does not comment openly on the morality of the time, *A Day in the Life* is an explicit consideration of late 1960s issues and attitudes.

A Day in the Life does contain one particularly strong philosophical passage, relating to the issue of freedom of choice, during the Prisoner's confrontation with Sir John on page 120: 'But surely, in these times, none of us are where we are entirely from choice. It seems clear to me that the forces of environment and heredity have channelled us down certain *inescapable* paths. What Negro in America is entirely free; what white in China is entirely safe? Aren't certain of your thoughts and attitudes a result of your upbringing? ... Are we not, in this world of ours, subjected to constant and inescapable manipulation? As subtle and pervasive as mother's instructions not to play with our penises ... As crude and overt as the public school's indoctrination of its pupils with Judaeo-Christian morality ... And these pressures affect us in ways that are not entirely conscious.' In including this sequence, Stine manages to capture and develop another of the series' understated themes, that of individual choice versus the influence of the collective. Like the series itself, this allows the reader to speculate on the degree to which individuals are, in fact, free to act, or are all – the Prisoner included – the products of social forces greater than themselves. Unfortunately, however, Stine does not develop this idea much further, and so it remains only an interesting notion or point for debate.

A Day in the Life is thus a book that develops the themes of the series in certain ways, and contributes to philosophical debates surrounding them. However, the strong, almost heavy-handed focus on 1960s concerns, popular culture and philosophy unfortunately tend to take precedence and to obscure the periodic thought-provoking passages within the narrative.

Shattered Visage

Publisher: DC Comics (as individual comics) (1988-1989)/DC Comics (collected edition) (1990)/Titan Books (1990)
Author: Dean Motter and Mark Askwith

SYNOPSIS: A British agent, Thomas Drake, prepares a report for MI5 on the publication of the memoirs of a former Number Two of the Village, observing that the whereabouts of Prisoner Number Six is unknown. Later, Drake's estranged wife Alice, a recently-resigned British agent, shops in preparation for a solo yachting expedition and for books to give her daughter, Meagan, who is away at boarding school. Thomas follows her to her house, where she reveals that they have been followed in turn. Thomas demands of his superior, Ross, what is happening, but he denies knowledge. Thomas then goes to Colonel J and threatens to resign over restrictions on his department's mandate; Colonel J refuses the request, and gives him tacit permission to continue investigating Number Two. Thomas, it transpires, is also helping an American agent, Lee, in his own investigations, which concern the Village. Alice sets out on her voyage, but runs into a storm and, as Lee has apparently sabotaged her computer equipment, is shipwrecked on the island where the Village is located; she discovers the Prisoner, 20 years older, still living in the ruins of the abandoned Village. Number Two returns while she is there, and he and the Prisoner resume their power struggle. Thomas and Lee plan an expedition to the Village, as Ross appears suspicious of Thomas's investigation and Thomas's flat has been searched. The Prisoner and Two stage their final confrontation as Thomas attends the funeral of the agent who has been tailing him, Lake; Ross discovers that Thomas has destroyed the files on the Village, and goes to visit Mrs Butterworth, who is subsequently murdered. Ross finds a copy of the Village files on floppy disk in Thomas's office, and sends paratroopers to the island to disrupt Thomas's and Lee's investigations. When they arrive, the insane Number Two lets off a rocket, destroying the Village; Ross discovers that Colonel J has been replaced, and his new superior demands his resignation. When Ross refuses to give it, he is gassed at home and taken away by undertakers in a hearse. The Prisoner and Alice Drake return to life in England, and Alice is reunited with her daughter.

ANALYSIS: *Shattered Visage* was first published as a series of four individual comics (entitled simply *The Prisoner*) in 1988-1989, and then republished in graphic novel format in 1990 (when the *Shattered Visage* title was appended), with official permission from the copyright holders to *The Prisoner*.[20] The author and artist are both Canadian: Dean Motter, a professional artist and illustrator; and Mark Askwith, formerly a manager at the Silver Snail comic store in Toronto, and story editor and producer of the cult Canadian sci-fi/news/comedy series *Prisoners of Gravity*, among other things.

The book is an example of a particular genre of graphic novel/speculative fiction that flourished during the 1980s, involving the reinterpretation of icons of earlier eras from a 1980s viewpoint. Other notable examples include Frank Miller's *The Dark Knight Returns* (featuring an aging Batman finding it difficult to cope with the contemporary crime world), Alan Moore's and Dave Gibbons' *Watchmen* (revolving around thinly disguised Charlton, Marvel and MLJ Comics superheroes) and Karen Joy Fowler's short story 'The Faithful Companion at Forty' (about a middle-aged and retired Lone Ranger and Tonto). The decision to subject *The Prisoner* to similar treatment is perhaps somewhat surprising, though, as whereas superheroes and cowboys were considered debased, irrelevant and in need of reinvention by the 1980s, this series never really stopped being relevant to the modern world. The fact that

---

20 This series has no connection with an earlier attempt to adapt *The Prisoner* into comic-book form in the 1970s, when Marvel initially commissioned a treatment of the series from artist Gil Kane and writer Steve Englehart, before shelving this in favour of another one by artist Jack Kirby, and finally abandoning the project altogether in 1977.

Shattered Visage is very much of its time is both a blessing and a curse in other ways: while there is some nice use of recoloured stills from the series, the 1980s impressionistic art style makes it difficult to tell when a character is supposed to be one from the original series making a cameo or a completely different person; and the occasional use of postmodern visual puns (the title of the first volume is 'A(r)rival', for instance) is either amusing or annoying, depending on personal taste. While *Shattered Visage* is in keeping with a literary trend of the day, it is questionable what it contributes to the genre.

THE SPIES WHO CAME IN FROM THE COLD: *SHATTERED VISAGE* AS LATE-COLD-WAR FICTION

Although it may be a dubious example of the reinterpretative-fiction genre, *Shattered Visage* manages to use its premise to explore issues relating to the Cold War through the portrayal of the Prisoner and Number Two (who is clearly the Leo McKern edition). In the late 1980s, the Cold War was slowly coming to an end, and writers, filmmakers and television producers were beginning to question the implications of this for such related activities as space flight, nuclear proliferation and, in this particular case, large-scale espionage. The glamourisation of the spy in the 1960s had given way to a more mundane, shabby and bureaucratic portrayal of intelligence (specifically in the television adaptations of John le Carré's works, which are briefly referenced in *Shattered Visage* when Lee mentions George Smiley); James Bond, around this time, went from foiling international espionage plots to chasing drug thieves. The Drakes, in *Shattered Visage*, are thus playing out an increasingly redundant political game, as the form of espionage they practice gradually goes out of favour.

This situation metaphorically comes across in the portrayal of the Village. Although it is still seen to have relevance – several live nuclear missiles are housed beneath it, and Number Two argues that it, like everything else, is all about power and control – the specific battle that spawned it has now been fought (as the fear in the 1980s was less about a nuclear war breaking out than about nuclear missiles being let off by accident, so a rocket under the

Village is triggered not as an act of war, but as a result of Two's increasing madness). This is portrayed in the way the decayed Village continues its activities automatically: when Alice triggers one of the surveillance busts accidentally, it sends Rover after her, even though she wasn't trying to escape, indicating that the meaning and relevance of the Village machinery is gone, but the mechanical routines continue. The imagery of the decaying Village is thus not only atmospheric and well-done, but develops the late-Cold-War themes of the story.

This is also seen in the depiction of the central characters. The Prisoner's information is no longer valuable; and yet he stays on in the Village, fighting his old battle with Number Two regardless of whether or not it is important ('I've stumbled across a private war and I'm sick of those! I won't be part of it!' says Alice, the voice of the contemporary world, to Number Two). The now-numberless Prisoner retells his story as a fairy-tale about knights fighting dragons, but then asks at the end which side won: the knights or the dragons? The story also repeatedly inverts the initial events of *The Prisoner*; for instance, Ross is kidnapped not for resigning but for refusing to resign, and Thomas's Prisoneresque attempt at resignation is halted and his letter burnt.

The story is also heavily indebted to a well-known mid-1980s British television series that challenged the premises of Cold War espionage, *Edge of Darkness*. The character Lee in *Shattered Visage* is very close to Darius Jedburgh, the amusingly uncultured, but deadly and intelligent, American CIA agent in *Edge of Darkness*, and the sequence in the former in which Lee and Thomas investigate the rocket chamber recalls that in the latter in which Jedburgh and British policeman Ronald Craven break into an underground nuclear hot cell. This connection might explain why the *Shattered Visage* sequence involves the chamber becoming flooded with water (as a sudden flood featured in the parallel sequence in *Edge of Darkness*), although, whereas there was a rational explanation for the water in *Edge of Darkness*, in *Shattered Visage* it seems to be there merely to make the story more dramatic. Elsewhere, a Magnox nuclear reactor is referred to (*Magnox* was the original title for *Edge of Darkness*), and 'The Arch-Angels' is the name given to a mysterious group or organisation associated with the Village ('angels' are also referenced in *Edge of Darkness*, although as a metaphor for human concerns about good and evil versus the natural world's simple push for survival; when, in the climax, Jedburgh prefaces his showdown with his former CIA colleagues by saying that he is on the side of the angels, Craven retorts that he, turning his back on the whole system, is on the side of the planet).

The concerns and issues of the 1980s are very much to the fore. The presence of a female protagonist with a family reflects the greater interest of the 1980s in action stories with either heroines or (as in *The Dark Knight Returns*) strong female sidekicks; the trigger for the events of the story, the publication of Number Two's memoirs of his time as Village chairman, and the subsequent press and governmental reaction, links in with the events surrounding the 1985 publication of (and efforts by the British government to suppress) *Spycatcher*, the memoirs of former MI5 officer Peter Wright. The name of Terry Waite (who had been taken hostage by the Lebanese organisation Islamic Jihad in 1987, and would not be released until 1991), is also visible on a newspaper advertising poster at one point. Conspiracy theories, and the fear of government, becoming prominent at the time, also appear: as Thomas prepares to go out in one sequence, a radio broadcast makes reference to a number of real-life incidents in which British scientists working for Marconi on the 'Star Wars' (SDI) programme (a proposed American defence system, which is also referenced in *Edge of Darkness*) died under mysterious circumstances.

More importantly, we also see a reinterpretation of the series' central character through the concerns of the time when the book was written. When Number Two plays the recording of the Prisoner making his famous 'I will not be pushed ...' speech, which in 'Fall Out' becomes stuck on 'I, I, I,' it sticks on 'numbered, numbered, numbered ...' reflecting a change from concerns about the expression of individuality in the 1960s, to obsessive fears about surveillance and numbering in the 1980s. The Prisoner himself makes a pun on the words 'information' and 'in formation.' Number Two's description of the Prisoner – 'I can't help but feel responsible for his fate. Number Six is merely a symptom of a distressed society ... if we condemn him, do we not condemn ourselves? There's something of Number Six in all of us. I have only compassion for the poor man. The system imprisoned him, interrogated him, broke him, drove him mad' – recalls how the

1960s were being reconsidered in the 1980s, and characterised by some as a period of intense creativity and social disorder that, although initially positive, gave way to madness, destruction and governmental repression in the 1970s. The Prisoner is therefore portrayed here as the spirit of the 1960s as seen by the 1980s establishment: less as an individualist and more as a mad aberration.

DRAKE IS IN HIS HAMMOCK:
THE CHARACTERS AND THE SERIES

The central figures of *Shattered Visage*, Thomas and Alice Drake, are visually and narratively linked with, and likened to, the Prisoner himself. Superficially, connections are made between the Drakes and the Prisoner: their surname, of course, references the 'Is the Prisoner really John Drake?' controversy; Alice's computer satellite monitor looks like a large white globe; the date on Thomas' desk calendar is November 6 (a pun: No 6?); and Thomas drives the KAR 120C Lotus 7, which was apparently a present from Mrs Butterworth (possibly a sly reference to the fact that the original Lotus's final appearance was in 'Many Happy Returns', suggesting as it does that Mrs Butterworth kept the car). Thomas, at one point, stands in an Orbit cylinder. Visually, the scenes of Thomas driving the car, and of Alice waking up in the Village, reference the series' title sequence: there are also two panels, of Thomas shaving and the Prisoner shaving, in which their poses and expressions mirror each other. The entries made in the Prisoner's diary and the *Tally Ho* headline, seen later in the ruined cottage, play out over the start of Alice's journey ('Today … a beautiful day … made very welcome … holiday begins …'). The Prisoner likens the Stone Boat to Alice's catamaran. Finally, the Drakes' daughter Meagan is attending a Catholic boarding school, the same one her mother attended as a girl (referencing McGoohan's own faith); this is explicitly likened to imprisonment, and the gates close in on her as they do on the Prisoner in the title sequence. The book thus does not feature a solitary 'new' protagonist, but two (or possibly three) characters who take on his attributes.

There are, however, also connections between all of the story's central characters. Number Two and the Prisoner, in an extension of the links developed between them in 'Once Upon a Time' and 'Fall Out', are identified with each other: both sport beards and assume each other's identities. Number Two quotes the Prisoner's lines at the climax of the story, much as the Prisoner quotes his in his first encounter with Alice, in which he is seen sitting in Number Two's chair sporting a scarf and shooting-stick. He later plays something of a Number Two-style mental trick on Alice, when he asks her to pick a number between one and four, presents her with a piece of paper upon which he has apparently written her response in advance and informs her that she is predictable, but Alice later discovers that he had four pre-prepared pieces of paper in his pocket. Both Number Two and the Prisoner call Alice Number Six, and it is unclear which of the men has scrawled the word 'My' over the word 'Your' on the Village information board, changing 'Your Village' to 'My Village.' Thomas's superior, Ross, is also identified with Number Two, through his actions and his relationship to Thomas, and Lee sports a football shirt with a number 5 on it. Alice encounters the ape mask seen in 'Fall Out' (drawn so as also to resemble the one seen in 'The General'), which is shaded such that it also slightly resembles Leo McKern, and, as she does so, the Prisoner sings the song 'Pop goes the weasel,' including the line 'The monkey thought it was all in fun' (bringing home the whole ego-focused idea of the series through one of its key songs). Thus, the different protagonists merge with each other, in effect combining their identities through their associations with the Village.

As well as in the way in which it plays with identity, *Shattered Visage* has other links to the themes and ideas of the series itself. The themes of religion and faith are extensively featured, with references to 'Gods' and 'Arch-Angels' being connected with the Village; at Lake's funeral, the hymn 'They Whose Course on Earth is O'er' is sung, with Prisoneresque lyrics such as 'We the captives, they the freed; we and they are one indeed. One in all we seek or shun; one – because our Lord is one.' We also see the repeated imagery of death; Lake, like the Prisoner – and like Ross, at the end of the book – is taken away in a hearse, with undertakers. The Village, as Alice says, has become a ghost town, picking up on the death imagery as well as the portrayal of ghost-towns as the Village in 'The Girl Who Was Death' and, obliquely 'Living in Harmony' (in the scenes of the deserted fake town towards the end). The connections between the Village and the world are explicit here, as the Village is seen to have a bearing on real-world politics and vice versa (though once again its location remains mysterious, aside from it apparently being on an island); the imagery of the Village at night is echoed in the final image of Westminster under the stars.

There is also a certain amount of discussion regarding the ending of 'Fall Out'. The explanation given at the outset of the graphic novel is that Number Two staged an intervention using psychedelic drugs, role-playing and faking his own death, which sent the Prisoner insane (as he faced the contradiction between his insistence that he was not a number and his realisation that he was Number One);[21] the Village was then evacuated by the UN of all its inhabitants except Number Six, who was declared legally dead. While none of this actually contradicts what we see on screen, it does seem a rather prosaic explanation; however, this does not preclude the possibility that these are post-hoc explanations for something considerably less easy to explain, given that the characters in the story deal in secrets and disinformation.

ANSWERS ARE A BURDEN: UNEXPLAINED SEQUENCES AND SELF-REFERENTIALITY

Within the story itself, certainly, a number of things are unexplained: these include the identity of the 'Arch-Angels'; what sort of game the 'Gods' are playing; and what is indicated by the man with the moustache who is seen in a number of crucial locations throughout the story and later appears to take over from Colonel J. This is not a problem, however, as it leaves the story with a sense of mystery – that there exists a wider picture that neither the characters, nor the readers, are privy to, and thus that some of the things that seem to have an ordinary explanation (for example 'Fall Out', as discussed above), are in fact not as straightforward as they seem.

---

21 As a side point, however, it is worth noting that in Aristotelian philosophy, 'one' is not a number, as the classical Greeks defined a number as 'one of a plurality of units', and 'one' as being separate from that; thus, as the Prisoner is Number One, he is not a number.

We also are left with questions regarding the Village. We are told that it was, and is, the only one, and yet, at the end, Ross is taken away by undertakers in an echo of the Prisoner's own kidnapping; we also see the final image of Alice and her daughter play out over the viewing screen in what appears to be the Green Dome, with the scene making it unclear if anyone is in the chair or not (recalling the earlier imagery of the machinery continuing to work even if no-one is there to direct it). However, the Green Dome was blown up with the rest of the Village earlier; and in any case the set-up at the end is visibly more complex, with more controls, tiers and so forth, than the one we have seen up until now. It is, therefore, likely that the meaning of all this is that, whatever we hear to the contrary, there is another Village, or simply another office from which the world is observed (perhaps, given the images that follow, in Whitehall). Significantly, however, the images on the screen at the end are of the wider world, whereas in the series they are simply of the Village; the intention may be to point the reader to the conclusion that, while the Village itself may be gone, the world is the Village, and surveillance continues on a wider level.

More problematically, however, there are things that don't make sense that are crucial to the story. For one thing, it is unexplained how Number Two has learned about the Zircon spy satellite system (a government project of the 1980s) if he has been imprisoned since 1968. More seriously, while a conversation between Thomas and Lee indicates that Alice is supposed to sail by the island containing the Village, this begs the question of why they would want her to do so, since she is unaware of their plans regarding it; it is also something of a lucky break for Lee that he is able to time the satellite tracker breakdown to coincide both with her passing by the island and with the transit of Hurricane Judith (possibly a reference to Toronto science fiction writer Judith Merril, a regular guest on *Prisoners of Gravity* well-known for her outspokenness). It is possible that Lee is just trying to rig the satellite tracker breakdown so that Alice will lose contact near the Village (necessitating an investigation), and that the storm is a convenient accident; but that still leaves the question of how it would benefit Thomas and Lee to have her just sail by. Even leaving aside the implausibility that Thomas (who still cares for his wife) would put her at risk with a plan like that, her disappearance would cause people to make the connection between the location of her disappearance and his investigation. The idea that Thomas's investigation into the Village is providing a cover for Lee's deeper one also does not hold water, since Thomas's work is going ahead with only tacit approval from Colonel J rather than full official support, which thus does not provide much credibility for Lee's operation. While the storm that brings Alice to the island works on a metaphorical level, linking her arrival there with the lightening storm in the series' title sequence, the rationale behind it does not really work on a practical level.

The book also contains a number of references, some significant but others less so, to *The Prisoner* and other telefantasy series (sometimes to the point where it becomes slightly intrusive), in keeping with the tendency towards self-referentiality in 1980s postmodern works. As well as all the connections drawn between the Drakes, the Prisoner and Number Two, we have Mrs Butterworth turning up as a retired division director of MI5, Number Two at one point dressing up as Napoleon (*a la* Schnipps), and Thomas and Lee having a drink at the Hope and Anchor (the Prisoner's former local mentioned in 'Checkmate') and later attending a cricket game. Colonel J appears (although the artwork makes it hard to tell if it is intended to be the same person or not, since the man we see in no way resembles actor Kevin Stoney), as do undertakers (who may or may not be the Village undertakers); Lee mentions the 'High Eye' at one point (referencing the eye/surveillance motif of the series); and the modified Albertus font is seen in a number of places throughout. The name of the doctor on an autopsy report is 'Dr Sid Rafferty', referring to the character Patrick McGoohan would later play in the TV series *Rafferty*. The Butler appears, though we never see his face. The names of Prisoner cast and crew members appear throughout: for instance, the *Vorpal Blade* sails from Port Muscat; we see a jukebox emblazoned with the company name 'Tomblin'; and minor characters with the names Vincent, Racoff (sic) and Stafford appear.

We also see references to other telefantasy and spy series as well. Mrs Peel and John Steed from *The Avengers* turn up at Lake's funeral, and Ross is said to have been 'trained by Mr Smiley himself' (referring to John le Carré's well-known fictional spy). Mention is made, as Thomas listens to the radio, of the Oldbury nuclear power station, where certain episodes of *Blake's 7* and *Doctor*

Who were filmed. We also see references to film and literary sources. The sequence of the Village blowing up, for instance, resembles the sequence at the end of one cut of Fracis Ford Coppola's *Apocalypse Now* in which Kurtz's compound is bombed (possibly suggesting a connection between the Prisoner's isolation, and insanity, in the decaying Village and the similar situation of Mr Kurtz in Joseph Conrad's *Heart of Darkness*, the novella on which Coppola's film was based). The authors also keep shoehorning *Alice in Wonderland* references into the story – specifically the female protagonist's name, the book she buys for her daughter (along with *The Secret Garden*, which is at least a bit more subtle and links in with the Prisoner's own self-description later in the story as 'just a gardener') and the name of her boat, the *Vorpal Blade* (from the *Jabberwocky* poem in *Through the Looking-Glass*).

Shattered Visage is very much of its time, which is both a good thing (in that it develops the story of *The Prisoner* in terms of subsequent geopolitical activities, and uses this to reflect upon both contemporary and 1960s society) and a bad thing (in that the interesting aspects of the story can get lost under the inside references, the impressionistic art style and the abovementioned plot problems). It should, however, be of note both to fans of *The Prisoner* and to those interested in late-Cold-War spy fiction.

The Prisoner's Dilemma

Publisher: Powys Media (2005)
Author: Jonathan Blum and Rupert Booth

SYNOPSIS: While scoping out escape possibilities in the woods around the Village, the Prisoner encounters a young woman, Number Eighteen, who has apparently just murdered her Observer, claiming that the constant cycle of brainwashing has sent her over the edge. He is later interrogated about this by Number Fifty Four, a policeman investigating the murder, who says that Number Eighteen claimed the Prisoner was responsible, but the Prisoner recognises the strategy Number Fifty Four is using, the Prisoner's Dilemma, and refuses to implicate Number Eighteen. The Prisoner makes contact with Number Eighteen again; she is a reporter for *Village Weekly* magazine, and is gathering data on her late Observer (who had apparently been engaging in criminal acts, to wit, keeping surveillance tapes for personal use) under cover of writing her stories. He goes with her to meet Number One Hundred and One, a genius who is building a supercomputer, called Juliet, which, he discovers, is being used to predict the actions of all Villagers, including him, and doing so with preternatural accuracy. They also make contact with the Irrationals, a group of young Villagers who are in rebellion against their society. The Prisoner learns that his old boss, the Minister, is now in the village, as assistant manager of the old age home.

In collaboration with Number Eighteen, Number One Hundred and One and the Irrationals, the Prisoner plots against the Village, but Juliet's intervention means the Village anticipates his strategies; he then discovers that he has actually been attempting similar stratagems for an unknown period of time, with his memories being repeatedly wiped, as the Village authorities test the computer. The Prisoner then wakes up to discover that the Village has vanished, and that he and Number Eighteen are in a desert. They set off to find a way out, traversing a snowy wasteland, a jungle and a cliff-face, only to find that this is all a reality-TV game and they are now celebrities in the Village. An unknown force apparently attacks the Village, blowing up the bell tower with a bomb (with several houses being destroyed in the tower's subsequent collapse). The Prisoner is accused and tortured, then released to find the Village, gripped by paranoia, going onto a military footing. The Village is then apparently invaded by Eastern European soldiers wanting to seize control of Juliet, and the Minister reveals himself to have betrayed the Village to the other side. Their general gives the Prisoner the means of destroying Juliet, a computer virus that will take down all the Village's defences, but a dilemma with it: if he does not do what they ask, he will be turned over to their authorities for interrogation, but if he does, he has to trust the general's assurance that both he, and the people involved in the Juliet project, will be released unharmed. He agrees to help them but, instead of releasing the virus, he confronts Number Two, gives him the virus, and claims that in fact Juliet is working for the other side, knowing that Number Two will isolate the Juliet system and release the virus against it, so that the Village's other defences will remain intact. The computer is destroyed and life in the Village continues – albeit without Number Eighteen, who has either escaped or been removed.

ANALYSIS: The idea of reviving the series of original novels based on *The Prisoner* could easily have been a problematic one, in terms of making the series relevant for a post-millennial audience without sacrificing the quintessentially late-'60s atmosphere of the original episodes. However, the first book from Powys Media does an admirable job of maintaining the balance between political comment and retro surrealism, without coming across as too contrived or too dated.

REALITY AND TV: THE BACKGROUND TO THE NOVEL

Powys Media, an American small press that had previously had some success with a series of original novels based on the Gerry and Sylvia Anderson series *Space: 1999*, acquired the rights to do original novels based on *The Prisoner* from Granada Television (the owner of the series) around 2003. Their stated aim was to avoid retreading ground covered in the original series, but to produce new *The Prisoner* fiction for a contemporary audience. At the time of writing, one title has been published, with five more planned. The authors of *The Prisoner's Dilemma*, the first in the series, are Jonathan Blum, an award-winning American writer resident in Australia who is best known for his *Doctor Who* and *Doctor Who* spin-off novels and audio scripts, and Rupert Booth, a British actor and writer associated with film production company MEV Productions. The book also includes a foreword by J Michael Straczynski of *Babylon 5* fame. At the time of writing, two more novels have been announced, *The Other* by *Doctor Who* novelist and spin-off writer Lance Parkin, and *Miss Freedom* by former *Doctor Who* script editor and novelist Andrew Cartmel. Renowned science-fiction novelist Robert Sheckley was also commissioned to contribute to the series, but this was forestalled by his death at the end of 2005.

Authors Blum and Booth clearly know the series but are not afraid to experiment with it; they have avoided the problems that periodically plagued the earlier books in their descriptions and characterisations, and the story seldom feels bogged down by the detail. Also, perhaps since Booth is British, the novel does not have the occasional 'voice' problems found in those written by Americans only. The story bears comparison with Disch's work; although it is less weird than that, this does not detract from its overall quality, but simply makes it more in the tradition of 'The General' or 'The Schizoid Man' than 'Free for All'. It reads less like a single episode of *The Prisoner* than a linked series of episodes all building up to a final revelation, giving it the feel of a series within a series.

In terms of its antecedents, the story clearly owes much to 'The General', with its plot about a computer being used for social control and subplot about an attempt to break into the Town Hall to neutralise it, and also to 'It's Your Funeral', with its idea of a computer that can predict people's movements and actions. The reality-TV sequence, in which the Prisoner and a female companion travel across diverse landscapes only to find themselves back in the Village, recalls 'The Chimes of Big Ben' and an unused sequence in 'The Girl Who Was Death'. Minor elements also reference earlier stories: the necessity for an electropass is taken from 'Arrival', and the character of the Minister/Number Thirteen echoes other acquaintances of the Prisoner's who show up in the Village over the course of the series, most notably in 'Arrival' and 'Dance of the Dead'. An exterior dance sequence, described in terms recalling 'The General' and 'Dance of the Dead', also features briefly; and one passage, where the Prisoner is summoned to Number Two's office but Number Two refuses to give a reason, mirrors the scene in 'Hammer into Anvil' in which the Prisoner similarly attempts to disconcert Number Two by turning up at his office claiming that he was called when in fact he was not. There are also connections with a number of the unused stories from the TV series; the Prisoner's discovery of a note to himself that he has no recollection of writing resembles his rediscovery of his diary in Eric Mival's 'Ticket to Eternity', a computer program that maps out the Prisoner's mind in order to predict his actions also is mentioned in Gerald Kelsey's 'Don't Get Yourself Killed'; and the Prisoner's attempts at figuring out possible escape routes under an innocent pretext recall the opening of Moris Farhi's 'The Outsider' (and there is also, on that score, a brief reference to the Palace of Fun). The story lifts Disch's idea about the Prisoner discovering that he has been performing the same actions over and over, with his memory being wiped each time; the cat of 'Many Happy Returns' and 'Dance of the Dead' also makes an appearance; and there is another reference, as in *Who is No. 2?*, to the idea that it may be a surveillance device.

Looking outside of the series, the idea of a computer re-running social control programmes over and over in order to test the system, and that of rebellion and individualism being tacitly part of the very social structure these reject, are close to elements of the film *The Matrix: Reloaded*, a connection also flagged up in *The Prisoner's Dilemma* by the presence of an array of video screens, each showing a possible action that a character might conceivably take at a given moment. One might also claim an influence from the *Doctor Who* story 'The Curse of Fenric', which featured a character based on

Alan Turing and references to a number of logic problems, including, at one point, the Prisoner's Dilemma itself. Other TV shows also get brief mentions: *Gilligan's Island* and *The Teletubbies* (a pre-school children's programme involving surveillance systems, bright surreal landscapes and a dome-shaped underground control centre) both feature briefly on Village television, and the popular British chat-shows *The Kumars at Number 42* and *Richard and Judy* are merged in the form of a Village chat-show featuring a married couple of Number Forty Twos (a and b).

The book is, however, not without its problems. Number Eighteen is somewhat flatly written, reminding one less of a *The Prisoner* woman and more of the sort of plucky but irritating girl who permeates the *Doctor Who* spin-off genre, most notably Virgin's *Doctor Who New Adventures* novels. Parts of the book are long-winded, making the message difficult to discern, and its episodic structure causes it to lack a sense of flow. The secondary characters can be hard to keep track of. The Fish, for instance, gets an extensive set-up and then, having done only one useful thing in plot terms, effectively vanishes from the story. However, the book is able to rise above these minor problems and remain an interesting and readable addition to the canon.

GENERAL AUDIENCES:
JULIET, NUMBER 101 AND COMPUTING

As its title suggests, the novel focuses around the use of computers, computing and game theory. The titular logic puzzle, the Prisoner's Dilemma, runs through the story. This puzzle, formulated by Merrill Flood and Melvin Dresher, involves two prisoners arrested by the police, who have insufficient evidence for a conviction. The police isolate the prisoners and give each the choice of cooperating by providing evidence against their colleague, or staying silent: if the prisoner cooperates and his colleague stays silent, the prisoner goes free; if neither cooperates, they both serve a short sentence; if both cooperate, they both serve a longer (but still reduced) sentence; but if the prisoner stays silent and his colleague provides evidence, he serves a full sentence. Several iterations of this occur throughout the story. In particular, it runs through the relationship between the

Prisoner and Number Eighteen: when both are interrogated by Number Fifty Four about the Observer's murder; when they are in the reality-TV game; when both are interrogated following the 'terrorist' attack on the Village; and finally, when both infiltrate the Town Hall to destroy Juliet. It also recurs in more complex form in a sequence in which the Irrationals individually debate the value of betraying the group to the Village before another member has a chance to do so, and is referenced again when the Minister explains that his decision to choose a 'cooperate first, then defect' strategy against the Village was motivated by the Prisoner's Dilemma. Finally, the Prisoner is set the ultimate Prisoner's Dilemma at the end of the story, when he is given the choice of destroying Juliet or allowing it to remain, and ultimately chooses a third, compromise option.

This metaphor highlights the nature of the Prisoner's main opponent throughout the story: the Juliet computer system. While the computer has 1960s features, it also possesses more modern characteristics, such as vast power and the ability to link up in a network (resulting, slightly to the book's detriment, in a series of explanations to the Prisoner and Number Eighteen about the potential of computing and the possibility of the internet that verge on the contrived, along the lines of Disney historical-comedy films in which the viewer has full knowledge of the later impact of the technology that the characters hail as innovative). This computer is used to bring in the modern themes of digital surveillance and its ability to violate the freedom of individuals without them feeling as if their privacy has been breached. The name is explained as an allusion to Shakespeare's Juliet, the point being the idea that classical tragedy is inevitable, the result of crucial decisions by the characters from which the consequences flow, as reflected in the computer's role in predicting human behaviour and thus, depending on one's perspective, either creating or forestalling inevitable tragedy. In the end, also, the Prisoner chooses not to destroy the whole computer system, but simply to isolate the machines in it, forcing them to stand as individuals, in keeping with the series' themes of individualism.

Juliet's creator, Number One Hundred and One, also deserves a mention. From the description of him, and hints about his sexuality and his past, he is clearly intended to be the famed British mathematician Alan Turing, who played a key role in the development of computing and who invented the Turing Test for artificial intelligence (and it is implied in the story that he is hoping to actually develop such an intelligence through Juliet). Turing's real-life story, alluded to at key moments, is a tragedy, as he committed suicide in despair after having been convicted on charges relating to then-illegal homosexual activity; his treatment by British society is compared openly to the Village's treatment of the Prisoner, and of course his number recalls Room 101, the instrument of the totalitarian society in George Orwell's *Nineteen Eighty-Four*. Number One Hundred and One's relationships within the story are ambivalent; his loyalty appears to be focused around the computer system alone and, at the end, after the Juliet system has been shown to be vulnerable, as it can be attacked through its users, he is engaged in trying to figure out a way of making it user-proof, suggesting that the controlling power of technology is, in a surveillance society, ultimately unstoppable.

PHILOSOPHER'S STONE:
THE PRISONER'S DILEMMA AND IDEOLOGY

Juliet's ultimate fate also picks up on the story's theme of individualism, and its ethical limits. Early on, when the Prisoner challenges Number Fifty Four's hypocrisy in claiming to believe in justice and yet still working for the Village, Number Fifty Four responds by demanding to know how the Prisoner can claim to believe in the value of the individual and yet still believe that the Observer deserved his death. Later, when the Prisoner reacts with fury on learning that the Observer had been making private tapes of women in the Village, Number Fifty Four remarks 'Man, I thought you *wanted* them to keep their nose out of people's private business' (page 65), suggesting that the ultimate price of freedom may be the tolerance of abuse. The Observer's crime also reflects the modern tension between security and invasion of privacy, as highlighted in cases in which, for instance, CCTV footage has been included in television programmes without permission having been sought from the people shown in it. Number Fifty Four also alludes to the Prisoner's egotism, commenting that he thinks that the world revolves around him (which, in a sense, it apparently does), and the story later picks up on Disch's idea that the Village authorities 'don't just want you broken, they want you *willing*' (page 50); the Village is an exercise not so much in interrogation as in psychological remodelling. Finally, the idea that the Village is anti-individualist is questioned when Number Eighteen observes that there are no team sports there; the aim is not so much to absorb individuals into groups as such, as to remodel their psyches into what the system wants them to be.

We also get some exploration of what it is that drives the Prisoner himself. The final sequence of the story sees the Prisoner still refusing to have his faith in Number Eighteen shaken by the Minister's persistent questioning of it, or by the fact that he does not know whether she escaped or whether she was a Village agent all along. This is an interesting reversal of the ending of *Nineteen Eighty-Four*, in which Winston Smith's belief in an objective truth is shattered by O'Brien's causing him to lose faith in Julia; here, the Prisoner, like O'Brien rather than Smith, believes in a subjective truth rather than an objective one – which, if one follows Orwell's logic, is a kind of insanity, but is ultimately what keeps the Prisoner from breaking down under pressure.

The presence of Juliet also highlights the themes of narrative and interpretation. Number Two explicitly says that the Juliet system is less about predicting the future than about creating stories, providing narratives for people; he adds that the private self of the individual is irrelevant, as it is people's public faces that have an impact on the world. This is reinforced in a crucial sequence on page 306, in which, through Juliet's program, we see the Minister perform the same actions with two different interpretations placed on his motivation, highlighting that narrative is as much about interpretation as about action. The death of the Observer makes the man, however reprehensible, a 'retroactive saint' (page 44). The story is thus about the power of narrative and the interpretation of activities as a means of social control.

This is also reflected in the reality-TV subplot, an idea that could have come across as rather contrived but actually fits very well in the surveillance-obsessed world of the Village. At the apparent conclusion of the survival programme appropriately named *Be Seeing You*, the Prisoner's rebellion is taken from him by virtue of his being deemed a celebrity; his resistance becomes nothing more than a gimmick. More than this, however, the Prisoner remarks on how the cult of celebrity has encouraged Villagers to collaborate in their own surveillance, and their own loss of identity: 'Is that what they're giving you to aspire to? To being *watched?'* (page 223). He himself is induced to collaborate by virtue of lending his celebrity status, and thus a form of legitimacy, to the funeral service for the victims of the 'terrorist attack', demonstrating also that sometimes to not resist a regime is to lend support to it. Number Eighteen writes for a gossip magazine *Village Weekly* (the name of which, incidentally, appears to be taken from that of one of the magazines seen in 'Hammer into Anvil'), which encourages Villagers to spy on their neighbours in exchange for the dubious reward of seeing their name in print; the editor of the magazine is none other than Number Two. The Irrationals, similarly, disdain the Prisoner when he becomes, in their view, 'mainstream', revealing the shallowness of supposedly counter-cultural people who respect resistance only when it is obscure and 'cult', even if the person in question is still the same. X remarks at one point that, as an acquaintance of the Prisoner's, he is considering selling his story to the papers to get a bit of attention. At the end of the book, in shades of *The Truman Show*, there is the implication that the Village itself may be some form of reality-TV programme, with viewers voting people out and the potential for cash rewards at the end. The Village is therefore reinterpreted in light of modern forms of surveillance and self-censorship.

AL-QAEDA BELONGS TO US: TERRORISM AND SURVEILLANCE

The novel also contains an incident that is a close parallel to the events of 11 September 2001. This is, if one thinks about it, a fairly obvious thing to put in a Prisoner novel, considering its impact on civil liberties, but it does work well here. Its inclusion highlights the Prisoneresque nature of both the event itself and subsequent activities involving the detention, surveillance and 'extraordinary rendition' of so-called 'enemy combatants'. The conversation on page 255 between the Prisoner and Number Eighteen, in which the latter voices the concern that their resistance activities could leave the Village vulnerable to outside attack, and that the hypothetical invaders could be worse than the Village, indicates how such events can be used to suppress opposition and bring counter-cultural elements in line with the state. When the Prisoner argues that the attack may have been good for the Village, as it reminds them of the presence of the outside world and challenges their complacency, his discourse is promptly suppressed in a wave of accusations that he is defending the terrorist attack, in the same way that media figures and politicians who did not totally support the American government's response to the real-life events were accused of being 'soft on terrorism' or 'supporting al-Qaeda'. The Village, therefore, becomes a metaphor for post-9/11 America, and the observation that 'the paranoia of civic vigilance now intersects with the eternal gaze of celebrity' (page 274) an effective summing-up of the present socio-political system.

Mention must also be made of the Irrationals, a group of counter-cultural young Villagers who identify themselves with the Village equivalent of *noms de guerre*, pseudonymous numbers that, in keeping with their group name, form a set of mathematical puns (X, Theta, e, Pi and so on). While they resemble, in concept, the young rebels of *A Day in the Life*, they do work rather better in terms of portraying the problematic nature of youthful rebellion. While the Irrationals deplore the Village system, they support it by buying their clothes and music at its shops, and their idolisation of the Prisoner puts them in the same position as the celebrity-worshipping older villagers. They attempt to justify their position through reinterpreting the Prisoner's famous 'I am not a number' catchphrase through the fact that i, in mathematical terms, is the square root of minus one; therefore, I, although rebellious, *is* a number. Because they are essentially conforming under their rebellious facade, they are tolerated by the Village; when they show genuinely threatening rebellion, the Village crushes it to a degree that surprises and demoralises them, with X, the last one, eventually going off to become a file clerk after a confrontation with Rover, showing how rebellion can, ultimately, be conformist.

The book does an excellent job of capturing the Village, with the surreal announcements, the atmosphere of Portmeirion and the air of mingled gaiety and paranoia being well portrayed. The Village is still multicultural: Number Fifty Four is Black, the Fish is European, and minor characters turn up from Australia, Germany, Eastern Europe and so forth throughout. The Buddha statue, never seen in the series, makes a brief appearance. The sequence where every day is Thursday for a number of days picks up on the surrealism and social control aspects of the series, as well as indicating that the Village has the ability to control what day it is simply by way of a declaration (picking up on the apparent time discrepancies in 'A, B and C' and 'The Schizoid Man'). The fact that members of the Village justify the repeated sequence of Thursdays also indicates how people can rationalise any bizarre occurrence (and seems like a nod to G K Chesterton's *The Man Who Was Thursday: a Nightmare*, a short novel that anticipates *The Prisoner* in many of its themes and imagery, and the title of which is also perhaps referenced by 'The Girl Who Was Death'). A scene in which the Prisoner passes through the seasons of the year as he walks through the Village picks up on the way that – due to the fact that the location filming in Portmeirion took place at different times of the year – the original series shows sometimes quite marked differences in light, foliage and so forth from scene to scene (see especially 'It's Your Funeral'). The surveillance busts not only make an appearance, but are also revealed to double as an advance weapons system in case of attack. The ambiguity of who owns the Village is maintained (with hints being dropped that it is the Communists, the Prisoner's own side, or even, in a more modern twist, a multinational corporation using it as a kind of meta-focus group), as in the series. The authors also provide a different interpretation for the hand-around-the-eye greeting gesture, not as a Christian symbol or salute, but as a lowercase b, making the meaning of the gesture 'b seeing you.' We get a brief insight into the nature of Number Two in the sequence where the Prisoner finds a former Number Two (evidently the one from 'A Change of Mind') who, reduced to a mindless creature, is playing solitaire; the dialogue that follows hints that Number Two is a kind of program that is put into various individuals in turn, with each incumbent being 'retired' when the program is moved to the next. There also is the implication in the scene that the man has been lobotomised, suggesting that the Villagers seen pursuing him at the end of 'A Change of Mind' did succeed in subjecting him to 'instant social conversion'.

At the end of the story, the Prisoner, despite the fact that he must on some level realise that he is a product of society, and that his rebellion is useful to the Village, continues to fight on. The Prisoner's absolute faith in himself, and at the same time total denial of his place in society, is the series' ultimate enigma, as symbolised by the seashell the Prisoner finds, with a note reading 'How did I get this?' The seashell symbolises the Prisoner's inviolate core, with the question never being answered, indicating that the central enigma of the series is the nature of the Prisoner himself.

Selected Bibliography

What follows is a limited selection of the resources we have found most useful in preparing this volume. Interested readers are encouraged to consult any or all of these for further information on *The Prisoner*, particularly regarding issues outside our remit.

BOOKS

Britton, Piers D and Barker, Simon J (2003). *Reading Between Designs: Design and the Generation of Meaning in* The Avengers, The Prisoner *and* Doctor Who. Austin: University of Texas Press.

Carrazé, Alain and Oswald, Hélène (1989). *The Prisoner: a Televisionary Masterpiece*. London: Virgin.

Cornell, Paul, Day, Martin and Topping, Keith (1996) *The Guinness Book of Classic British TV* (2nd ed.) London: Guinness Publishing Ltd.

Fairclough, Robert (2002). *The Prisoner: The Official Companion to the Classic TV Series*. London: Carleton Books

--- (2005). The Prisoner: *The Original Scripts* vol. 1. London: Reynolds and Hearn

--- (2006). The Prisoner: *The Original Scripts* vol. 2. London: Reynolds and Hearn

Frumerman, Catherine Nemeth (2003) *On The Trail of* The Prisoner: *A Walking Guide To Portmeirion's* Prisoner *Sites*. PrizBiz.

Gregory, Chris (1997). *Be Seeing You: Decoding* The Prisoner. Luton: University of Luton Press.

Hora, Max. 1985) *The Prisoner of Portmeirion*. Publisher Unknown ('A Number Six Publication').

--- (1985) *Portmeirion* Prisoner *Production*. Publisher Unknown ('A Number Six Publication').

Langley, Roger (1985) *The Making of* The Prisoner. Ipswich: ESCAPE.

--- (1985) *Escape Book of* Prisoner *Episode Reviews* . Ipswich: ESCAPE.

--- (1999). *The Prisoner in Portmeirion*. Portmeirion: Portmeirion Ltd.

Rakoff, Ian (1998). *Inside* The Prisoner. London: Batsford.

Ricks, Steven (2000) *The Prisoner: I am Not a Number!* TR 7
Publications.
Sellers, Robert (2006) *Cult TV: The Golden Age of ITV*. London: Plexus
Publishing Ltd.
Stevens, Alan and Moore, Fiona (2003) *Liberation: the Unofficial and
Unauthorised Guide to* Blake's 7. London: Telos Publishing.
White, Matthew and Ali, Jaffer (1988). *The Official Prisoner
Companion*. London: Sidgwick and Jackson.

SERIAL PUBLICATIONS

In The Village and *Free for All*, the publications of Six of One: The
Official Prisoner Appreciation Society
The Prisoner: The Official Fact File and *The Danger Man Collection* De
Agostini UK Ltd. (a set of DVDs with accompanying magazines
brought out in 2005, edited by Robert Fairclough and Marcus
Hearn)
The Prisoner Puzzle, Ontario Education and Communication
Authority, 1978.
Starlog issue 135, October 1988.
Time Screen, in particular issues 9 (March 1987), 11 (Spring 1988),
and 12 (Winter 1988).

WEBSITES

Danger Man Website, www.danger-man.co.uk
PrizBiz (*The Prisoner* merchandise), www.priz.biz
The Prisoner Scripts,
http://www.prisoner.demon.co.uk/scripts.htm
Interview with Jean Marie Stine on Anorak Zone,
http://www.anorakzone.com/prisoner/interview.html
Six of One (the official *The Prisoner* fan club website),
www.sixofone.org; Six of One can also be contacted at Six of
One, Box 66, Ipswich IP2 9TZ.
The Unmutual, www.theunmutual.co.uk
Virtual Portmeirion (online home of the resort),
www.virtualportmeirion.com

DVDS

Brand (1959) – Network
Casino Royale (1967) – MGM Home Entertainment.
Secret Agent/Danger Man (1960-1) – ITV DVD; (1964-6) – A&E Home
    Video
The Prisoner (1967-8) – ITV DVD.

DOCUMENTARIES

Six Into One: The Prisoner File (1984). Channel 4.
On the Trail of The Prisoner: *The Goodman Interview.* CD audio,
    produced by PrizBiz.

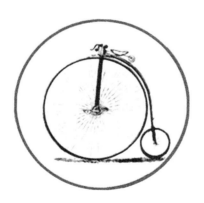

Index

391

About The Authors

ALAN STEVENS has written, edited and developed numerous publications on telefantasy series, including *The Prisoner, Doctor Who* and *Blake's 7* (notably *Liberation: the Unofficial and Unauthorised Guide to* Blake's 7, and *By Your Command: The Official and Unauthorised Guide to* Battlestar Galactica *vols. I and II,* also from Telos). Since the early 1990s, he has produced a number of documentaries, serials and dramas for radio and independent audio release, including the *The Prisoner*-inspired *Blake's 7/Doctor Who* spin-off series *Kaldor City* and the Gothic horror time-travelling adventure *Faction Paradox*. He is currently based in the South East of England, where he runs his own audio production company, Magic Bullet Productions (www.kaldorcity.com), and writes for the theatre, the Web, and print publications.

FIONA MOORE was born and raised in Toronto, Canada. In 1997 she moved to the UK and has lived there ever since. She has a doctorate in Social Anthropology from the University of Oxford, and is currently Reader in International Human Resource Management at Royal Holloway, University of London. She has written on a wide variety of subjects, from the entrepreneurial activities of Korean expatriates to the culture of drag queens, and is co-author of *Liberation: the Unofficial and Unauthorised Guide to* Blake's 7 and *By Your Command: The Unofficial and Unauthorised Guide to* Battlestar Galactica *vols. I and II.* Her fiction and poetry have been published in, among others, *Asimov, Interzone* and *Dark Horizons.* She used to own a black and white Mini Cooper Classic with racing modifications.

Printed in Great Britain
by Amazon